WOMEN

John Philip Lundin, Ph.D.

 The Autobiographical Reflections of a Frustrated Male

INTRODUCTION BY R. E. L. MASTERS

The Julian Press, Inc., Publishers, New York, 1963

WOMEN

Published by The Julian Press, Inc.
80 East 11th Street, New York 3
© Copyright 1963 by the Julian Press, Inc.
Library of Congress Catalog Card Number 63–13191
Manufactured in the United States of America
The Book Press, Brattleboro, Vermont
Designed by Leda Arensberg

Second printing

Come, fill the cup, and in the fire of Spring
Your Winter-garment of Repentance fling;
The Bird of Time has but a little way
To flutter—and the Bird is on the Wing.

Omar the Tent-Maker

. . . das Ewig-Weibliche hebt uns empor.

Goethe

Contents

Introduction

John Philip Lundin's *Women* is an erotic memoir somewhat in the tradition of Casanova and Frank Harris. For the most part, it describes the author's sexual experiences with ten women.

I am pleased to introduce this book for two reasons. For one, I find *Women* both instructive and thoroughly entertaining; for another, John Philip Lundin (pseudonym of a world-traveler and scholar) is an old and valued friend.

In keeping with the climate of candor Lundin has created, I should probably confess to a third reason: my agreement with much that he has to say. His view of the female, as far as it goes, is in the main realistic; and his remarks on the prostitute are particularly in accord with some conclusions of my own.

The erotic memoir, or autobiography with heavy emphasis on sexual experience, has a legitimate place in literature. Moreover, it is likely to have value for historians and scientific workers. With regard to the latter, here at least is a welcome change of pace from the usual case studies. An account of a man who is not consciously troubled by guilt, impotence, perversion, and other assorted psychosexual afflictions, is valuable if only to remind us that such persons exist.

Lundin's book takes on added interest when we note that his travels have led him to many of the places where American troops have been stationed in the period since World War II. Through him, we learn something of the sexual life of those countries as Americans have experienced it; and we get some answers to that perennial question: What does the U.S. male "see in" foreign women?

Fortunately, Lundin lives on the same plane as many of the rest of us, and his relationships are with women such as most of us might find accessible. He has no advantage of wealth or of "connections" and must work for what he receives sexually and otherwise. It is true that he is more intelligent and better-educated than the typical American. But his problems are almost universal: the same hungers drive him as drive most of us; his methods of appeasing them are similar to our own. His, it might be said, are the sexual adventures of the average man.

As a bachelor on the move, living in the cities and towns of America, Europe, and the Orient, Lundin has had ample opportunity to study the women of many lands. But particularly he has studied those women who make a business of sex.

These women are not all prostitutes within any ordinary definition of that term. By making a business of sex, we may understand trading on sex appeal, exploiting one's sexual nature and talents, using sex as a vehicle for securing a variety of quite different rewards. This, in Lundin's view, is done by most women; and the ability of the female to control her desires, to make the male the supplicant for pleasures which are mutually desired, is the key to the success of "the matriarchy." In general, he confines himself to some of the more obvious examples.

Claudine, a bar girl, is one. With strong erotic appetites of her own, she preys upon the desires of males, holding out to them the promise of a satisfaction that is never forthcoming. Night after night, she sits on a bar stool, drinking cold tea that is supposed to be whisky, while males who can ill afford to do so spend their money buying her drinks. One man squanders his life's savings in this way, always with the hope, never fulfilled, that she will respond to his desires. At the end of the evening, she goes home to her lover (Lundin), to express her contempt for the "fools" who are thus parted from their money. Clearly, her business is sex, rather; broken promises of sex; yet by none of the usual definitions could one term her a prostitute.

Lynn, a co-worker in an office where Lundin was employed, sought to use her sex to exploit and ensnare him in two ways. For one, she attempted, by hinting at rewards later on, to make him her errand boy and provider of her coffee and lunches. Second, by stimulating his desires without fulfilling them, she hoped to extract a proposal of marriage. These are such common forms of trading on sex by the female that they are taken for granted. Nonetheless, the immorality of such maneuvers is plain.

Odette, a Parisian streetwalker, is one of several women in this book who are professional prostitutes. Yet it is with Odette that the author manages to find one of the most intense and moving emotional experiences he has recorded—giving the lie to our spurious insistence that such relationships are invariably degrading.

Other prostitutes are Suzie, a Korean; Hisako-San, a Japanese; and Anne, an American, who specializes in rich, elderly businessmen. The chapters describing the first two are highly amusing. They also well illustrate the gulf between East and West—and, in the case of Hisako-San, between a money-hungry prostitute and her customer, whatever their cultural backgrounds.

I do not wish to give the impression that this book is mainly about prostitution. In fact, much of its interest stems from the fact that it so often deals with the little-explored fringe area between the so-called respectable world and the underworld, an area where the women are not quite prostitutes but are not regarded as respectable, either—the world of bar girls, good-time girls, sometime mistresses, etc. Nonetheless, I would like to say more about Lundin's attitude toward prostitution and prostitutes since his conclusions are sound ones.

As he points out in his concluding chapter, and as he manages to make plain at other points in his book, Lundin regards prostitution as a legitimate activity. He is quite aware of what may be the occupational diseases of the prostitute: greed, laziness, wasteful extravagance, selfishness, etc. But he understands, too, the urgent need for the commodity she offers.

The prostitute sells a service: sex. Unless she adds some crime, such as thievery, to her repertoire, she operates honestly. The customer receives what he pays for; and, if he is disappointed, it is usually because his expectations were unreasonably high. Thus, in many respects, the prostitute, doing business in good faith, is morally superior not only to the bar girl and good-time girl, who tease and then give nothing, but also to those wives whose feigned passions have provided them with security.

Like many another contemporary American, Lundin both rejects and condemns our antisexual ethic. He pays no attention to those moralists who condemn his behavior as sinful; he is not deterred by those authorities who brand it illicit. Our society officially regards such behavior and attitudes as reprehensible; but we do well to inquire if there exist any reasonable alternatives.

Today, science, not theology, is increasingly becoming the arbiter of sexual morality. Physicians and psychologists, sociologists and anthropologists, not clergymen, are the effective authorities on sexual behavior. Their mistakes are many, but the best of them, unlimited by preconception and dogma, seek sane and sensible standards of conduct. Their findings seldom lend any support to the view that continence is a desirable way of life.

No distinction is to be found between the sexual needs of the married and the unmarried. A young man's appetites do not wait to awaken at the moment of his marriage. A widow's desires are not extinguished at the death of her husband. If marriage affects desires, it makes them less urgent.

The conflict between scientific findings and the practices of our citizens, on the one hand, and our professed morality and legal structure, on the other, produces grave emotional conflicts. We are operating a vast neurosis factory, and few escape without damage. This is a point I have made repeatedly in various books: in *Forbidden Sexual Behavior and Morality,* in *Eros and Evil,* in *The Homosexual Revolution,* in *Patterns of Incest* and in *The Cradle of Erotica.* Lundin, by some of his examples, makes the point again here.

Like Lundin, many have a plan for escaping the damage. They would do it by rejecting the old values and establishing new ones—values in accord with their beliefs and, as it follows, with their conduct. Surely, a revision of values is the only solution; but society's values, not just those of some individuals, will have to be altered.

To terminate the lecture, what else do we have in this book?

It is, perhaps first of all, a record of one man's attempt to live honestly. Believing that he is entitled to sexual expression, and refusing to marry solely for the purpose of obtaining it, Lundin has sought pleasure and affection with a variety of women. He has behaved rather well; to his sexual relationships he has brought an inherent courtesy, good humor, and the wish for a reciprocal respect. He has never regarded the sex act as dirty or debasing to himself, or to his partners.

There is no abuse, no physical mistreatment. He has looked for beauty and affection, along with a maximum of pleasure, for both his partner and himself. Sometimes, when strong emotions have been involved, he has had the worst of it; sometimes, the best. But there are few human intimacies where someone is not eventually wounded.

One might wish that all sexual relationships were conducted on an equally high plane.

We have no way of knowing how truthful or accurate Lundin has been. The pleasure so unanimously enjoyed by prostitutes in their intercourse with him might arouse some suspicions; so, too, might the claims of extraordinary potency which the author advances. Yet some prostitutes *do* sometimes pleasurably respond to the sex act, even with their customers; and some men *are* exceptionally potent.

However that may be, we are given encounters with prostitutes in which there is no sordidness. The episodes are humorous, affectionate, and sometimes ecstatic; but never are they dirty or mean. Never is the prostitute reduced to flesh alone; never does Lundin lose sight of the other's human value. And, additionally, we learn much that is of interest about prostitution in the countries involved.

The reader may wonder why a book containing so many erotic episodes should be regarded as a chronicle of frustrations. At the beginning of this Introduction I mentioned such comparable memoirs as those of Casanova and Frank Harris. Surely, those works, too, are as much about frustration as about conquest.

Every man looks for the relationship that will completely satisfy his needs. Only once, with Florence, did Lundin approach this ideal, and then it was the flawed character of the woman capable of giving him fulfillment that provided, instead, frustration. We are left to speculate as to whether, if her character had been different, Lundin would or could have loved her.

It is true that realistic men do not seek, or hope to find, a complete fulfillment in every relationship. A man (or a woman) may be quite willing in some cases to settle for the lesser pleasures of the moment—pleasures that sustain the seeker as he moves along his way. Yet a core of frustration is always present at the heart of such pleasures. Who settles for half a loaf cannot avoid the knowledge that his experience is less than it might be. If this were not true, one attractive, skillful partner would serve as well as another.

The "craving for variety," common to so many of us, is always an admission of inadequacy—of the inadequacy of the partner *for us,* and probably of our inadequacy *for her.* Usually, it also testifies to our optimism: Somewhere, out there, *she* is. The next woman, or the one after her, will be *the* woman for whom we have been searching.

Which, then, is better? To abandon the quest, to accept as one's life-partner a woman who only partly measures up to one's dream, or to push on with the search, savoring the incomplete fulfillments along the way while continuing the pursuit of the possibly unattainable ideal? Some men and some women choose one course, some another. We know which course our official moralists would prefer that they take; but are we able to say, for every member of our society, which course is the wiser or the more admirable? And are we able to say that the same course is possible for everyone?

I hope that future historians of our society will not pass over Lundin's book. Better than most novelists, and better than most authors of psychological case studies, he has presented a slice of the sexual life of our time.

R. E. L. Masters

New York City
January, 1963

WOMEN

I Diverse Women, Especially Claudine

If you tried to buy the favors of a fairly presentable American whore for ten dollars, you wouldn't get very far. Any girl worth looking at would probably send you packing. And, what's more, she'd have the verdict of society on her side: Everybody knows that a fifty-dollar bill is *de rigueur* these days, and that many of the girls ask and get more. Inflation has hit the U.S. flesh-market. Civic cleanups and crackdowns have helped hike the price of vice. Next to plumbers and TV repairmen, the whores of America are among the most overpaid wage-earners in the country.

Elsewhere, a harlot is obliged to give more for less money.

If you hand about ten dollars to a German prostitute, you won't be sent packing. She's ready for whatever your potency permits and she'll sleep with you all night. If you proved yourself talented, maybe she'll let you repeat the performance in the morning. She may, that is, if she doesn't have an appointment with her hair-dresser, her seamstress, her manicurist, the girlfriend who introduces her to her better-paying clients, or any of the other members of that enormous general staff who seem to be necessary to the girl's operations. She wouldn't miss one of those appointments for the world.

If you give about ten dollars to a Jananese whore, she'll take you to a small hotel hidden from the curious eyes of the world by a fence, and after mutual bows, welcomes, compliments, and exchanges of information with the Mama-San of the establishment, you'll find yourself in a well-scrubbed Japanese bathroom, being washed under an open faucet and getting anointed for your immersion in hot water, which must never be contaminated by soap or—perish the thought —dirt. The girl will scrub your back and cleanse your toes, test the hot water for you, rinse you off painstakingly before you climb into the tub with her, and playfully fondle you while the two of you are sitting in the bath, letting all impurities out through your pores. She'll take you to bed, let you love her backwards and forwards, and gently tell you when to stop and curl up to rest. When you rise in the morning, she'll get beancurd soup, fish, and rice for your breakfast and make the inevitable tea. Finally, she'll put you in a taxi and make sure that the driver knows the shortest way to your home.

If you hire a Korean prostitute for about ten dollars, she'll walk you to her tiny room in a cozy mud-hovel, undress you and herself, and play with your virile endowments and hers to observe your reaction. By the time you've been stimulated so far that you could take on the girl, her mother, and her grandmother besides, she'll let you mount her. She'll ride you and squeeze you, raise one leg to let you exercise sideways, and turn over to let you play dog. She'll share her food with you and lick your sweet body while you're eating her rice. And if you've managed to spend the night on her hard horse's hair mattress, she may stuff you with raw eggs and spiced cabbage in hopes of obtaining additional satisfaction from you before you depart.

If you give about ten dollars to a French whore, she'll walk you to a cheap flophouse, and the first thing you can be sure of is that you owe more money for the rent. Having paid the chambermaid and the whore, you may then take your clothes off and lie down, but no matter how speedy you may be, the girl will be down to her garter-belt and her stockings before you. It's a funny thing about France: All the street-walkers strip down to their garter-belts and stockings in record time, and that's as far as they go. You have to graduate into the forty-dollars-a-night trade before you're able to put your arm around the girl's posterior without scratching yourself on the confounded garter-belt. She'll be ready to make love to you as soon as her flesh hits the worn mattress, and within five minutes' time she'll show signs of impatience. She'll hurry you through the rites of Eros, and as soon as you've started to decline she'll jump up and squat on the bidette like a hen setting on her eggs, washing out the liquid blessings that you've bestowed upon her. She won't require five minutes to get dressed, and before you know it she'll have you out on the street and wave good-bye as she begins to look for the next customer.

Women are said to be the same the world over, but within

their similarity they're as divergent as it's possible for members of the same species to be. They have only one thing in common: They like to be rewarded for enjoying their pleasure. Who wouldn't?

Naturally, there are great differences in the currency they use. The girls who await the approach of their patrons in the clubs of Las Vegas, Atlantic City, San Remo, Monte Carlo, Baden-Baden, and Acapulco have price tags attached to them that the poor little slut from the Boulevard de Clichy in Paris or the street-walker from the Bahnhof district of Frankfurt on the Main wouldn't dream of. The girls who wink at customers in the sidewalk cafés of Rome and Marseilles, or start conversations by bumming cigarettes from customers in the bars of Hamburg and London, will never be promoted into the class of females who nonchalantly ask their acquaintances to rooms in the Waldorf-Astoria in New York, the Ritz in London, the George V in Paris, or the Sacher in Vienna.

Certainly, our society is stratified largely for men only. Women can cross the boundaries with the slightest effort, having only to permit intimacies to the right class of admirer. If a man uses obscene language in public, he's expelled, but if a woman with a good figure does it, and especially if her voice carries that certain suggestive intonation, people consider it highly amusing. If a man were to wave aphrodisiacs before young ladies in a hotel lobby, he'd probably be arrested. But a woman isn't in style unless she wends her way in a cloud of perfume designed to bring out the beast in man —the very beast he mustn't exhibit on penalty of ostracism or worse. Were a man to slap a well-dressed woman in polite society, champions would arise immediately to spring gallantly to her defense, whereas a woman may hit a man in the face and be considered to have acted within her natural rights. And provided that her bustline is sufficiently large, her hips not too flaccid, and her dress tight enough, a woman could plunk herself down in the middle of a table and hurl smiling insults at everyone in the room. The rules of etiquette don't apply to women who please the eye and parade their charms without fear. If there is a single currency that all women need it isn't money but daring. The more audacious they are, the better they're liked. Those who merely ask for a ten-dollar bill will never receive very high wages in either money or the things it will buy. Those who don't ask for specific sums often receive more in the long run, for they put the man on his honor. The more obstreperous, inconsiderate, and shrewish they are, the better they're paid, if only they'll hold out a promise to the right men and curl up under the proper blanket.

I once knew a forty-year-old redhead in Los Angeles who stopped any male conversation by just walking into the room. She made a specialty of crashing parties. Rarely did anyone ask who had invited her. All she had to do to be admitted was to smile at the ticket-taker at the door, walk past him, and sidle up to the first man she discovered. She was always invited. Her husband was some sort of petty official who usually was out of town on secret government business. This arrangement suited her perfectly. She had the poor sucker trained to such a point that he actually phoned her to give "fair warning" before he dared show his ugly face around his own house. Not only that, he always called her from the same bar, about half an hour's drive away from home, so that he could wait for her to pick him up in the family car. This arrangement gave her lovers plenty of time to make the bed and escape. If one of her admirers happened to call her when her husband was in town, she'd say, "I can't talk to you now,

I'm not alone." The jackass of a husband put up with it all of his married days. He may still be doing it. On week ends, if he can manage to slip home from his assignments, she sandwiches him in between her other lovers.

This woman and I once went to a furrier's shop. She decided to look at some Persian lambs. The manager came out to greet her. He kept making silly mistakes, because he couldn't take his eyes off her neckline.

"But, madam, you needn't make a down payment," he said, when she objected to the price of a stole she liked.

"Well, I couldn't make the monthly installments, either."

"You needn't make any payments, madam. You never need to pay one cent for your furs. Have anything you like. It'll be my pleasure."

"And what would it cost me to buy these furs without money?" she demanded.

"Come with me and let's talk it over," he stammered.

"You must be out of your mind!" she mocked him. "To propose a thing like that with my escort listening."

He held open the door for her and bowed like a servant. His eyes rested upon her bosom. He wanted her so badly he could taste her.

"If ever you change your mind, here's my card," he mumbled, pressing a visiting card into her hand.

We left him standing and gaping in the door. I was thunderstruck by his behavior. It was the first time I'd ever seen or heard of such a conversation outside the movies.

"Do people often make such propositions to you?" I inquired.

"All the time. He'll find out who I am in a few days and lay siege to my door," she answered, as if it were the most natural thing in the world.

I couldn't help wondering how many such propositions she had heeded. She was the type that scratched, bit, and clawed during the act, and after a night with her one felt as if one had been in battle. People recognized her wherever she went, in shops, in nightclubs, even at taxi stands. The men invariably got that certain transfigured look on their faces, and some of them grinned the smile of the wise. I wondered how many salesmen and taxi drivers had borne the marks of her fingernails upon their shoulderblades, how many of them had felt her teeth sink into their biceps, how many of them had felt her spittle upon their collarbones. She could never get enough, and it was always like the taming of a tigress.

She wasn't outstandingly beautiful, and she didn't affect the mannerisms that we associate with the glamor of the movie queens. Her figure, to be sure, was of startling proportions, but there are many women with excellent figures who don't have that strong an effect on men. It was more than that; something intangible, invisible, indefinable, something that hovered in the air when she was in the vicinity and communicated itself to everything male from fourteen to eighty; something our language isn't articulate enough to express and which is infinitely stronger than anything we can describe. Some women have it and others don't, and when you find one who has it, you're not only her slave but you've got a lifelong battle on your hands to determine who'll have her tomorrow. Neither wedding rings nor private detectives will ever keep the suitors away from such a woman. The best precaution you could take would be to make her have a child every year until she was too old to attract the competition. But this particular girl wouldn't have a child. She wanted to keep that figure, so that she'd be able to enjoy herself until she became so old that it didn't matter any longer.

She told me that one time she had asked her aged grand-mother when it was that a woman lost interest in sex. She had thought for sure that her grandmother, who was in her eighties, would be able to give her a satisfactory answer.

"I'm sorry, my child," the old lady had answered, "but I don't know. You'll have to ask a woman older than me." Apparently, it ran in the family.

Getting old was the only thing that ever worried the red-head. And since aging was one process she couldn't stop by crossing her shapely legs and adjusting the seams of her blouse, she was determined to derive all the pleasure she could from life before it was too late. From one lover to the next, she worried that she'd never find another. It was an obsession with her. She knew that forty was the borderline, and she worried night and day that she had crossed the boundary and there was no turning back. I wonder if she ever was happy.

Though she craved her sex every day of the year, I don't know whether she was able to enjoy it when she had it. When she was aroused, her whole body started working overtime, and from the waistline down she was like two clockworks rolled into one, moving in two directions at the same time. One of these motions threw her upward against the man's pelvis with a desperate, whipping fury, while she gasped, panted, and screamed. When she came near her climax, her screeching was enough to awaken the whole neighborhood. It was an eerie shouting, octaves higher than her normal tone of voice, of a strange, primitive, and orgiastic intensity that reminded me of a singing saw. It was impossible to stay at a hotel with her; she'd have the manager and the hotel de-tective at the door within minutes, with everyone wondering why I was trying to beat her to death. With the force and regularity of a locomotive, she'd let off those yells, and there was nothing one could do to silence her. She'd simply continue screaming at the top of her lungs until she had an orgasm. And when she cooled off, and the beads of perspiration dripped from her face, she'd alternately laugh and cry as if she had lost her reason. Sometimes she cried for hours into the night, especially when she was sore or exhausted, but some devil inside of her still craved more sex. Sometimes she frightened me.

The most wonderful woman I've ever known was Claudine. She used to work as a bar girl at a large striptease joint, where the well-proportioned hoofers knocked themselves out for seventy-five dollars a week. The bar-girls sat still and earned twice that much. In her teens, her parents, who were very religious, sent her to a Baptist college for girls, in the fond hope that little Claudine would grow up to be a good religious creature. It wasn't very long, however, until the Very Reverend biology professor and his assistant were chasing after Claudine, with the obvious intention of performing some not very religious, biological experiments upon her blond body; and the woman who coached physical education classes began to make advances in the hope of a different kind of physical education in which she undoubtedly was an even more skilled expert. Claudine, according to her own story, had the most excruciating time in preserving herself intact against all these lecherous advances from males and females, not to mention the somewhat less determined members of the staff and student body who were bent on poisoning her little soul with strong drink and all that it might lead to. After a year of these defensive maneuvers, she determined never to return to the scenes of her embarrassment, and when her parents insisted, she caught the train to the town where the college was located, but went straight on to the nearest large city.

These grim reminiscences of hers are to be taken with at least three grains of salt, for among the characteristics that all loose women on earth have in common is the tendency to talk at length and with great embellishment about their stalwart defense of maidenly virtues. They tell inspired stories about the wealthy men—they're usually wealthy—who have made advances to them, and how difficult it was for them to withstand the great temptation of so immense a profit for such a harmless night of pleasure. But no! Their virginity escaped unsullied—to be proffered to the first comer upon some other occasion, it seems. I've heard the most incredible tales of ladies in distress, even from professional prostitutes. Listening to their epics of flight and hot pursuit, I've always wondered how they could ever have lowered themselves so far, when they'd been such impeccable paragons of virtue. Their attempts to convince the listener of their sturdy primitive-Christian morality when dealing with other suitors, young and old, are difficult to reconcile with their incumbent roles as more or less free-lancing strumpets. They'll accuse one another of being whores, but they themselves are, let it be understood once and for all, above such reproaches. Try as one might, he can't escape the virtuous trollop, telling all and sundry lascivious dotards to lay off her untainted body, and taking money only from friends. (She has no enemies.) Furthermore, she's probably about to get married. This peccadillo with you is just a last, mad fling!

Claudine was hardly different from the others in that respect, and though she spoke freely of the various good-looking young chaps whom she had invited to her bedroom whenever she felt the inclination, she claimed to have defended to the very last ditch her somewhat tarnished honor when it came to the rich and masterful but profligate males who, according to her story, were constantly chasing after her for the pleasures to be derived from her sweet body. And, if one lent credence to her reports, it was astounding what extravagant promises they made to her and to what satanic trickery they resorted in order to share the comforts of her bed. What unstained purity awaited my eager embrace! How honored I must feel to be privileged to creep under her newly-laundered sheets with her—and that for nothing!

We maintained a sort of unwritten agreement that whenever I had any money I'd spend it on her, and when she had any, she'd reciprocate the gesture. And since I was going to college and lived on my wages as a part-time worker, the times were few indeed when I could dispose of much money for that noble purpose, but since she drew a steady twenty-five per cent of all the money that her would-be lovers and admirers spent on her in the bar, she usually was in clover. Claudine, therefore, deserves a good part of the credit for making me the man I am today, and I hope she isn't ashamed of that rather dubious distinction. Putting me through college gave her a spiteful thrill, it made her think she was getting even with the sanctimonious lechers who had chased after her in the religious institution. And since she could afford to call the tune for a college-bred man, she felt superior to the world of universities and professors which she had left with a bad taste in her mouth. With all my brains, she was able and willing to point out, she was better able to make a living than I was. That certainly was a true, if partial, observation. In fact, with all my brains, education, and years of experience, I still don't always make as good a living as she made then. But for this I lack certain essential equipment with which a kindly Mother Nature had endowed her.

Her striptease joint closed at one-thirty and drove out the last drunks at two, after which she had to remain to get paid for the day's activities. It required about half an hour for her to argue out the daily wages with the greasy Mediterranean type who managed the establishment. She always won her arguments. Triumphantly, she placed her money in her purse, changed into a comfortable skirt and sweater, and picked up her new car at the parking lot. She drove directly to the late hour restaurant and bar where I sat and nursed my brandy and soda, waiting for her arrival. The place belonged to a fellow named Max, who was a friend of ours, and he had a little back room with crap tables, slot machines, blackjack tables, and sometimes a roulette wheel. It was highly illegal, naturally, but things being what they were, the local sheriff received his rake-off, the politicians got theirs, and Max operated a nice little business. Occasionally, crackdowns came from higher up in the state government. Then the deputy sheriffs, most of whom had put their money into Max's machines a few days before, arrived with warrants and carted all the equipment away. Sometimes, a really eager chief investigator had them carry hammers, axes, and picks, and they smashed all the equipment on the spot. Max, usually having been forewarned, would empty the slot machines on the afternoon before and hide his most expensive equipment in the basement, so that the deputies could have their fun without his losing too much money. The newspapers always carried lengthy accounts of the raids, of the confiscated money —which never amounted to very much—and of the gambling machines that had been taken out of commission. Max never minded. I think the syndicate that took most of his earnings probably replaced the equipment. It was like having an insured automobile stolen. The main inconvenience is the paperwork in having it replaced. A couple of weeks would pass, while the gambling room was being refurnished, and then one day I'd see the gigantic bouncer standing at the curtain that divided the room from the bar, and I'd know that business was being conducted as usual again. Tony the bouncer had the mission of turning away anyone he didn't know or who looked suspicious, and of throwing out anyone who objected too forcefully to losing his money. Actually, Tony was a mild-mannered man who wouldn't harm a fly unless he got paid for it. But if there was trouble, he could pick up a hundred-and-eighty-pounder and fling him into the alley like a flour sack. It was in this lovely place that Claudine and I used to meet after she finished with her work.

The first chapter every evening was a recital of the extraordinary stories with which her admirers had tried to impress her. Until I met Claudine, I'd never realized what atrocious lies men tell to bar girls before the inevitable proposition. She looked through her customers as if they were made of glass, but she always pretended to believe them, at least until they ran out of money. She had among her collection gunrunners from Cuba, owners of vast industrial combines, kings of gangster empires, lords of the sport world, inventors of machines that would alter the destinies of nations, salesmen who'd sold everything tangible in the United States at least once, and veritable knaves who were plotting crimes of unprecedented magnitude and cruelty, all of whom were peaceful little people without much of a past and with less of a future, who had never done anything significant and never would do anything more venturesome than tell the boss he was a son-of-a-bitch. These "soldiers of fortune" reappeared every payday and told her more of their yarns, spending their hard-earned paychecks, and thinking all the while that she was taking them seriously as prospective lovers. They probably didn't understand that they could've supported a wife on the money that they spent on her, and she never granted them in return what the wife would've offered in abundance. In fact, she gave them nothing but contempt.

If only they had known what she thought of them! Like most bar girls, she considered her customers the lowest of the low, a slimy aggregate of stupid, ill-mannered, lascivious, unreasonably demanding oafs. She'd sooner have indulged in sexual relations with her janitor or with the shoeshine boy on the corner than allow any one of them the privacy of her boudoir. I used to marvel at my own good fortune, when she rendered the case histories. After all, I had also been a customer of hers once—though only once.

Some girls would've felt touched in a soft spot of their hearts by the middle-aged man who drew all the savings of a lifetime of hard work out of the bank to buy "double shots of whiskey" for Claudine, which really were cold tea, and of which she could drink at least fifty a night, at two dollars apiece. He hoped, of course, that she might go home with him some day, and probably thought of marrying her, since he was a widower. Not Claudine. She laughed at his persistence, and the relations between those two turned into a kind of contest between the endurance of Claudine's kidneys and the old fellow's savings account. And since she was a determined little girl with an iron constitution, there was never any question about the outcome. He spent all of his money, and after that he turned up only twice a month to wince and whine, while she spent his paycheck for him. She was an expert at the noble art of spending money. There was always a flower vendor about, who sold roses, orchids, and bouquets of violets; they always were good for a few dollars, and Claudine received a regular commission out of the exorbitant price. There always was the necessity of buying cigarettes, which in that club were unreasonably expensive, coming not out of a machine but from a cigarette girl who more than doubled the price. Claudine not only received a commission from her but never allowed the customer to pick up his change, holding her protective, little hand over it. "Let the poor girl have something, too," she'd say, and the victim hardly ever had the audacity to say no. Tips like that used to go into a central tip fund, a clever idea which precluded any rivalry betwen the employees. At the end of the week, the fund was divided into equal parts for the bar girls, the bartender, the janitor, and a cut for the house. Claudine also promoted the cause of this fund by giving lavish tips to the bartender and the doorman at closing time, always with the customer's money. Then she ordered food to be brought into the bar, which the customer naturally paid for. Just for the heck of it, she'd made him give a large tip to the delivery boy who didn't even give her a kickback. The customer's money never went very far, no matter how much it was. And if he braved it until closing time, she'd tell him a cordial "goodnight," dash off to get her car, and drive to Max's place to meet me.

Now I know that I should've married Claudine, but at the time I was too blind and too conceited to realize it. She was just my type, and she was in love with me. I could've been on Easy Street for years, and all that she'd have asked of me would've been to make love to her every day. But then I was young and foolish, and I said to myself that I never wanted to tie myself to any one girl, because I liked the other girls too much. I thought that there would always be another

Claudine, and after her, still another. A man has to get older and a great deal wiser before he realizes that there aren't many Claudines in this world who'll regard him as an idol rather than as a member of the fraternity of oafs and idiots who should be fleeced of the contents of their pocketbooks. The man tends to flatter himself that he can charm any woman, but without knowing it he sooner or later becomes one of those who spend all their money and go home alone.

One reason why I couldn't marry Claudine was that even though she was just twenty-three years old, she was a "woman with a past." She had a little boy, the offspring of her illicit relations with an Ohio nightclub king. It seems that when she decided to leave college she could think of no better employment opportunities than nightclubs, and this gentleman glanced at her slim legs when she was a hat-check girl in one of his establishments. Before long she was living with him. The bright-eyed child was the progeny of their relationship. The nightclub king, it appeared, was the jealous type and set his chauffeur to watch over her when she was alone. Claudine looked at the chauffeur, liked what she saw, and started to seduce him. At first, he hesitated to touch his boss's sweetheart, but she was young, pretty, and willing. . . . The two of them whiled away their leisure hours together until she became a mother. After that, the nightclub king found them out. Soon she found herself out on the street with a child and no money. The chauffeur had lost all interest.

There are many nightclubs in the United States, and before the disastrous nightclub slump of the mid-1940's there were even more. Claudine still possessed good looks, and she knew how to use whatever advantage she had. It wasn't long before she'd started drinking cold tea with love-starved bachelors and straw-widowers. I used to note how modestly she dressed, in

contrast to her colleagues, who used their clothes to empha-
size the quality of the merchandise which they were constantly selling but never delivered: sex. Claudine wore plain
but elegant dresses, reaching all the way up to her throat and
below her knees, with long sleeves and plenty of room to
move around in.

"The imagination is the most wonderful thing on earth,"
she used to say. "I let it work for me. Why should I show what
I've got, when your imagination will make you believe you
see a lot more?"

This metaphysical strategy had advanced her materially
in every conceivable way, and I could observe its effectiveness.
Considering it, I could also understand how she managed
to set up housekeeping on a comparatively lavish scale, afford
a maid, and give her little boy the best of everything. She
was a calculating creature and always knew what she wanted.
Mostly, it was money. As far as I could tell, her son and I
were the only exceptions to that rule.

Although I liked the child, I didn't fancy the responsibilities of fatherhood for another man's son. Claudine, on
the other hand, would've refused any suggestion of separation
from the child. One could more easily have hit the double
jackpot on one of Max's slot machines than convinced her to
give him up. And if I assumed the job of fatherhood, there
always was the possibility that the nightclub king might decide he wanted the child for himself. Claudine would put up
a fight like a cornered lioness, and I'd be caught in the middle
of a shooting gallery.

There were occasional reminders of the past, and the nightclub king did occasionally indicate an interest in getting the
boy. One day there was a sinister individual waiting for her
in the living room, waving a long cane at me, and inquiring

about my identity. I wondered whether poisoned arrows shot out of the cane, or if it was the harmless kind that merely opened into a dagger.

"Who's he?" the character asked, still pointing at me.

"A friend. What's it to you?" she snapped.

"A long-lost cousin, I suppose," he growled.

After a furious glance failed to dispose of my inconvenient presence, he decided to ignore me instead of pursuing the subject further and inquired about the child. The two of them exchanged some very bitter repartee, in the course of which it became clear to me that the nightclub king seemed certain that the little boy was his and not his chauffeur's, that he was eager to get possession of the child to rear him in his own image, and that Daggers meant at all costs to have a look at him. On the other hand, I was surprised to see Claudine develop a profane vocabulary and an obstinate courage of which I'd never have suspected her little person. So determined was she not to let her child have the slightest contact with his father that she wouldn't even let Daggers have a look at him. Daggers, accustomed to having his own way, moved across the room and reached for the door leading to the nursery.

Claudine, even more to my surprise, suddenly produced from her purse a small ivory-handled pistol, which I would've guessed was one of those Belgian .22's that pass by the name of "ladies' special"—presumably to ensure the safety of the ladies' ladylike virtues. Incongruous as it was to see little Claudine handling that shooting-iron, there was no mistaking her determination when she spoke.

"If you touch him or do any harm to him, I'll kill you, so help me, I'll kill you!" she shrieked.

He must've turned the doorknob before she got through to him for the door slowly opened and revealed the person of Hattie, the colored maid, who stood there rather awkwardly, her lips trembling with fear. Behind her, the little boy made waking noises and raised himself in his bed. For some long minutes, no one spoke a word. Claudine, a little frightened of her own courage, was waving her pistol, Daggers twisted his neck to catch a glimpse of the boy behind the portly maid, and I certainly wasn't going to make any useless remarks.

Daggers mumbled something about not being foolish and promised to render a faithful account of the entire interview to his boss. Claudine told him to do exactly that and not to forget a single detail.

He walked across the room with deliberate coolness and placed himself in front of her. I expected at any moment to hear the report of the shot and to see his body drop on the rug. The colored maid was still standing in the door in silent horror, her lips moving as if she were trying to speak, but she didn't utter a single sound. Claudine never blinked. Her slim right hand raised the pistol gradually, until it was exactly level with one of the buttons on Daggers' overcoat. I found myself speculating on whether that button might deflect the bullet, and wondering why Daggers didn't use his cane.

But his intentions, for the moment at least, were peaceful. He bade her a formal farewell and, with a show of slowness, walked out of the apartment. The door closed behind him. Claudine stood motionless for several more long minutes, pointing her pistol toward the spot where the man had vanished. The colored maid sat down and started muttering and crying as if she had been hurt. I looked at the little boy who was sobbing noiselessly into his pillow, his hand warding off the light from the living room. For lack of anything better to do, I closed the door to let him sleep while we had the inevitable explanations.

Hattie, after she managed to calm herself and made sure there was nothing more she could do for Claudine, put on her coat with an audible sigh of relief and was on her way as quickly as possible.

"Pour me a drink, Phil, would you please?" Claudine said to me. "I need it."

"We both need one," I replied while going to get the ice cubes. As far as I was concerned, I knew I needed a stiff one.

Claudine snapped the safety catch back on the trigger and put away her ivory-handled pistol. For a while she said nothing at all. After Hattie had left, she sat on the sofa and sipped her Scotch and soda, which I had mixed for her. I anticipated that she'd want to talk, but I knew better than to cross-examine her. I stared out of the picture window at the streetlights turning weak against the pale sky, with the light blue morning rising from the east with edges of purple at the horizon.

"I loved him a lot, when I conceived the child," Claudine suddenly started. "I knew he was married and his wife would never let him get a divorce, but I didn't care. I might've stayed with him and let him spoil the child as he spoiled everything he touched, and I might still be sitting up nights and worrying about the chicks he'd take to the back room and the detectives he'd hire to shadow me. That's the way he was. He was the almighty boss, and he could do whatever he wanted. But me, I had to stay at home by my little lonesome and wait for my lord and master until it pleased him to enter my bedroom. And I might've done it for years longer, if he hadn't been so mean to me about the chauffeur."

"Well," I suggested, "you said yourself that there were grounds for suspicion."

"Grounds? Of course there were grounds! Do you think I'd let that rat get away with treating me like that? I wanted to have a little fun, too. So, I got the chauffeur to make love to me. Anything wrong with that? He used to do the same thing to me almost every day. And every morning he came home drunk."

I was as silent as the Great Sphinx, always amazed at women's logic.

"So, when I'd had my fun, he found me out. So what? I got the best of him. I got his child. There isn't anything he wouldn't do to get ahold of that boy, nothing he'd shy away from. He might send somebody to kill me next time. Before I let go of that child, that's what he'll have to do, kill me."

"Do you think that's what he sent Daggers here for?"

"Oh, him? That's Joe. He's his right-hand man. He'd never do the dirty work himself. He came here to scare me, so that I'd give in without a struggle. But I'm going to give them the fight of their lives."

I'd had enough of thoughts of violence and death for the day, but I didn't have the slightest idea what to do in order to snap her out of her mood. I resorted at last to my usual, and best, method of dealing with excited women: I kissed her and started taking her clothes off. At first, she didn't seem to react. She absentmindedly let me kiss her neck and her cheeks, as if I were hanging up a picture or washing her gloves while she thought of more important matters. She poured herself some more Scotch and sat there with the drink in both of her hands, trembling with nervousness like a cornered doe and staring down at the carpet. But when I began to unbutton her blouse, she gently kissed me behind the ears, and with a little jerk she kicked off her shoes. I had a habit of kissing her thighs under her skirt above her stockings while I undid my necktie and took off my clothes. It always made her shiver with delight. On this particular morning, she moaned with longing when I touched her with my lips. She placed her glass on the table, spread her arms wide open, as if she meant to embrace the earth, and flung herself on her back.

"Love me, honey, love me today!" she shouted, as if she were afraid in that tender moment that I'd leave her. "Please, Phil, make love to me! Give it to me, please, deep inside of me, where I need it!" And she panted like a hunted animal while she rubbed against me passionately.

Her hands passed up and down my back, and she bit crazily into the hair on my chest. When I undid her bra, she shook loose from it and put her firm little breasts in front of my lips with a wiggle, as if she were one of the strippers who threw their bodies around on the stage of her nightclub. She shook and wound loose from her panties like a prisoner shaking off her manacles and rope. Her entire body thrilled and writhed with anticipation next to mine.

"Make love to me, honey, please, don't make me wait! Deep inside of me, please! I'm hungry for you! It aches, I'm so hungry for you! I can't stand the empty feeling inside of me! Please come and fill me, honey! Ah!"

When I penetrated her, she gave forth a short, gasping cry every time she exhaled, and she was breathing furiously. It wasn't long until she screeched into my ears and held my hips with her legs, moving her abdomen in concentric circles. She propped herself up on her elbows and threw her sex at me as if she meant to spear me with her spine. At last, she pushed up at me with a gigantic lunge. I could feel the levels rising within me and demanding their release as if something were pumping inside. Her flesh was pulsating with a heat and fury that I had never sensed in another woman. She held me clasped with her thighs and pressed my chest against herself while her head struggled upwards toward mine and her tongue bathed me. We were both vibrating and gasping for air.

"Don't ever leave me!" she panted when I tried to climb down from her to wipe the beads of sweat off my back. "Don't ever leave me. Just stay with me that way, like we are now!"

We remained that way a long time. Women have a way of making even the most absurd requests seem possible. Her flesh, after a short while, began to convulse and pulsate once more, although I hadn't moved, and a happy grin lit up her face.

Excitement of all kinds, whether positive or negative, seems to agitate the sexual instinct in women, and they seek release in sex from all tensions of life. If they have a tiff with their parents—to bed, take it out on the patient flesh! If they have quarrels with their husbands—to bed, whether with their own husbands or with someone else's, to rid themselves of their surplus energy! If they can't get along with their bosses at work, at home there is always the couch waiting for them with all the pleasures it offers. If they get in trouble with the authorities—to bed for consolation! If they get into a fight with another woman—to bed, to shoot off their un- needed adrenalin! If they suffer from philosophical melan- choly—to bed, to enjoy the delights of the genitals! If they miss the streetcar—to bed, for a quick release from the taut anger of the moment! If the electricity won't work—to bed, to take advantage of the unexpected darkness! To bed! To bed for comfort and solace under any and all circumstances. Claudine was no exception. Even danger to their health and the proximity of death sends them into the arms of a lover. The more violent the heartbeat, the more passionate their embrace the next moment.

The mother instinct is possibly the strongest drive in women, and once it's aroused the craving for sex is greater than at any other time. I've known quite a few women who stood in danger of losing their children, either because they were divorced or because they weren't married when the child was born. And I've known others who were forced to give up their babies as soon as they had seen the light of day. In all cases, I learned that there was nothing stronger in the world than the mother instinct. Mothers love their children they've never seen, children who are complete strangers to them and whom they'd never recognize on the street, children who had been adopted through the offices of agencies for the placement of unwanted babies which make it a condition for their service that there never be any effort to contact the child, that the mother renounce all claims and never try to learn of its whereabouts. The mothers signed the papers, delivered their babies, and cried their hearts out whenever the subject was raised. I've known mothers who, because of their slovenly habits, because they took on lovers, or because they were ruled irresponsible and erratic by the court, lost their children to their ex-husbands, to their parents-in-law, or to orphanages, and they were all alcoholics. If there had been a way of kidnaping the child and abducting it to a foreign country, they would've sold their souls to do it. Even the most docile cat may attack a person if he moves between her and her kittens, and the human animal is no different. I had no doubt that Claudine would've shot Joe in cold blood if he had tried to take the little boy with him. And if Joe had ever set foot in her apartment again, I wouldn't have

given a plugged nickel for his life. And Claudine hated violence. Whenever there was a fight in her bar—and there are
fights in all bars—she got sick.

There probably is a good reason why women become especially passionate when their mother-instinct is irritated.
Axel Munthe says in his book, *The Story of San Michele,* that
the prevalence of epidemics stimulates the sex instinct in
man, and that this is nature's way of evening up the score
when thousands must die of disease. And woman's only way
of replacing a lost child is to have another. And so, she labors
and travails to produce another baby to make up for the one
that she lost or the one that is threatened. Threaten the child
and seduce the mother; or better still, protect the child and
seduce the mother! That would be one of the safest lines of
approach for a man to operate with.

II Lynn: Early Snow

When I was in my late twenties, I worked in the same office with a woman some eight or ten years older than I, who tried her level best to seduce me. She wanted to act refined about the whole thing. That was her undoing. If she had simply come out and said, "Come over and sleep with me tonight," I would've replied, "Gladly." But something inside of her made her hold out the bait like a highschool girl while making like Rabelais, and in the next moment, she'd play it coy and fish for compliments. One never knew where one stood with her. On the one hand, I was as sure that she wanted my body as I was of my own name, but on the other hand, she wouldn't get down to brass tacks. What she wanted, of course, was the lengthy courtship, the touching scenes, the tender gestures, the longing glance of the rolling eyes, and the words of worship that had remained in her mind the image of love. That's the way love starts out for most American women in their teens, and that's what they crave to have repeated when they're forty, giving them the false picture of themselves as the queen of the graduation ball.

Her name was Lynn. She wasn't at all a bad character. If I had only met her a few years later, I could've obliged her and made her happy, but at that stage of the game I wasn't ready for her. It wouldn't have been so bad if she hadn't had such a wrinkled face. She mustn't have taken care of her skin with the oils, salves, mud-packs, and ointments that most girls seem to use to the age of grandmotherhood. She had deep wrinkles across her forehead that looked like furrows in a field, crowfeet at the corners of her eyes that would've made her tears roll sideways, deep lines from her nostrils to the corners of her mouth, and the little monkey wrinkles between her nose and her eyeslits that make a woman look as if she had been through the mill. I could've put up with all of it except those monkey wrinkles which somehow hid her iris. Every once in a while, I'd take a good look at her breasts, which were fairly large and seemed to be firm enough, and at her legs, which were pretty shapely, and I'd take my heart in my hands and try to approach her with some compliments. I just couldn't ignore those monkey wrinkles, however. They wouldn't let me speak up.

She used to say that after thirty you just don't care any more, and that was the time when you really began having fun. I didn't think that she was having too much fun, and that she herself wasn't a living proof of her opinion, but it used to stimulate my lecherous imagination. Was it true? Did women stop caring after thirty and abandon themselves for the asking? Unfortunately, as I've learned since then, it was generalization. The opposite may well be the case.

What she really meant, I believe, was something else: That, before a person could really enjoy life to the fullest and drink the cup to the lees, he must have his heart broken into tiny bits, trampled on, and crushed into dust. He must have his emotions exposed and spat upon, and have his soul illuminated in a naked posture of embarrassment and scoffed at by someone that he has held very dear. And then, if that person has suffered the worst and found that it didn't destroy him, when he has found out that his heart can function on as a muscle that pumps blood without the faintest trace of emotion, when blame and guilt, reproach and recrimination, accusation and punishment, haunting memories and cruel blows of injustice have failed to wreck him, he's ready to accept life upon its own terms. Lynn looked as if she had been through the mill, and I imagine she had. Those monkey wrinkles were on her face for a good reason. And beyond the wrinkles, there was something about her that suggested that the blows of fate wouldn't touch her, because she had been whipped by them and had grown armor plating. I rather liked that quality in her, and I only wished it could've been combined with a more pleasant face. Wisdom and character are the prerequisites for a good friend, but in a mistress I require beauty to stimulate my desire.

It needed several more disappointments and many bitter blows before I had reached the stage where I could properly appreciate a woman like Lynn. Disappointments accustom a person to the sensation of an expanding rock crushing his chest between the heart and the windpipe, the choking of one's breath when the air is fine, and a childish desire to shed tears which run into the mouth and cause a salty flavor because they can't get out. Whenever I extend my hand and it's accepted, I've come to be grateful because no one raps me over the knuckles, for that kind of beating can be the harshest punishment in the world. But the harshest blows aren't even those of deliberate cruelty; the most cruel injustice is that of indifference. Being smashed, trampled, and beaten is hellish, but being ignored is infinitely worse. When the ego learns that the other person isn't flinging dung at it but merely happens to hit it with a stray piece in the normal course of activities, the remainders of pride rattle in their death throes and the child dies a thousand stinging deaths in the prostrate soul of the adult. That's where the crucible lies in which we're tested. Only those who manage to pass that fire test emerge into the ultimate kingdom, which is of this earth and not in the hereafter, where all bounds are shattered and man transcends himself.

I used to marvel at the ability of married people to survive years of carping, bickering, and nagging, and at their apparent willingness to continue in a state which appeared to be a bed of thorns rather than of roses. People married for several decades often seemed to make it a habit, to be followed throughout their waking hours, to give one another harsh words and spoil each other's lives. Only recently have I realized that their disagreeableness is their manner of letting each other know that they still are, indeed, important to each other, that for lack of anything good to say they're using nasty words to let each other know that they still care. They are, in other words, making social noises.

Once you've understood this fact of life with all your heart, your attitude toward people changes, because you dispense with your previous dependence upon them for bolstering your morale. And you may no longer seek in a love affair the incarnation of an essentially pagan worship of beauty. You mainly want the other person to refrain from trampling on the tender twigs of your emotions, to abstain from sitting down upon the delicate blossoms of your thoughts and crushing the breath out of them, to stay away from the idea that the entire relationship consists of a blind worship of her contours, and not to yield to her natural temptation to use her sex as an instrument for reducing you to a doting servant. What you want, once you've seen the light, is a companion who'll know enough to cover the bare spots which you expose to the chill of the morning. What you need is a friend who'll let you talk about things that matter to you and shut her mouth when she feels like interrupting with news about the butcher's dog or about what Mrs. Jones said to Mrs. Smith about Mrs. Thompson. And what you dream of is a mistress who'll give you a hug and a squeeze when you want to make love to her and who won't push you away to prevent her new nightgown from being soiled. If this female should happen to look like your favorite movie actress, so much the better. But after you've been seared and branded, the monkey wrinkles no longer matter nearly as much, and you can find a word of kindness now and then and make it sound good. It's like reaching a second adulthood.

Men and women really want very different things from each other, and that fact is at the bottom of the basic conflict that has raged between them ever since the first Cro-Magnon man carved the image of a fat pin-up on his cave wall. The older and wiser a man becomes, the more he will seek a relationship rather than an affair, but women don't seem to change their taste in their relationship with men and would

rather have an affair than a relationship even after their
menopause. For women, though they may prefer security
to excitement in their heads, have their hearts set on adventure. Even after their dreams have remained unfulfilled for
decades and their memories are crowded with heartbreaks,
the thought of romance whips up their emotions to a state
of pleasant violence—whether scepticism has taught them
to react negatively to certain advances or a childlike optimism
still moves their imagination at the idea of a gallant prince
on his white charger.

A relationship is as delicate as the golden sheen of the sun
on a blond woman's hair and as gentle as a fawn blinking at
its mother, while an affair may often burn with an angry
flame and consume its substance with the voraciousness of
an oil fire. A relationship is the evening breeze rustling in
the poplars on a warm day; an affair is the plumed breaker
crushing the dykes at the seashore, sweeping foam and land
before it. A relationship is the peace of a field of ripe grain
basking its brownness in the moonlight's silver; an affair is the
piercing cry of a mother giving birth and the hot fragrance
of fresh blood.

A man may choose a companion with monkey wrinkles
and think more highly of her than he does of the suggestive
aura of a divinely young body, but his mistress will always
be the latent promise of smiling passion, and his woman,
unable to stomach the thought of dividing his affections,
cannot bear the knowledge of what the monkey wrinkles
imply. Convenience and comfort dictate the relationship as
the most livable form of heterosexual companionship. While
passion may conduct the man into the arms of a fiery princess,
he'd tend to return into the peace of compatibility, if his
companion would permit it. Our society rather frowns upon

the toleration of passion for a third person in a marriage of compatibility and peace, and thus it turns the instincts of the male animal into a subterranean volcano which smolders in the earth of convention and threatens to erupt whenever the heat of fury melts the sand.

We have millions of such smoldering volcanoes beneath the surface of bourgeois respectability yet we pretend surprise when one of them erupts and buries in its glowing lava the rafters of a presumably happy home, to leave nothing but the ashes. Along the path, myriads of embers are still smoking from the eruptions of yesteryear, but we still refuse to recognize the dangers of repetition today and tomorrow. We refuse to accept the factuality of fire, heat, and explosion. But when you sit on top of a volcanic mountain and deny the truth of its impending eruption, you have nothing to which to look forward but being crushed and cremated. The molten lava has buried cities of happiness and burned out empires of bliss. White-hot flames of ghastly fires lick to the skies of our institutionalized world, singeing the walls we create between us and collapsing the foundations of artificial buildings. We're dying daily of the after-effects of the age of Puritanical coldness and Pauline virtue, when the cities of the mind were built upon the quicksands of superstition. We're burning out our passions in frustration and madness, because "Thou Shalt Not" is still more powerful magic than "I Will." We're tormenting ourselves with the icicles of Hibernia because we fear the heat of igneous streams. We're vegetating in a gigantic Pompeii and pretending that our emotions are still alive. It's small wonder that the incidence of insanity is steadily on the rise for in our society normality is the only condition that doesn't exist.

It's probably because ours is a matriarchal society that

we're made to pretend that the affair of marriage will never become the more mature relationship, and that the idea of having affairs must perish with the first experiment. And so, when she makes believe that there will be hot fury at a late age for romance, woman serves her own cause and that of her sisters, for any acknowledgment that there could be such a thing as a relationship serving the convenience of both parties would essentially obviate the idea of marriage and thus destroy the clever foundation for woman's security within the home. It matters little whether the particular woman under consideration is married or not; she won't betray her sisters. Consequently, if she is to live with a man, there must be romance, ardor, and passionate devotion.

It became a game between Lynn and me, a game in which there could be no winner. I thought at first that the best manner of solving the problem was to treat her simply as a fellow worker and pretend that I didn't notice her in what she was trying to do, but no woman will let a man get away with such an easy solution or admit that her charms might've failed to attract the object of her affection, and she hinted more and more broadly that she wanted to be adored by me. She must've thought me very stupid to imagine that I was oblivious to her tricks. In these circumstances, I imagined the best thing would be to proceed as though her infatuation with me were some sort of disease which might pass, and I attempted to remain as quiet and unobtrusive as possible, but that only intensified her efforts for it showed a certain concern about her person and thus could be interpreted as a triumph or a challenge. There was, of course, the alternative of telling her to shut up and take her emotions and park them somewhere else, but she was too nice a person to insult, and I didn't know whether such remarks mightn't provoke a violent scene, with name-calling and much shouting, which I tried to avoid like the plague. At work, there aren't too many ways of protecting oneself from one's fellow employees. Unless one has a private office, which I didn't, one is exposed to whatever they care to babble about. For me, the most difficult part of working has never been the performance of my actual duties but rather the demand that I also act as companion to my fellow workers. I deemed it bad enough to have to serve as a sounding board for a superior who was a silly old woman, and for the dull-minded people in the office, whose intellectual limits were stretched to their utmost by a discussion of the weather and the latest news. I could consent to serving as a stud-horse for love-starved colleagues of the feminine gender, if they'd just invite me for some after-hour drinks with no pretext about their purpose. But I strenuously objected to the role of an unpaid gigolo as part of the conditions for my employment. The game was no fun. I wished that she'd concentrate her amorous attentions upon someone else and try to be friends with me. I've always enjoyed friendships with women who knew what the score was, though that didn't mean I was madly in love with them.

My surprise was rather great when Lynn took an apartment across the hall from mine and told me of her efforts to furnish it in a style becoming to her and the surroundings. Did I have any suggestions? Had I ever seen the place?

I answered in a dispassionate and objective fashion, spoke of the problem of interior decoration without the suggestion of a personal involvement, and offered to be of help whenever there was anything concrete that I could do.

I wonder whether she sat behind her front door in her living room and waited for me to ring the bell. If so, she must've spent some humiliating hours, for by now I was far too embarrassed simply to ring the bell and look at the arrangement of her furniture. Nor was I in any mood to adopt subtle excuses. If I went to her apartment to go to bed with her, I wouldn't make believe that I was "taking advantage" of the role of interior decorator. And if she wanted me for a stud-horse, I didn't want her to expect the pattern of behavior of a lap-dog. For a short while, I entertained the idea of knocking on her door, walking into the apartment when admitted, and saying, "Let's you and me have fun," taking her by surprise, and throwing her on the bed. But I rejected the idea as likely to lead to bitterness and recriminations. The best plan, I still thought, was to let her become discouraged and hope for her to discover a more attractive and a more devoted man.

How many nights, I wonder, did she sit in her living room and think of me while I sat in mine and wanted a woman, and we were only fifty feet apart? Walls of superstition, emotions, and personal conceit separated us, when the ring of a bell might've united our bodies in mutual ardor and created the all-forgiving intoxication that we call love. Walls of faith in reverse, walls of empty concepts fostered by old wives tales, class-B movies, and calendar art.

I thought of her. She was half an inch taller than I. Perhaps everything would've been all right if she'd only learned how to take care of her hair. A woman's hair is half her beauty. Hers was naturally of a dark-brown color, not in itself unattractive, but she dyed it light red. To dye hair, unfortunately, means undertaking a hard and regular commitment, for as soon as the hair grows an eighth of an inch, the dark roots show up very prominently and give it a shaggy-dog effect which I find quite repulsive. Moreover, bleaching and ordinary dying result in an elimination of the natural oils of the scalp by the oxygen in the dye, and the hair dries up and becomes kinky, loses its luster, and appears more like the stuffing of a mattress than the natural adornment of a woman's head. It requires frequent massages with fatty substances and two thorough dye jobs per week to render a bleached head of hair attractive. If a woman is willing to invest that much care, effort, and time to it, the dyed hair can be very seductive, but if she isn't it becomes the mark of a slattern. Lynn, with the indifference of a lonely middle age, had her hair dyed about once a month, and so it grew in all shades of red and brown, looked about as tidy as an unmade bed, and stood out in all directions. Now and then she combed it in front of everybody and set it with hairpins—a ludicrous effort, since she never looked better afterwards than she had before. The silliest thing was that occasionally she'd look into her pocket-mirror and seek to adjust some little end of her coiffure, as if it were the only obstacle between her and perfection. Having adjusted the recalcitrant hair, she'd smile with satisfaction, as if she were saying, "Once more, I look my old, desirable self." Meanwhile, the dandruff gathered on her dark hair roots.

Her eyebrows were another case in point. Women often paint their eyebrows to reinforce their color and accentuate the contrast to their white lids. Others shave their eyebrows or pluck out parts of them and paint new eyebrows on themselves, presumably improving the position of the brows with relation to the eye-slits. Both techniques can be used with skill and to great advantage, if the woman knows the strengths and weaknesses of her facial appearance and acts accordingly. The one thing that makes a woman's eyebrows ridiculous and repulsive is first to have them shaved and then to let them grow in, or simply to ignore the natural contours of the brow and to paint a second set on top of the first. Lynn, with the neglect exemplified in her hair, plucked them now and then, and then waited until there was quite a promising harvest before repeating the operation—good economy of time, but bad feminine strategy. On top of the first and natural set, she painted a pair of slanting brows that looked like copies of the Chinese devil pictures. They formed a triangle with her natural eyebrows, open toward the temples like forks. Between the remainder of the natural and the line of the artificial brows, there were spotty remnants of the larger ones that would've been hers, had she not occasionally plucked them. I always had to think of a mangy cat when I studied her face.

Her eyes sat under the coarse, granular structure of her upper lids and next to the monkey wrinkles, squeezed in by her crows feet. They were small, round, and dark-brown, with extremely small pupils, like those of a small ape. The white parts of her orbs were quaintly yellowed as if she had nicotine stains on them, and occasionally a blood-shot pattern of red veins showed in the yellow part to make her look ill and mouldy. It gave her the appearance of advanced age.

Her nose was small and thin and the youngest-looking part of her face, an incongruous nose in a countenance that showed enough wear and tear to belong to a persecuted refugee. It sat between the deep lines that framed her cheeks and the monkey wrinkles which made her eyes look even more rounded than they were. There also was a curious contrast between the raw, almost virginal whiteness of her nostrils and the leathery quality of her cheeks. It made the nose look almost superimposed, as if she'd bought a clown's nose in a novelty store and pasted it on her oldish face.

Under a long upper lip there sat the mouth whose lips were

well-shaped like those of a college girl and conveyed the idea of strength and kissability. It was a nice mouth, curved in two rather narrow lips with very pronounced angles in its corners. When she smiled it was flanked by dimples which had lined her with two odd wrinkles, the meaning of which became apparent only with the smile. Something kittenish and coy hung about that mouth which, with the little nose, made her face appear in two parts, the old part and the young. It reminded me of some men, whose faces look as if an old mask had been superimposed upon the child's face which was afraid to show itself to the world.

Her chin was well-formed and curved, but she had under it a second chin, although otherwise she wasn't fat. The double chin, ruddy and firm, again stood in strange contrast to the flaccid, large-pored skin of her neck, an epidermis which indicated that she must've been much heavier in her more prosperous days. Her skin became even more coarse and red around the lower portion of her neck, and when she wore a dress with a V-line, she showed that large skin texture all the way down to her breasts. It's always a sure giveaway for middleage.

Her body sometimes showed to good advantage underneath her clothes, but since she'd had trouble keeping jobs before, owing to her various adventures with younger men, she now garbed herself in shapeless tunics and drab sacks so as to indicate that she was accepting middle age with good grace. Only when all of her new, unimaginative wardrobe was at the cleaner's did she appear in clothing which revealed that she might have points of physical interest to a man: a pair of well-developed breasts, a strong, muscular waist, and well-shaped legs, usually draped in heavy silk stockings. When she wore her old shoes from her more glamorous days, her legs showed up to particularly good advantage, and one remembered Keats's line, "She walks in beauty like the night."

Perhaps, then, it was her new pose of middle-aged office worker without hope that made her seem less desirable than the usual woman that one cares to date. At any rate, her carelessness of appearance and traces of extravagant and strenuous living spoiled whatever appreciation I might've had for her physical charms. She often spoke of the days when she held two jobs in order to pay off some of her debts, days when she worked sixteen hours and got little sleep. I'd attribute the deterioration in her appearance to that period, if I were to judge without additional information. Lack of sleep, in my experience, is the deadliest factor when it comes to the question of youthful versus aged appearance. The skin around the eyes, more than any other portion of the physiognomy, betrays late hours. A good-time girl who sleeps all day can look infinitely better than a woman who earns an honest living sixteen hours a day.

One reason that I didn't go to see her when she lived so near me was that I used to become utterly enraged at her form of coyness. She must've read somewhere that silly adage about mystery making up half a woman's charm, for she used to start tales of the most astounding frankness and lead one to believe that she was about to launch into discreet confidences, and then she'd break off her narrative when she came to the interesting part and leave one suspended in mid-air. She also used to drop dark hints about maintaining an active love life and knowing all there was to know about the noble art of sex, but when it came right down to saying so, she dropped back into the gossamer of obscurity. Her most accomplished gesture was the mysterious smile. Having led her listener right to the brink of feverish interest, she had the effrontery to push one back into a feeling of distance and distrust. She worked indefatigably at arousing one's curiosity about her private life and then pretended to be offended at the scrutiny to which one subjected her activities. After she succeeded in evoking one's sympathy, she veiled herself in her protective shell.

When anyone, male or female, plays such games with me, my first instinct is to turn my back on him and leave him to his own devices. But being forced to collaborate in the same room with her it was difficult to isolate myself from Lynn's trickery and escape being caught in the net. And being caught was exactly what I was trying my best to avoid. For once a woman has caught a man in the webs of her schemes, she can dominate him and exact her price—a price, in most instances, not of love-making and physical satisfaction, but of flattery, ostentatious readiness to run errands, and subordination of his sphere of action to her own world of housekeeping details, neighborhood gossip, and intricate relationships between friends, relatives, acquaintances, and passers-by. I actively fought against being included in Lynn's world, which was no more interesting than that of most middle-aged women with a third-rate clerical job. We actually played two simultaneous games: One, to see whether she could make me fall in love with her, and the second to determine whether I was going to carry her parcels and listen to what her sister said to her landlady last Tuesday, what she said to a man who'd made in-decent propositions to her, and what she did for entertain-ment when she worked in Phoenix, Arizona. It became diffi-cult for me to do my work, which, after all, I was paid for, while she babbled and giggled on. I tried mentally to turn my back on her by thinking of good books.

The affair—if that's what one would call it—came to a head when Lynn invited me officially to her apartment. She said something about the mountain which had come to Mohammed, since Mohammed wouldn't come to the mountain, and asked me in for drinks. Now, I thought, we're getting to the point at last. She has seen the light. We're through making pretenses and laying traps and coming out into the open. I filled myself full of bulky and fatty food, the better to withstand the effects of the alcohol, and knocked on her door.

She had drawn the drapes and lit a couple of little lamps in a corner, dressed herself in an elegant cocktail outfit and draped herself all over an overstuffed armchair, which she never left during the course of the evening. I was sent to the kitchen to mix the drinks, empty the ashtrays, and refill the little sandwich plate from a pile of prepared and stacked victuals she had spread on the table by the sink, sufficiently large for a crowd of callers. During the entire evening, I listened to her dark hints regarding her adventures as a teenager, which were too stale to attract much interest, her family troubles, which didn't concern me in the least, her college days, which she embellished with an unreal glory, and her domestic cares, which I couldn't know if she performed or not, because it was too dark in the room. I hardly ever got a word in edgewise, and since there wasn't any chance of things working out as I wanted them to, I seized on the occasion to get gloriously plastered. In my memory, it appears to me as if her mouth had enlarged itself that night to consist of gigantic organs of speech, and they were working overtime throughout the ticking of the clock until three o'clock in the morning, at which time I'd had enough. Her dimples grew deeper, as her mysterious smile was called into being once more, and her glass kept swaying back and forth, because she talked with her hands like a Frenchwoman. The cigarettes piled up into stinking heaps of debris, and I made things easy for myself by letting the ashtrays spill over before I staggered into the kitchen again and looked for the garbage can. The bottle went on the wane fairly soon, and we started another one, which we managed to consume halfway before I quit. And I found out that she was a much more experienced drinker than I. With all my fatty and bulky foods, I was getting intoxicated more quickly than she was. It turned out that during one of her unfortunate marriages—she'd had a couple of them—she spent most of her waking hours drinking herself to sleep. Gradually, the enchantment of the dim lighting and the alcohol evaporated, and I again perceived things with that stark sense of reality which always accompanies drinking in my case when I'm not losing control. I saw Lynn's decaying facial skin stretched taut over her prominent skull, with the monkey wrinkles shading her cheeks so as to increase the death-head effect she imparted under the halo of her red-and-brown, coarse, and dried-up hair. I saw her flabby neck under her double chin, and the drops of water dripping down on her dress from the bottom of the glass, where the chill of the ice made the dew gather. I saw the cigarette ashes on her ruffled cocktail dress and wondered whether she had burned any holes into it, and I noticed a somewhat soiled bra showing above the top of the dress, forced up by the pressure of her body. I saw the heel of her left stocking sitting on her crooked, and I wondered if she'd be able to walk like that. I saw the stains on her new shoes and thought she must be suffering agonies because the upper parts of those shoes seemed to be eating into her flesh. Above it all, there was the constant din of her voice, uttering words which had no more coherence for me, interrupted every now and then by a laugh of self-indulgence. And I asked myself, Is that what I'm supposed to adore and worship on my knees, profess my undying love for, and get hot for like a rutty roe-buck? Is that the object of my affections for the next few months? Should I tell *her* that I'm overwhelmed by her beauty?

I thought very seriously of saying, "Look, Lynn, shut up, take off that ridiculous old bunch of ruffles, and spread your legs!" But a serious consideration told me, even in my drunken stupor, that she would've laughed at me. What she wanted me to do was to drink champagne out of her sweaty shoes like the Parisians in the operettas and tell her that she looked like Miss America, only better. She used to say, "Words, they're the most potent weapons a man has. With words, a man can do anything." I took that to mean that, in her case at least, flattery would get me everywhere. Only I've always been a bad liar, and I prefer not to lie at all. That may be the reason I've never succeeded in seducing a woman whom I didn't deem very beautiful. In those cases, I could say it and mean it.

When I was tight enough to suspect that I might go to sleep next time I blinked my eyes, I thanked her for her hospitality and left. I staggered across the corridor and went to bed in my apartment, still thinking of those lips of hers moving with a constant stream of sounds and her voice continuing through the hours to envelop all the subjects and objects of feminine attention.

Not to be outdone in hospitality, I invited her over next week. Maybe, I thought, she'd be more relaxed and relapse into that state of active eroticism which she so often hinted at in the office, when she actually found herself in a bachelor's apartment. I bought her favorite whiskey and put fresh sheets on the bed and laid in a supply of cigarettes and soda water.

She appeared at exactly the stipulated hour, dressed up in an even more ancient party dress and a pair of tight shoes that made her feet swell out under them. Her hair was straggly as usual, and her face was covered with a heavy mask of powder and make-up, which made her look grotesquely like a clown. In spite of all the war paint and the cake of flour, the monkey wrinkles broke through within five minutes. There was flaky powder on the sofa on which she sat.

The evening went exactly like the one the week before. She talked a blue streak of banalities while I filled up the glasses. I had decided to get her drunk that day, and several times I cheated on the mixing of the drinks and used gin instead of soda water to mix with her whiskey. It must've tasted bad and strong enough to dope a horse, but she sat there quietly and went on talking as if I had given her a glass of orange juice. On the other hand, in spite of all my precautions, I drank myself into a stupor, just matching her strong drinks with weak ones of my own, and I not only didn't feel like saying anything, but I wasn't able to say anything in reply to all the torrents of words that gushed forth from her like water from a geyser. I sat and studied the powder crumbling on her cheeks and falling down on my furniture, the latches of her worn-out shoes cutting into her arches, the fluffy curls bobbing up and down above her forehead when she laughed, and her yellowish eyeballs rolling in amusement from the monkey wrinkles to the crows' feet. I estimated the angle between her natural and her painted eyebrows and tried to guess when she had last bothered to pluck the area in between. I looked down her dress and discovered the same soiled brassiere showing under it, only the posture in which she sat that evening permitted me to peek further down her tits. She had good breasts, there was no denying it. The only question was one of getting past the torrential downpour of words, past the cold whiskey glass in her hand, and at the mildewed zipper on her back. I never managed it. She frightened me off by seeming not to notice my interest in her body. Women always notice it when a man becomes covetous of their fleshy contours; many of them see it in one's eyes and immediately start having a reaction between their legs. She must've known what I wanted, but she wanted to let me beg for it. And so, all she got was my whiskey, and all I got was a terrible hangover the next day. When my eyes turned glassy, she took her leave and casually strolled out of the door. She probably had a nightcap in her bedroom.

We sat in the same office day after day as usual, and neither of us mentioned those evenings again. I didn't, because I felt it would be a waste of time and good whiskey to repeat the performance. Apparently, it took something stronger than the bottled stuff to make her do what I wanted. It wasn't until a few weeks later that I learned why she never said a word about our têtes-à-tête.

"Well, Phil, I tried everything I knew to make you fall in love with me," she burst out one day, when I got back after lunch, "and I didn't succeed. What you want is a woman who looks like Marilyn Monroe and has a mind like Margaret Mead."

I looked at her to see if she was serious. She was. I wanted to answer her, Don't be an idiot, old girl. What I want is a woman who will climb into bed with me without my making an ass of myself, but somehow I couldn't say it. What she wanted me to say, of course, was something like, Oh, darling, my dearest one, I haven't had the courage to speak out what's in my heart. I've been in love with you since the first day I laid eyes upon you. Please, please, forgive me for my natural reticence and be mine! And then, it would've been the time to try to press my lips upon hers and ravish her behind the file cabinet, where the first half of the alphabet left off and the second half started with M. The boss would then have come into the office and caught us right in the act, and there would've been nothing honorable for me to do but to marry her in order to protect her somewhat sullied reputation. But since I didn't feel like it, I didn't say a word and made check-marks on an index card. She sat quietly for a couple of minutes, evidently waiting for me to pronounce the words that would release her from her bonds one way or another.

"So," she finally resumed, "I'm getting myself a new boyfriend, somebody who'll appreciate me for the woman I am."

"Aha, you've found yourself a boyfriend!" I replied. "Anybody I know?"

"Wouldn't you like to know!" she smiled the smile of mystery again. Her face enshrouded itself in that look of the Inscrutable Orient which I knew so well on her.

I couldn't possibly have cared less about the identity of the object of her affections and so I didn't pursue the subject, although evidently she was on tenterhooks, waiting impatiently for me to pry the secret loose from her. As far as I was concerned, it was a relief to see someone else in the role of the fox when the hounds were running. I didn't do her the favor of breaking down the guise of Trappism, and she didn't have the pleasure of taking me into her confidence. She must've suffered.

Shortly after that, she gave up her apartment without letting the office manager know about it—always a sure sign of the fact that a woman has gone to live with a man, without benefit of clergy. She became more close-mouthed, and for the first time in months I was able to concentrate on my work again. It was a relief, and I breathed even easier when she arranged to have herself transferred to another department of the firm. Now she had vanished out of my life completely, and I only rarely saw her at lunch. She put on an enormous amount of weight, especially around the hips, and I was glad that I hadn't committed myself to her in any way, for she began increasingly to remind me of Ethel Barrymore in her old age.

I guess it was simply that sex agreed with her, for she did even more physical labor in her new job than she had in the old one, and she never was a big eater. It works that way with some hypertense people who grind themselves up in nervous despair when they don't have sexual satisfaction. So long as they can rip off a couple of pieces a day they blossom out like red tulips, but if they're deprived of their mates for any reason they wither away. I imagine Lynn was fairly hot, and she was in her mid-thirties, just at the critical age when women are most desperate for regular intercourse.

It wasn't long until she announced that one of the executives and she were secretly married, and soon it became apparent to everyone that she was pregnant. The date of the marriage was never determined; it didn't particularly matter to me, but the old gossips around the office naturally assumed that the marriage was performed when it was clear to her that she was with child. She remained on her job until six weeks before the day of the expected birth, saying that she was going to spend "the last three months" at home. It was a "very premature" birth, though neither mother nor child seem to have suffered from the lack of hatching time.

We met strolling down a walk in the park one day. She was pushing a baby carriage and fussing over the squalling infant.

"That could've been yours," she remarked, "but you didn't want it that way."

"I didn't say that," I protested. "But you know, a bachelor is a man with no children to speak of."

"I didn't want it that way," she mused, as if I had opened a new vista to her. It seemed that at last she realized what her position was with me.

We talked banalities of life for two minutes and took leave. It was like a meeting between two people who had never exchanged more than Christmas cards. All the former tension and excitement were gone. I knew I could run into her anywhere and there'd never be a word spoken about our curious relations before.

I often wondered what she would've been like, if she had been hot, and if she had loved me enough to sleep with me without getting a free meal ticket out of it. I think she might've done anything I asked, if only I'd had the sense or the hypocrisy to ask for it in the right manner. I did her a favor by jilting her, possibly the biggest favor she ever received.

III Odette: Paris *Par Excellence*

Paris was beginning to pall on me before I met Odette. At the hotel, the service was marvelous and the furnishings were meticulous, the orders from the restaurant and bar were only slightly confused, and the view from my window was enough to warrant making several color slides. Everything was fine, except that the servants woke me up in the morning with hour-long conversations at the top of their voices. In the little rooms set aside for the use of the personnel on each floor the management had affixed huge signs reading "Silence! Respect the tranquillity of our guests!" But the servants rarely went to those rooms, so that they must've forgotten what it said on the signs; instead, they preferred to stand in the halls and to shout at one another with stentorian voices. The women were worse than the men. In order to work there, they had to be pretty hefty. I think they had barrel chests, every last one of them, and if you hitched them to a wagon they would've run a race with a team of horses. Their huge chest boxes made terrific sounding boards, and they could communicate all through the block-long building and thus avoid walking. In the process, they imparted their "thoughts" not only to one another but to all the guests in the hotel. But that made little difference to them, since they were already awake, and they probably thought that all good people ought to be out of their beds and working at that hour anyway, so they were just performing a service to the welfare of mankind by waking us up. Or perhaps they chose this means of equalizing the inequalities of the capitalist system. A customer might pay ten dollars a day for a hotel room to sleep until he chose to wake up, but the maids saw to it that in spite of all his money he was placed on a democratically even level with themselves. Maybe, too, they used this means to wake up everybody in time for them to get around to the rooms, for I've noticed in five years of hotel living that the maids the world over try to arouse everyone early in the morning so that they can perform all their chores before dinner. In the afternoon they take it easy, do their personal washing, or talk their bosses and the administrators in charge of various supplies out of items which might be useful in their own households. Making a maid work in the afternoon is considered something of a breach of democratic etiquette, and if one makes a habit of it, one is punished by the morning conversations being carried on regularly in front of the

door, including, of course, a round condemnation of one's
unco-operative private habits.

After I had photographed the Champs Élysées and the
Place de la Concord, tired myself out in two days of walking
around the Louvre, shaken off the whores at the Pigalle and
the Clichy, listened to the drunken students at St. Germain
de Prés speak in a dozen languages, and visited whatever
museums weren't closed for repairs, I felt like a tourist who
has done his job and started sitting in cafés and sipping wine
like the Frenchmen. That was an improvement over the
tourist routine, but something was still missing. I felt that
Paris still owed me something. No one goes to Paris expecting it to be like other cities. Paris is one place that everyone,
all over the world, wants to see once, and where everyone
expects to find something that he dreamed of when he went
through puberty. Paris is a place you feel you know when
you arrive there the first time, a city you feel you've visited
before, something like a hometown away from home, a hometown that many people never see yet would recognize if
they were dropped into it from a helicopter. Paris is a magic
word, a fetish almost, a formula that evokes sparkles of utopia
whenever you mention it, whether you're talking to a Japanese prostitute or a Swedish countess. Paris is everybody's
city, the center of whatever you care to mention, whether
it's painting or horse racing, music or military history,
NATO or car manufacture, fashions or jazz. And because
it's everybody's city, I felt that I still had been cheated, for
I hadn't found its soul.

Until I met Odette. It's funny how a woman may make
all the difference in the world. The difference between a
city you love and a city you hate may only be that between a

good woman and a bad one. If there's a good woman in your memory, you like the city. If you had an unfortunate affair, you hate the place. Even countries work like that. Every man loves the countries where the women are beautiful and accessible, and every man hates those where the women are ugly and don't make themselves available. I believe a good part of the popularity of Paris is the result of its spirit of easy morals, because the male tourist can always find a woman, and the female tourist feels that in Paris she has a right to shed conventional rules and throw herself at the first man whose nose appeals to her. Paris is full of American school-teachers looking for a Frenchman to thrill them. Sometimes an American businessman looking for an easy Frenchwoman finds an American steno-typist looking for a lewd Frenchman. Sometimes each pretends to the other that he doesn't speak a word of English. That's Paris.

Odette was a street-walker on the Montmartre. She couldn't have been more than twenty-two years old, gracious, well-mannered, and sophisticated. Heaven knows what drove her out on the street.

You meet all kinds of prostitutes: Girl students and former students who happened to run out of money, clerks who gave birth to an unplanned baby, upper-class girls who were kicked out of their homes because they were caught seducing their boyfriends, singers and dancers who weren't quite good enough to make the grade and are "between jobs," nice girls in search of quick and easy money to pay their unexpected hospital bills, waitresses and factory workers who've decided to build up private emergency funds for future strikes or diseases, high school girls whose mothers won't let them have enough pocket-money, nymphomaniacs who can't get enough action out of their boyfriends, sluts who won't work for a living and would rather screw lepers and hunch-backs than stir a finger in honest labor, and well-preserved divorcées who somehow never learned a trade except forni-cation. The streets abound with tales of woes. Every corner in downtown Paris has a dozen hardship cases waiting for a man to pay for an insertion of his erect private parts into those soft lips with the curly beard. It isn't worth one's trouble to inquire too closely into the origins of the girls' fall from grace, even if you understand enough French to ask and un-derstand the answers. If one tells you the truth—which is un-likely—you often find that she's taken the only intelligent way out and you couldn't help her worth a damn. And chances are she won't tell you the truth but whatever story is calculated to make you bleed your bankroll. They're all full of stories, romances, novels, and atrocity tales; a new one every day, a different one for every customer, an appropri-ate one for every age bracket, for each and every type of sympathetic male listener. The imagination will supply them with enough mental ammunition to stir the heart of the most close-fisted pawnbroker. Their business is the extraction of money from your pocket, and they think up new ways of doing it while they're standing on the street in hot weather and cold, rain and sunshine, wind and smog, Sundays and workdays.

If you have a young son who still has illusions about women, take him to Paris and let him find out what they're like. Once I couldn't find a hotel room because it was the tourist season and everybody from the United States who could find an airplane or a ship to transport him to Europe seemed to be in the Old World, most of them in Paris. Fi-nally, I happened across a small hotel at a corner where I used to observe the dames in tight dresses and peroxide-blond hair parade themselves. It provided me with a rare opportunity for observing their technique. Some day I must return to my alma mater and get a Ph.D. in sociology with a descriptive dissertation entitled something like "The Modus Operandi of the Parisian Prostitute as Analyzed from the Perspective of Close Propinquity with the Benefit of Personal Contact, Observation, and Statistical Computation."

On Sundays and holidays the whores arrived between 3:30 and 4:30 in the afternoon, on weekdays between 6:00 and 7:00 at night. Their first move was to meet and exchange news and information at a coffee-shop or bar near their beat. There they sat and ogled the customers, and sometimes they'd find a man without even going out and pounding the pavement. That was an auspicious beginning. It was considered an omen of good luck for the rest of the shift. Their customary drink was Cinzano, and they had another chocolate-colored, sweetish liquid behind which they could sit hour after hour and dream. To me, their taste in liquor was abominable. Some of the older types had to down a few cognacs before they could bear to face the public. All of them underwent a sort of act volition before they could muster the courage to get out and try once more. It reminded me of the time I was in college and needed quick cash and, imbecile that I was, thought that the way to obtain it was to sell magazine subscriptions. The crew of teenagers always met first and drank a few glasses of whatever spirits could be scrounged to whip up courage before running upstairs and downstairs, knocking at a thousand doors, and entering the damp, clammy, and unkempt hovels of the working proletariat that subscribed to our magazines of slushy romance, phoney confessions, and crude criminology. In a way, we were prostitutes, too. Like prostitutes, we accosted anyone promiscuously; like prostitutes, we pretended to have a hard-luck story of grave and critical importance if anyone asked us; like prostitutes, we tried hour after hour to sell perfect strangers an article which they didn't actually need; and like prostitutes, we had no esteem for the merchandise we sold. Only, unlike prostitutes, most of us earned very little money at our trade.

Every girl had a definite beat to patrol, and she wasn't allowed to deviate from it, since she then would be muscling in on another girl's territory. Most of the better corners had a bunch of girls assigned to them, and they could stroll up and down the block in either direction on either side of the street, but that was their limit. They almost invariably had a little hotel along their block to which to repair with their customers. The price of the room was the contribution they made to the madam, so that they ordinarily didn't go to any other hotel. At the rate they were going, a twenty-bed hotel could accommodate at least forty customers an hour, which, during the rush-hours, could amount to a neat pile of francs. Naturally, the madams weren't usually that lucky, for it was rare that all the rooms were engaged; half a dozen customers at any one time was considered a good complement. Even so, that meant a gross intake of about twelve dollars an hour, which, for a tiny hotel, was fairly good. If the large, respectable hotels could earn as much money per bed as the tiny whores' havens, they'd rake in the millions quicker than their stockholders could count them. Usually, the girl also lived in the hotel or near it, so that her whole life centered on the area of a block or two of Paris, and there were some who hardly ever saw anything of the city outside this narrow sphere of activity. They let Life come to them.

Hour after hour, I stood by my window and watched the

whores in action. At first, when they saw me watching and
didn't understand that I was going to remain at my post for
several days, they glanced up at me and left. When I leaned
out and looked around, I realized that they walked down the
block a bit, one group in one direction and others in the
opposite one, more or less out of my sight, and a number of
them had crossed the street to join the girls standing at the
corner directly downstairs, whom I couldn't normally observe
from the fourth floor, where I lived. They were aware of the
fact that it might hurt their business to have anyone watch
them, or perhaps they suspected me of having some connection with governmental or clerical authorities, whom all
good whores hate, detest, despise, and abhor. But as individual girls returned to their corners from their assignations
and found me still at the window, or as they glanced up to
check on me and found that I hadn't budged, they gave up
all thought of preserving my illusions and paraded in front
of my window, disregarding whatever fear they might've
entertained of my being a dangerous agent of the state.

I think there were sixteen of them who made their headquarters at that corner, though no more than eight or ten
were present at any one time. Some were always attending
to their duties in the hotels to which they belonged, one up
one street and another down the block the other way. Now
and then, they also took time to enjoy a drink, though I
never saw them eat during "business" hours. If they ate anything, they had it before they arrived or, in a state of collapse, after quitting time between eleven at night and one
o'clock in the morning. Occasionally, they gathered at one
of the local bars around midnight, all of them talking at the
same time. Talking, chattering, and prating appeared to be

their main common characteristic. Even during working-
hours, they often gathered in a cluster and babbled away like
a barrel of monkeys, missing out on well-dressed men who
walked past them slowly and ogled them with curiosity. Talking was the one thing they preferred to money. I wondered
what those miserable creatures, standing on the same street-
corner most of the day and seeing each other try to catch
men eight hours a day, seven days a week, could possibly find
to talk about. I remember from my office days, however, that
the lower people's educational level and the narrower their
horizon and experience, the more they seem to have to gossip.
Maybe the girls compared notes about the techniques of the
men they met.

It was quite a task to get into and out of the hotel. The
girls, of course, took it for granted that anyone renting a
room in that neighborhood must be after at least one woman
a day, and so, they figured that I was after them. Whenever I
left the front door or tried to walk in, I was besieged by a
ring of these females, nudging and pulling at my clothes,
chattering in rapid French, and flashing their dark eyes at
me to arouse my virile fire. Some of them put their arms
around my waist and felt me up. At night, I thought they'd
rape me on the street. I wondered how it would feel. Others,
understanding from the map of Paris that I always carried,
from my shoes, and from my clothes, that I was a foreigner,
muttered, "Cheri, we go make love, no?" or "Listen, darling,
you want to sleep with me?" or something equally subtle.
There was just one major difficulty: I knew every one of
them would be preparing to leave the minute she entered
the room. I've seen these girls walk off with men they had
enticed with fair words, disappear from their corner, go to

their hotel, and return, all within the space of less than half an hour. I'm a man who hates to eat off a dirty tablecloth, and so I declined all invitations.

They varied a lot, considering the fact that they were all working at the same street corner. Some had dyed their hair red or blond, others kept it in the original black or brown. Some had enough makeup on their faces to cover up the sins of Jezebel, others barely used any at all. Some were dressed as if they just moved out of a haystack, others were perfectly attired for attending a diplomats' ball. On the whole, I thought it spoke for the good taste of the French males that the better-dressed street walkers had by far the most thriving business, while the sloppily attired ones found hardly any takers. The weatherbeaten types in slinking muslin dresses stood at the corner all night and rarely found a customer. Occasionally, there was a whistle like from a football coach, or a wave of the arms, from the doorman of a dusty nightclub entrance located near one of their hotels, probably when someone in the club asked for a girl to take to bed. When that happened, the whole gang of them ran like track stars to the club and sauntered up the last few paces to the door, straightening out the hems of their stockings and stroking their hair back into place. Often it was a false alarm, and they all came trotting back to their corner in defeat. The club must've accommodated girls on a first-come-first-served basis, for when the signal was given, they all raced with ferocious speed and each tried to outrun the others, with handbags and umbrellas waving on high, stiletto heels slipping on the pavement, and an occasional casualty falling down in the scuffle. It was quite amusing to see. There were two or three among them who practically skidded the last few yards to the door, like a baseball player sliding into base.

One of the girls at that corner was a perfect doll. Unlike the others, she never walked out in front of the male passers-by, never threw her arms around a stranger's waist, never clutched an indifferent man's arm, and never accosted any-one of her own accord. She didn't have to resort to such tactics. She was rather tall for a French girl, with a very good figure, bleached blond hair, hazel eyes, and a very young face. Usually she wore a tailor-made, scarlet-red suit, nylons, white shoes, a white belt, and white gloves, going all the way up to her elbows. These gloves were the best sales promotion stunt since the invention of television commercials. I watched the men giving the once-over to the girls, and their eyes almost invariably fastened on those long, white gloves of hers. And no matter how much the others talked, clutched, and rubbed themselves against the man, he'd choose her every time. She barely gave him a smile of recognition and started walking off, with him in hot pursuit, like a jet interceptor behind a hostile bomber. She'd grab him by the hand and walk him to the hotel next door to the nightclub, walking in ahead of him to ensure that the management recognized who was bringing the customer. She'd be gone for somewhere between fifteen and twenty minutes and stand back on that corner again, squeezing her fingers into those taut, white gloves. Sometimes she barely had sufficient time to get her hands back into them when the next man took her aside to ask the price. It was like an assembly line from seven P.M. till one A.M. That girl must've made twice as much money as all the rest of them put together. Whoever managed that girl's finances had found himself a gold mine.

Some procurers who operate a whole string of such women fall in love with them and have heart throb affairs with each one of their charges. For a man who never had any ideals about women, that's pretty hard to believe, although we all know it to be true. I observed them for hour after hour, watching their street for any likely looking men. Some of them took a few steps back into the other street and then came walking back slowly, timing their arrival with that of the man, to make it look "accidental." Taking a step forward, and inclining the upper part of their bodies a little, they'd accost him, "Monsieur . . ." If he didn't pay any attention to them, they'd shout, "Ecoutez-vous . . ." as if something awfully important depended on his listening. And if he still brushed them off, they'd turn around and be just as happy or unhappy as before. The same pose every time. The same facial expression: innocence, anxious pleading, urgent prayer, and ah, sexual attraction! Every man, of course, was precisely the ideal one that they were looking for—for the next fifteen minutes or less! Still, their approach held within it a certain element of cleverness. What man, if faced with open admiration, isn't flattered? What man wouldn't like to justify such desires?

Sometimes, when a man stopped to chat and haggle with them and then didn't choose a woman after all, the prostitutes became embittered and showed what they really thought of their customers. I saw them walk after such men, imitate their gait with all the mimicry of an accomplished actress, and gesticulate in a manner more eloquent than words, kicks, or blows could ever have been. Often they gathered in groups and discussed the cases of particularly difficult fellows—at last they had something to talk about when they put their indefatigable mouths to work. And nothing could possibly have illustrated the atmosphere of street prostitutes more adequately than those gestures of pleased surprise upon seeing the man, beseeching glances of the innocent eyes, the touching prayers to heed the poor maiden's call of love, followed by gestures that a stable boy would've been ashamed to use toward his pigs. Their real natures showed in sharp contours under the flimsy taffeta of business amity. In the course of a few months of prostitution, whatever love they'd had for their fellow men necessarily chokes on cold semen, and their minds compensate for the humiliation of their bodies by denigrating their customers to a level below the gutter in which they know that they're constantly moving. I have no use for people who try to make martyrs of a degenerate civilization out of prostitutes. They're not martyrs but leeches, feeding on the weakness and ignorance, the frustrations and disturbances, the inadequacies and prejudices of a bigoted society. If we could all do as we pleased, there wouldn't be a prostitute alive who could make a living.

As I looked out of my window, I saw men window-shopping like housewives, only the wares they were examining were females on the hoof. They walked by time and again, looking the girls over, seeing if any new ones had arrived, or how these compared with those on the other side of the big boulevard. Nor were the girls surprised at this procedure. The first couple of times they saw a man, they walked up to him and went through their act of joyous enthrallment with his bald-headed looks. After that, they merely glanced at him. They recognized each one for what he was. If a man came back and gave them a second look, they warned each other to be on the alert. Sometimes, one or two of the girls had already been in bed with the fellow, and he was making up his mind whether he should make the rounds with them all.

"Have you had him yet, Yvonne?" one of them would ask.

"Oh, the one with the bald spot on the back? Yes, he was with me last night."

"That's funny, he was with me the night before."

"Maybe he wants to taste them all. How was he?"

"Much stronger than his old face would indicate."

"That's what I thought. He wanted it a second time, but I said, 'Nothing doing, you pay once, you screw once.' He didn't have enough money for a second time. Maybe he wants it now."

"No, he's looking at Lucienne. He likes variety."

"Too bad, I could've used the three thousand francs."

"Who couldn't, on a slow night like this?"

And so on and so forth. It was a merry-go-round. The old customers had already ridden all the old war horses and only selected the best for seconds. That's one of the greatest conveniences about having a definite corner assigned to each girl. A man knows precisely what he'll find if he returns to the neighborhood. If it's a special position he likes, he simply finds an expert at it, and if she isn't teaching it to somebody else at the moment, she'll be at her customary street corner. Otherwise, the man can always walk around the block and wait, for he knows that she never takes very long. . . .

My destiny was named Odette. She was standing on the corner, shifting her weight from one foot to the other like someone who either needs to go to the bathroom very badly or who has extremely sore feet. I didn't say anything to her when I approached but, good old professional that she was, she noticed at once that I was looking at her and accosted me. I tried to persuade her to walk to my hotel with me, but she said she didn't think she'd be admitted. She took me to her permanent headquarters, where I owed twelve hundred francs before I closed the door. Odette wanted three thousand, but I didn't have any change and gave her a five-thousand spot. Naturally, she had no money on her. They never do. After this business transaction, we could get down to cases.

She was a tall girl, very tall and statuesque for a French-woman. Her natural color of hair was Titian-red, which she dyed dark-blond; her eyes were gray, and she had long, naturally curved eyebrows. Her high forehead, narrow temples, and slender nose gave her an aristocratic appearance out of keeping with her occupation, and she had a full mouth which needed no cosmetics to appear desirable. Her skin was well-cared-for and smooth, light, and young. She had wide shoulders and a white body that could've been chiseled by Rodin. Her breasts were bulbous and large, with delicious little nipples to crown them, her waist was as narrow as that of an athlete, and her thighs were pleasantly heavy, of the type that one often sees on artists' models. She had unusually long legs, both in the thighs and the calves, which made her seem larger than she was and rather big feet, which ached her something terrible, since she stood at that corner for six hours a day. I didn't realize it when I shelled out the money, but at the moment I could've had her at a cut rate, just to get her off her feet, if I'd only had the good sense to argue over the price.

"Take it easy," she said, "there's no hurry. It's better slow."

But the mere sight of her excited me beyond all reason. I wanted to grasp her waist tightly with my arms, suckle on her breasts, and unite my throbbing flesh with the forest of red hair that sealed off her belly. Her soft skin burned on my fingertips. I was a mere mass of palpitating, yearning, grasping protoplasm, devoid of all self-control and discipline. All I wanted to do was to sink myself into her, squeeze her, kiss her, squash her, stick my tongue into her mouth and drink her dry. I needed to possess her. It was as if someone had pressed a steel-helmet upon my head and wouldn't let go of it. All of my natural self-possession and collected calm had evaporated, and the animal within my body took over. Only in states of extreme anger, when I was ready to throw an apoplectic fit, had I ever experienced anything like it. My blood was boiling in my arteries, and the two arms of a huge vise closed in on my skull above the ears, grabbing my head at the temples and hurling me at this woman, whom ten minutes before I didn't even know. I clutched her and stroked her, grabbed her and pulled her, stabbed deeply inside her very being and tried to bury all of myself inside her. My whole spinal column itched to crawl up into her belly above the red hair as if I were an embryo returning to his mother's womb. I shot my wad once without her realizing it and went right on riding her, in and out, up and down, back and forth, with a savage rhythm like a race horse galloping to win the Kentucky Derby. She didn't catch me at it, for she continued with the act as if nothing had happened.

It was a delirious experience to sense how reason deserted me. I was pumping out the energies raised by a thousand useless meals taken for the purpose of sustaining a pointless existence. Her breasts surged towards my mouth, asking to be taken, begging to be grasped by lips eager to help tickle her nerves. Her white skin radiated gentle submission and ardent desire. I licked her forearms all the way to the armpits, she seemed so delectable. The odd thought struck me that, if it were legal, one ought to try eating human flesh, that perhaps a new sexual thrill could be derived from masticating a hunk of woman's thigh or virgin's breast, broiled lightly on either side, and garnished with parsley. Her flat belly throbbed as if someone had touched an electric needle to it. She breathed heavily under the weight of my torso. I kept her pressed tightly to myself, because I didn't want to miss the touch of her skin any longer than was necessary for her to catch her breath. She squirmed and whined now and then, and beneath me I could feel her throbbing and trembling. I felt the liquid squirting out of her and all over my abdomen and thighs. It was delicious and stimulating, and I became stronger and more passionate than ever. I looked down: Her entire bush of red hair was white with foam, and we were united by a puddle of juice and sweat. The more I peered at it, the more passionate I became, and for the last half hour I must've been pumping away without a letup. She gasped and panted and begged for mercy, but the minute I slowed down even a little bit, she started to move her hips and begged me to go on. Her eyes rolled over as if she had taken heroin, and her breath rattled as if she had run the marathon. At last, my second release came shooting up and I barely managed to plunge it into her with a walloping jerk that would've burst asunder a less robust woman. She fell back into her pillow and stretched out her arms, while her big thighs twitched on my flanks. For a minute, she passed out. I wasn't far from it myself.

"Ah, *mon cheri*, you kill me," she shouted from the bathroom after she had washed herself out. "I won't be able to walk tonight."

I was stretched out comfortably on the bed, resting myself

after the strenuous exercise. It didn't occur to me until she arrived from the bathroom that she'd be putting her clothes back on and going out to look for another customer. Furthermore, I was expected to get dressed and go home. The thought didn't even suggest itself until my glance struck her garter-belt and stockings which, in the mad rush of my first desire, I'd ripped off her body with one forceful jerk, determined just this once not to conform to Parisian street-walkers' habits and to do it *my* way. She tried to hold on to them to the very last. Convention is strong, even with whores.

I saw her beautiful body before me, newly laundered and dried, and ready to go to work again, and the thought of losing her again so quickly gave me a feeling of strange nostalgia entirely out of keeping with the situation.

"Don't stay," she exhorted me, "you must leave. The hotel will want the room."

"Nonsense, we paid for it," I said. "Let's be different and stay."

"*Non, cheri,* we can't stay. I must go back and you must go home."

"Don't be silly," I retorted angrily. "Why the hell shouldn't we stay?"

She stood there, wearing nothing but her wristwatch, with her legs apart, her sex showing underneath the matted, wet hair, her white body still breathing a bit heavily, her hair falling over her ample shoulders. I looked at her, at every square millimeter of her, and drank her in, and somehow, although we had difficulties in communicating when it came to abstract matters, she understood me. She stood and didn't move for at least fifteen minutes, barely letting her arms revolve in their sockets and shaking her hair into new poses for me to feast my eyes upon. She smiled, and for the first time since I'd met her, her eyes expressed something of a human emotion. I was so entranced by her that I couldn't move, and we remained that way, with me lying upon my stomach, in the middle of the puddle on the bed, and her standing there, stark naked, returning my stares and looking into my eyes to read all the thoughts which my French wasn't good enough to express. I wondered whether she had ever been in love, but I didn't dare ask her, for fear that she'd give me one of those sob-stories which the street-walkers are so ready to hand out. I even wondered whether I was in love with this girl. I watched her breasts following the rhythmical movement of her breathing, let my eyes wander down the faultless curve of her waist and stomach, stared into the red magic of her pubic hair, and feasted upon the radiant whiteness of her legs.

She followed the direction of my glance to her feet. "Ooooh, my legs are killing me," she said, painfully raising one foot upon the bed to examine the ankle and stroke the swelling. When she moved, I could see an irregular strip of red flesh under the folds of her skin.

"Then stay here with me. You don't want to go down there again," I suggested.

"Then I need more money. We must give the hotel another three thousand francs."

"Don't be silly. I only pay forty-five hundred in the best hotel in town."

"Three thousand, or we leave," she said. "Do you want to stay?"

"Take down two thousand, and they'll be glad to get it."

"No use. If you don't want to pay, we must go."

"All right," I said in disgust. "But they're taking advantage of me."

She walked downstairs, wearing her garter-belt and stockings, her black panties, and a blouse, which she carried rather than wore on one arm, covering up her bare breasts with it. In the free hand, she held the money which I'd given to her for the hotel desk. I wondered if anyone would see her, and if it was customary for girls to take walks in Paris hotels in such attire.

"And now for me, *cheri*," she said, when she returned. "Another five thousand."

When it came to questions of money, there was no arguing with her, and her face served as a stone mask whenever I objected. I decided not to argue with her any longer, regardless of what she might have to say, or what the outcome, for it would only waste time, and five thousand francs was only about ten dollars. I gave it to her. I noticed that although she had proved to me at first that she had no money by showing me an empty wallet, she placed the first five-thousand spot in the lining of her purse, and when she put away the second, she hid it inside the powder cushion of her compact. I called her attention to this curious manner of handling money.

"You see too much," she grinned. "You ask too many questions."

She cleaned off the bed as best she could and went out again to obtain some towels to provide for all future emergencies. And while I lay there and admired her, she prosaically pulled up her feet as close as she could to her face and examined them. There wasn't a thing in the world wrong with them, except that she stood on them all night long in her high-heeled shoes. I tried to explain to her that if she was going to be on her feet that long, the practical thing would be to wear lower heels, and since she was so tall anyway and had nice, long legs, she didn't need the high heels. But she rebuffed the suggestion before I was quite finished explaining it. It seems that all street-walkers in Paris wear high heels, and Odette couldn't be an exception. It was convention again. If one walks along the streets of the city, one sees the common characteristics of street-walkers: high heels, stockings, heavy make-up, stylish hair, tight-fitting clothes of poor quality, large purses to hide all of their sanitary equipment, and a slow gait to make it easy to catch up with them. I suppose they're reluctant to give up any of their trademarks, because they need to be easily identified. If they looked like ladies no one would have the courage to accost them, and if they lacked the fashionable traits they'd be afraid they couldn't stand the competition of their sisters. Odette was going to wear four-inch heels on her big feet, even if it killed her.

When she convinced herself that she didn't have any blisters, she turned playful and offered me her body to practice my arts upon. I got the impression that she was curious to see whether I could teach her anything new. Her body was an instrument that had been played so often that any new chords one might strike would be a thrill to her. As for her instincts, there was nothing wrong with them. Like a sixth sense, they told her where my sensitive spots lay and where a simple caress would almost send me jumping to the ceiling or lay me out flat on my back, asking for more. She was more expert than a trained masseuse.

Her best trick was an intricate massage she performed with her tongue while her fingers roamed up and down the abdomen and assisted her in eliciting every last vestige of energy that the man might have in reserve. This little maneuver could continue indefinitely, until she thought of something better. As far as I was concerned, it brought the entire nerv-

ous system into coital rapport, and I grew madly passionate
and searched for a way to satisfy a desire I had never felt before. I pulled her over me and had her spread out the im-
mortal triangle over my ears, gradually lowering the image
of her womanhood in front of me and setting her backside
on a slant, as one could do only with a woman taller than oneself. Leaning my head against one of her thighs, I then started
working on the folds of her skin as if there were ice cream
hidden within her lap. I could plainly see her trembling and
pulsating under my touch, and the sight of her excited flesh
made me launch into an ecstasy of my own. Her kiss was wet
and hot and firm against me, and she seemed to be drawing
me out more than I knew was possible. Meanwhile, I saw
her squirm and shake in her most sensitive spots. She asked
me to use my fingers where they'd do the most good. I sank
four fingers into a receding moisture. She pulled apart before my touch and almost exploded with passion. Gurgling
and screeching with heat, she merged her whole face with
my body and her long hair wrapped itself around me. It was
almost too much to take, and there was no escape from the
tremendous catharsis that liberated me from passion temporarily. I was afraid she'd be insulted, but she greedily consumed it. At the end, she panted for more. Her own secretions turned the sheets into a sea of love. She never stopped
vibrating. The sides of her opening rubbed against each other
while her thighs pressed alternately against my head, each
time shifting the weight upon her sheath.

When her thighs grew tired, she let go of me and turned
around. Her arms closed around my neck and pulled me
down upon her face. Her tongue twisted around mine, and
her hands seized the object of her affections and guided it to

the spot where it was wanted. I didn't have to move. She did all the raising and lowering, moving up and down and sideways at the same time. Her lower lips closed in upon me and held me in tight captivity, as if she was never going to let me go.

I don't know how long we lay like that. It could've been twenty minutes or six hours. My heart was pounding with exhaustion and my eyes refused to stay open. All I could feel was sex, sex, sex. There had never been anyone like her. Every particle of me was partaking of the feeling of exuberance that goes along with the possession of a gorgeous and skilled female body. I thought I felt her vibrating to the tip of my toes, to the sinews in my tibia, and the roots of my hair. There was no dingy hotel room, there was no squeaking bedstead, there was no moist mattress, there were no soiled sheets, there was only the act of sacrificial union. Her thighs were the twin pillars of eternity. Her mouth bore the ripe fruit of the orchards in the fall. Her waist was the jump of a stallion across the hedges. Her hips were the clouds that carried me to the seventh heaven. Her breasts were the cornucopias of everlasting potency. Her hair was the horizon at the time when all men sleep and one hears the voice of one's guardian angel. Her breath was the music of life giving birth to the minutes that weave into years. She was a great white omnipresence such as any god would envy.

Before I knew it, I had fallen asleep, dreaming of odd fairy tales mixed with hues of reality. I dreamed of a twin-headed swan; one head was that of the first woman whom I truly loved and the other one was that of Odette. The swan carried me off in mad flights, and so rapid was his motion and so fluctuating the course of the twin-headed bird that my insides tickled just as in a fast elevator ride. The bird soared forward and sideways, carrying me on its back, and burned its wings on the rays of the sun.

"Remember Daedalus and Icarus!" I shouted. "Don't get too near the sun!"

The twin heads turned around and looked at me smilingly, and lo and behold, one of the heads had changed into that of another girl with whom I spent the happiest two years of my life. My true love had disappeared.

But soon I was flying down a Grecian staircase, all in ruins, and a dog was chasing me. The husband of one of my girl-friends was egging him on, and the beast came after me, slavering at the mouth with a foul-reeking saliva. I was terror-stricken and ran down the stairs, and when the dog gained on me I decided to fly down.

"Lucky that I can fly and they can't," I thought.

By now, there was a whole tribe of pursuers behind me: one of my old teachers, and a boy whom I had knocked half deaf when he insulted me in grade school, and various husbands who had grounds for complaints against me, and a grouchy giant who was mean to me when I was a small boy, and a pug-nosed monster whose features I couldn't recognize because I was scared to look back. Off the chase went, and I flew down stairs after stairs, gained on my pursuers, and looked up at the swan which was going on without me.

"Wait! Wait for me!" I shouted. "Don't leave me in the temple of fallen gods! They're dead, all of them! The dogs will get me!"

When I awoke, Odette was shaking me by my shoulders. Her red hair fell over my neck, and her mouth was next to mine. I lay on my left side, contrary to my usual habit, and I was clutching the pillow.

"Let me sleep, honey, you're talking too loud," she said.
"I love you," I said, and put my arms around her.

"You're bad for me, *cheri*," she said. "If I fall in love with you, I'll starve to death. I never loved anyone like you. I never knew a Frenchman like you, nor an American, nor a German, nor an Italian. No one is like you. If I sleep with you again, I'll be a poor girl. Now, let me sleep."

Soon I heard her breathing regularly. Her face relaxed into a childish smile. She held her left hand clasped in front of her mouth, touching her lips with her thumb. Her red hair was spread on the pillow behind her. Her beautiful body was stretched out sideways. I turned around and was lying on my right side, which is my sleeping side. Her left leg was slightly bent forward, her right one was pointed into my end of the bed. Its rosy flesh was exposed next to me. I then remembered that I must've fallen asleep in the act of making love to her, lying prone upon her belly. She must've gently lowered me on the sheets and covered me up without waking me. A thoughtful girl. I lent her a piece of my blanket for her right leg. My watch said it was six-thirty in the morning. Our friendship was seven hours old and unlikely to grow much older. And there was nothing for me to do but sleep. I closed my eyes with the salty flavor of sadness in my throat.

Before we parted, I promised to come to see her again in a couple of days when I'd be properly rested from our amatory exploits. But I received an urgent telephone call and was unable to go. Not knowing her full name or her address I had no way of letting her know. She had told me that she always stood at the street corner where I had picked her up. That seemed as good as an address. But when I returned to Paris a few weeks later, I spent an hour waiting for her at that corner and didn't see her. I went back several more times, but Odette was gone. The only girl of the streets worth her money had faded into that limbo of obscurity that surrounds girls of her profession and engulfs them at last.

Soon there was nothing left of her but the dream of the swan. I dreamed it again, and her head never failed to appear first in the sequence, though others might be added. When I awoke, I half expected to see her beside me and felt a keen loss because I was alone.

IV Florence: Fire and Ice

The other girl on the swan's double-head was also red-haired. I met her when I was seventeen, and she was the only girl with whom I was ever really in love. At least if you call it love when you become entirely different, incomparably prouder and happier when you're with the object of your affections, when you'd do anything to please her, and when you've got a magic bond between you which pays no heed to reason and logic. I thought that she was the most beautiful woman in world, which manifestly was an absurdity, because I hadn't seen all the women in the world. Generalizations of that type, I think, make up the semi-pathological state to which we laymen refer as "love."

From the beginning, the whole affair was insane, because she was my boss's wife and I was a starveling, all of which gave it the additional spice of romance and intrigue. I walked into his office after a week in his employment, ready to give it up. The job involved door-to-door selling, and I couldn't sell gold bricks for a dollar bill if my life depended on it. I was an obvious misfit, and I was ready to draw the logical inference and quit.

When I walked into the room, Florence sat at the side of the desk with her legs crossed, revealing a shapely knee. She had on a tight, black dress, and her petite figure showed to the best advantage. Her skin was of that pure white color which is peculiar to certain redheads, and her hair was flaming red. She had green eyes which, by their constant sparkle and fire, almost had to be Irish. And when she saw me, in my shabby clothes, needing a haircut, and looking dejected and listless, she still gulped. I knew from her unconscious reaction that she had the same kind of instantaneous, involuntary, all-powerful, and fateful moment of realization that I had when I saw her. Later on, she always referred to it as our "moment of the electric spark." No electric spark that ever hit me when I got into the way of an electric short ever hit me as powerfully as seeing Florence. My heart was pounding, my blood shot through my veins as if I had a fever, and a lump of lead squeezed itself between my windpipe and my aorta. My stomach was going down an elevator shaft, as if I were afraid for my life. And I felt a stirring of the testicles as if they knew independently that this woman would swing them into action. It was small wonder that I forgot what I was going to say.

Of course, there wasn't any question of quitting now. I haven't any idea of what was said; it was immaterial. They invited me to their house for dinner. Grover, my boss, wanted to be friends. He hadn't caught the electric spark. Maybe he was too old to notice. She was twenty and he was twice as old. People often mistook him for her father, even though—or perhaps because—he always gave his age as thirty-two.

There were more evenings at Grover's house. Florence and I stole glances. She knew the score from the beginning. I don't know if she wanted me more than I wanted her, but it was close. When I touched her hand lighting her cigarettes or handing her the dirty dishes, she shivered as if she were cold. In conversations with me, her voice took on a strange, shrill quality. A child might have predicted what our relationship was going to be. But not Grover. He was too sure of himself and what he had to offer her to speculate that she could prefer one of his boys to himself. He treated us like children. I tolerated this indignity, which I never would've taken from anybody else, because it didn't make any difference what he said or did. As long as I could be near her, nothing made the slightest difference. He could've beaten me regularly, for all I cared. If she was there with me, it didn't matter.

One day, she went out with the sales crew and told Grover that she wanted to see how we operated. As soon as my gang separated to work our first block, she paired off with me. I sat her down beneath an elm tree and told her that I loved her. She barely had time to say that she reciprocated my sentiments, when one of the other salesmen found us and wanted to show off his arts of salesmanship to her. When I went home that evening, my heart was still beating in a furious rhythm, the world stood upon its silly head and kicked all the Grovers in the neck. She loved me! She wanted to be mine!

There was just one obstacle to our happiness: lack of money. I spent more money on cigarettes, drinks, and soda-pop to keep up my spirits than I earned in my selling endeavors. Everybody else on the team raked in the dollars while I failed time and again. Boys of twelve and thirteen rang doorbells, pounded on brass knockers, and came back with piles of orders while I produced one or two a day. Not having an outside income, I couldn't keep it up indefinitely, yet I couldn't quit because of Florence. If I did, there wouldn't be any more possibility of meeting her, and if we met on the sly, we'd certainly be found out and there would be trouble. Nor did I know of a better means of earning a livelihood. Everybody in the whole United States seemed to know the science of making money except for me. I was born deficient. And without money, how could I take her away from Grover and go away to begin a new life?

Since I spent so much time at her house, she, too, was affected by the situation. She was quite a little trickster. She used to send poor Grover out to buy her sandwiches, make telephone calls for her, and get cigarettes. She deliberately hid full packs of cigarettes to be able to say she had run out of them, just to send him away. She was clever at thinking up errands which only he could attend to. Sometimes, other salesmen were invited with me, but she was so adept at this game that she could have them all out there, running errands. She also became so demanding in her requirements that Grover had to get another selling job and had to absent himself from his home at night.

That's how I learned about some tricks of another sort: the

trickery of love. She was such a passionate creature that she couldn't stay away from me. Hardly had the last person been maneuvered out of the room when we fell into a deep clinch. There were several close calls when we were almost surprised. Grover would come back when he had forgotten his change or his keys, the boys returned to ask exactly where the place was where they were going, and deliveries were made. Occasionally, we forgot to check if the door was locked and other people just walked in to find her blouse in disarray, her hair ruffled, my necktie undone, and my belt unbuckled. The neighbors occasionally dropped in. One of them found us together on the couch when the door wasn't properly locked, with her skirt up to her ribs, her panties on the dresser, and my trousers wrapped around my shoes. Fortunately, he was a jovial man who liked to take the married women of the neighborhood to bed when his wife wasn't looking, and he didn't dare or care to say anything. The boys were a more serious problem. They all knew, or at least suspected, what was going on, and their jobs depended on Grover. If one of them took it into his head that he'd serve his standing with the company by ratting on us, our goose would naturally be cooked. I suspect that's how Grover finally got wise to us.

Before he did discover the most obvious doublecross of his whole life, he made things easy for us temporarily. His nighttime selling operations freed us of his unwanted presence. We both sat and watched him with impatient glances all through supper, which usually consisted of spaghetti and meatloaf, because Florence didn't know how to cook anything else. I got sick and tired of spaghetti and meatloaf, but food became a matter of secondary consideration. What I wanted sat across the table from me; it wasn't eaten with knife and fork. And now and then, an eager, stolen glance from her green eyes told me that she felt the same way. I'd sit there and talk to Grover about how hard the work was and how tricky the customers in rejecting our selling advances, but what I'd think of would be the red hair that graced the most protected and delicate portions of Florence's body, the creamy skin, the muscular buttocks below her pelvis, rotating with the precision of a steam engine to meet me, and the abundance of secretions that attracted the cats and dogs on my walk home. I'd sit and eat his food and drink his wine, but I never spent a moment with him when I wasn't planning to cuckold him. The oddest thing about the affair was that I didn't even have a bad conscience about it. I felt that rightfully Florence and I belonged together, and that somehow, in the eyes of a Higher Justice, our union was infinitely more sacred than the mere bonds of matrimony that bound her to Grover. I could look him straight into the eye and lie like a trooper and never have a pang of remorse, because in my own values and mores he was the intruder rather than I, and his presence in his own marriage bed was a travesty upon human justice. Florence felt the same way. The only fear and qualm she had was that she'd hate to get caught.

She had a blue dressing gown that she was very fond of wearing. It was a wide, sweeping garment with ruffles and quilted plaids, held together only by a blue cord of the same material. From below it, the intoxicating aroma of her body poured out, mingled with the subtle perfume that she sprayed between her bare breasts. I had been curious about that dressing gown from the first minute I saw it and wondered just what was under it. There was only one way of finding out, and that's the road I took. The first time she wore it after Grover began his second job, we got up simultaneously from the dinner table, as if by a mutually agreed signal that was as overpowering as the electric spark we had felt when we first set eyes upon one another. I embraced her and thought back to the day, a few weeks before, when I took her to a dingy hotel room for our first meeting alone. I was nervous and almost incapable of giving her any satisfaction. She excited me to such a pitch that I made a lousy lover, from our first stealthy assignation to our last meeting in private. I wondered whether people who truly loved each other were predestined to cause each other frustration.

While I thought of that first day and kissed her behind the ears, she tugged at the cord and undid the knot. She wore a mysterious smile, as if she wondered what my reaction would be. The cord fell to the ground, the dressing gown opened, and my entire body trembled with excitement because of the naked glory that stood before me. In the dark hotel room, I didn't really see her, but now she stood before me like the statue of a master sculptor come to life. Below the roots of her red hair on her neck, the creamy, white skin stood out with incredible softness. Her breasts rose and fell with the fast pace of her breath, as if her nipples sought my mouth. I felt as if two gigantic hands grabbed me by the neck and pushed me toward her, into her radiant, naked body, which she offered to me without a word. Her narrow waist rippled lightly. She kept rubbing her thighs together and shifting her weight from foot to foot. My arms reached around her waist, sank down to her hips, and followed the undulations of her thighs, while my lips sought to cover every bit of her round breasts, enclose the nipples that stood up like taps waiting to be drawn upon, worked their way down to her navel, and strayed into her pubic hair. Before this, I was always afraid of touching a woman in that region for fear that I'd be repelled. But so much in love was I with her that such thoughts never even entered my mind. All I could think of was the idea of possessing her. It was as if I were compelled to gulp her down like a delicious apple. Soon I was drinking her dry, kneeling before her like a calf with its mother-cow, while she parted her legs to accommodate me and forced her abdomen forward with her hands on her pelvis. Her head leaning back, her mouth piped out her breath, as if she had just finished running around an obstacle course. She raised and lowered herself, balancing herself upon her toes, to bring every bit of her vaginal folds within range of my caresses.

We heard footsteps on the corridor leading to the apartment. Was it Grover? Was it one of his boys? She shrank back in terror, while I wiped my face and tried to cope with the monstrous excitement that gave my trousers the outline of the coverlet upon a dromedary. Thank God—delighted yells of welcome from the couple next door! The neighbors were having company. We were not found out—as yet. I looked at my watch: Grover had been gone for about an hour.

"Think he'll be back soon?" I asked fearfully.

"I don't think so," she whispered.

She let her dressing gown drop on the rug and raised one leg on the sofa, testing out its springs. Using a pillow to support her back, she lay down on it and raised one leg on the back of the sofa. I could see the white foam that betrayed her excitement. Her eyes bespoke the appetite of a wolverine, her hair scattered like a red cloud around her head, her nipples were still the size and shape of wild strawberries, and the floor-lamp made her skin glow with the yellowish pink luster of alabaster at sunset. I escaped from my clothes as if they were on fire and stepped on them in the rush to reach her before the mood was spoiled. I threw myself upon her and forced back her fingers that reached out in an attempt to guide me in gently. I whipped her insides as if I needed to punish her for the temptation which she presented to me. Somewhere, inside of her, I felt, there was the Holy Grail which I needed to touch. If there was no contact, all would be lost forever. Deep inside her, there was the pond of perennial happiness, and if I didn't reach it, I'd never know what was at the fountains of Life. Dig, dig, dig! Thrust into the white contours of womanhood! Wedge in between the lobes of forgetfulness and titillation!

And then there is the chasm of the end, when heat and chill follow one another in close succession, and reality slowly creeps back upon one's shoulders like snow settling upon a country town at Christmas-time. The question: Does she love me in her heart as she does during the act?

"I've never loved anybody like you," she said, guessing at the substance of my thoughts. "I don't know what it is about you, but you drive me wild!"

She raised her hands to my cheeks and drew my head upon hers to press a kiss on my lips. The flaming green in her eyes lit up with a quaint fire.

"I want you, and yet I'm afraid of you. I'm just sure I'll get a child. Even Grover doesn't scare me like you, and he's just like a dog. But you're like a stallion, uncontrolled, greedy, and stern, always taking more and more of me, as if you wanted everything I've got."

"I'd never be satisfied with anything less."

"I know. I love you."

There were steps on the floor of the corridor again, resounding like gavels in a court-room. Terrified, I grabbed my clothes and rushed into the bathroom. The last I saw of her was that she picked up her blue dressing-gown from the rug.

"Oh, hello, Grover, did you have a good evening?" she said with as casual a voice as if she had done nothing but listen to the radio all night.

"Fine. Pour me a drink, will you, honey?"

I don't remember what was said during the rest of the evening. It was like floating on a cloud. All I could think of was that he'd sleep with her that night and I had to go home to the bare walls of my room. I hated him.

It was odd how we broke up, that first time. The most outstanding thing about Florence was her sex. Everyone reacted to it instantaneously. When she walked across a busy street, cars with lonely men at the steering wheel came to a screeching halt or wandered into the wrong lane of traffic. She was a major traffic hazard. When she walked into a crowded restaurant, the conversation died down and all the men seemed to get that look on their faces that dogs have when they're straining on the leash and trying to mount a bitch in heat. When she walked into a bar, all the men stared at her as if she were their supper and their dessert, too, and all the women adopted the attitude of children fighting for their last piece of candy. The one thing that no one ever could have denied about her was her sexual attractiveness. And of all people, I wanted her most. I was so crazy about her that nothing else mattered.

And yet, she broke up with me because I didn't let her enjoy the junction of our bodies often enough. Whenever we were alone together in her apartment, she wanted sex. Whenever we sat in a car and Grover wasn't there, all she wanted me to do was whip out that erect organ and let her have its throbbing feel. Whenever we were waiting in the dark, she wanted me to stick my fingers into her to whip up the juice. She had no conception of time or danger, or of the likelihood of getting caught, or of the embarrassment of having the lights go on above you or having a policeman shine his flashlight on you when there is evidence of excitement running freely all over your thighs and your underwear is getting trampled under your toes. She was so hot that she lost all feelings of shame and didn't take the chance of personal catastrophe into consideration. All she could think of was to have her clitoris massaged and to feel that hard flesh palpitating inside her sheath. As far as she was concerned, there was no outside world, no risk of humiliation, no fear of being kicked out of the house, no care about tomorrow. All she wanted out of life was to work her white, freckled legs around a man and sense that stiff member striking bottom inside of her. Nothing else mattered an iota.

After a couple of very narrow escapes, I grew worried and more cautious than before, and this became the source of our break-up. I was up in her living room, caressing her, when Grover came home once unexpectedly. It was just our luck that I hadn't taken the bait of her nipples, which she had offered to my lips, and that I hadn't yielded to the immense desire to penetrate the overflowing part of her that was burning for me, because there surely wouldn't have been time enough to straighten ourselves out and for her to receive her lord and master in the proper manner for a wife to receive her beloved husband when a guest was present. Instead, when we saw his car parking in front of the building, we took a hasty leave of one another and buttoned ourselves up. He was already in the elevator, headed for his apartment when I closed the front door behind me, and when I walked down the hall his footsteps were ahead of me. Obviously, I couldn't let him catch me ducking out of his apartment, and so I looked for an easy way out. There were scarcely thirty seconds left until he must round the corner and see me. Fortunately, I discovered a broom closet and ducked into it. To my unmitigated horror, I stumbled against a tin bucket in the dark, and felt absolutely sure that he'd open the door, summon me to come out, and beat me up. Only later did it occur to me that my stumbling and causing all that racket made him less suspicious, for it convinced him that whoever was in the broom closet wasn't eager or anxious to hide his presence. The door was closed, though not fully shut, and my hand held on to the door-handle. I didn't dare remove it for fear that he'd notice the movement and left it there while he passed by. Apparently he gave no thought to the noise he heard, for he made no effort to come after me and pursue me. Some ten minutes later, I came out, looking in both directions and breathing heavily.

I remembered that in literature, illicit lovers are always taking refuge in broom closets, wells, pantries, and cupboards, and getting discovered in ludicrous embarrassment, usually to be chased across the roof-tops of the neighborhood in their long underwear. This made very funny reading and even excellent entertainment, if it happened on the stage, but now that the play was real and I was the principal actor, I didn't care at all for my humorous role.

It was difficult for me to know what to do, even after I escaped. My relationship with Florence was of such an intense character that it was inconceivable for me to break it up merely in order to save my threatened neck.

One day, Grover and the boys were sitting around in his apartment. We were helping him while the idle hours away, because Florence had gone to Chicago to see her mother. We

played poker and talked. The whole mob was poking fun at
me because of my poor performance in door-to-door selling.
I had to tell them that I was quitting fairly soon. Suddenly,
I weathered her. I picked up my head and held a finger to
my lips.

"Florence just walked into the building," I said.

"Nonsense, what're you talking about?" Grover derided
me. He was indignant that I'd even entertain such a thought
when he "knew" she was hundreds of miles away. Besides
that, his proprietary instincts as husband were aroused.

"I said Florence just walked into the building. She's in the
elevator, and in a couple of minutes she'll be here."

"Oh, sure!" Grover exclaimed mockingly. "Listen, Phil,
have you had too much to drink? You oughtta lay off that
stuff if you can't take it. You're too young anyway. Now, how
could she be walking into this building, when only two days
ago she went up to Chicago to see her mother?"

"Shshsh," I motioned to them. "Give her another minute."

"He's crazy," Danny the Rock said. Danny was a juvenile
delinquent who worked for Grover, zip-gun and switch-blade
ever at his beck and call. He never said a polite word to anyone in my presence as long as I knew him.

There was a clicking of female heels and thud like from a
suitcase being set down and a knock on the door.

"There she is!" I exclaimed.

"Like hell," Danny gurgled.

Grover went personally to answer the door. Before him
stood none other than Florence. There were the usual hellos
and cheerful noises. The boys brought in her suitcase, and
she pranced into the living room. She greeted me like everyone else, only a little chillier. And she proceeded to sit down

and pour herself a drink and tell the story of how everything had gone wrong at home, and how she had turned around and come back as quickly as possible.

All eyes fastened on me. I hadn't said a word.

"How did you know?" Grover asked me, planting himself next to me.

"I just knew," I answered.

"That's peculiar," he thought out loud. "How come I didn't 'just know'? I'm her husband. How can you just know?" He looked at Florence. "You sure you actually went to Chicago?"

"What do you mean, am I sure?" she replied, quite taken aback. "I ought to know if I was in Chicago or not, oughtn't I?"

"Yes, you ought to," Grover admitted. He briefly told her what happened.

She gave me a long, hard look, as if she meant to say, "What did you do a foolish thing like that for?" Actually, I couldn't have answered.

"Would it make you feel any better to phone my mother and ask her if I was there?" she asked Grover. "You can talk to her first, and you can go right ahead and ask. After all, I was there, arguing with her for most of the night."

"And how come you came back so soon?"

"I don't like arguing with my mother."

"Okay, don't worry about it," Grover tried to drop the subject. "Have another drink and make yourself comfortable. Anything I can get you?"

Though he tried to gloss over his questioning of Florence, there wasn't any more doubt in my mind that he was suspicious, and since his suspicions were well founded, he was bound sooner or later to confirm them. He was a man of very violent temper, and both Florence and I anticipated that he might either commit an act of violence himself or have Danny the Rock take some of the boys and do it for him.

There were a number of incidents when a kind of sixth sense seemed to connect Florence and me. When I was at home, tossing and turning on my lonely bed, I sometimes had an urgent flash run through my mind, as if I simply had to get up and help her, or I'd have such a lifelike vision of her that I could almost touch her. Usually she was reaching out for me.

"I thought of you last night," she sometimes confided in me later. "Something happened with Grover, and I felt in need of you."

We made it a point to compare the times when we thought of one another particularly strongly or when we felt need of each other particularly much, and the times always coincided. She could tell me within a minute or so the time when I had concentrated on her several miles away, and I could tell her the same about her. I always knew when she entered the building, even if she was supposed to be far away, and she usually knew when I was within range of her.

It was like having a private and very secret telephone line. Later on, after Grover had grown very suspicious and we could meet only on the sly, this proved a real asset. We had a corner where we always met, and if I stood there and thought very hard about her, she'd try to get away if she could and meet me there without the need of a messenger who might've betrayed us. Sometimes I hadn't been there for ten minutes when she'd appear up the street, smiling and looking for me at the familiar little shop.

But things couldn't continue like that indefinitely. I queried some of my friends and contacts regarding better jobs, but there wasn't much to be had. Papa Robeson wanted to put me to work selling jewelry in his shoddy pawnshop, but remembering my solid record of failure in selling, I didn't think that was a good bet, and besides that, I'd always suspected that Papa Robeson's merchandise wasn't entirely acquired in the above-board manner. In other words, if I'd ever contemplated selling some stolen merchandise, I would've approached Papa Robeson and made him a price, and it was a good bet that Papa would've been interested, if not eager. Then there was my rich friend who ran a restaurant of his own, but I didn't know how to do anything useful to him, and the best he could offer me was a job as food clerk at $34.50 a week. That would barely suffice for my personal needs, and if I was going to take Florence away from her husband, it wouldn't go very far. My contacts at the racetrack thought I ought to wait a few years before getting mixed up with the turf racket, and I didn't know enough about cards to get a job in any of the little joints I knew so well.

What can you do, if you're eighteen and you want to elope with your boss's wife? There isn't much of a choice. I considered turning to crime, but when I thought about it, it seemed to me that I'd be entering an even more competitive world there than I lived in right now, and that I'd be putting myself into a state of dependency upon experts at the cutting of the next fellow's throat—figuratively as well as literally. Besides, I didn't know any promising criminals, and I didn't know where one starts being a criminal any more than I knew where one starts being a millionaire. I certainly didn't intend to rob old ladies of their purses or steal pennies from blind men—that didn't yield enough of a profit to support Florence and me. And when it came to making off with the payroll of one of the few corporations that still paid in cash, I didn't think I could handle it. Amateurs, I thought, should never compete with experts, and as soon as you start parting people from large amounts of cash, you enter into competition with a whole army of professional crime-hunters whose lives are dedicated to the apprehension of petty, little would-be millionaires like myself. And so, I decided to stay honest.

The answer was easy but unpleasant: I couldn't be anything more than I was. An eighteen-year-old, unless he's born rich and doesn't have a family controlling him, hasn't any way of eloping with his boss's wife. If he works for a living, he doesn't earn enough. He isn't smart enough to steal and get away with it. He hasn't any collateral, so he can't borrow enough to set up housekeeping.

This truth must've dawned upon Florence, too, for she showed up less and less often at our rendezvous. After I had to quit working for Grover, I couldn't go to their house much any more. A few weeks after my last day with the company, I attended a little party Grover gave, and he didn't speak to me. Florence, too, kept away from me. I sensed that something had gone wrong.

"Listen, kid, let's take a walk," Danny the Rock said to me, when I was helping myself to some cheese and crackers.

"What's the hurry, Dan?"

"Come on, let's go," he motioned to me. His switch-knife was in his hand, and he motioned for some of the other fellows to come over. They formed a group around him and me, standing there and leering, their hands in their pockets. There were among them such outstanding citizens as Bobby, a hillbilly from Arkansas, whose huge feet always stank like

Liederkranz cheese, Timmy, a huge blockhead who made a mint selling his equals in the slums because he knew them inside out, and Marve, a scrawny engineering student, whom Grover was helping through college by keeping him on as supervisor in another district even though he was nothing but an educated fool. The three of them were quite enough for me, though, and I decided against risking a physical encounter on the premises of my boss's apartment. A couple of smaller boys, whom I had always helped along, watched the proceedings in silent terror and came along to see what would happen next. There may have been two or three more, but they remain more or less anonymous in my recollection.

Danny the Rock stayed right behind me while I walked down the stairs of the apartment building. He kept the pig-sticker open in his right hand, though he had it hidden in the loose sleeve of his raincoat. I felt sorely tempted to trip him on the stairs and see how much he'd cut himself up with the blade, but the others would probably take that as a deliberate declaration of war, and being this close to the apartment they'd probably massacre me. My two little friends wouldn't be too much help against the rest of the mob, and I wasn't sure they'd even try to fight people like Bobby, Timmy, and Marve. Being at a decided disadvantage for fighting troops, I therefore ambled along ahead of the switchblade, a humble prisoner. They walked me to a dark alley two blocks away.

"Listen, kid, you oughtta call yourself lucky we're lettin' you off this easy," Danny the Rock snarled. "Cause Grover is mad at you. Now, don't you go up there no more. Don't even come near the place. Don't have nothin' to do with the whole stinkin' neighborhood. You don't belong here, see?"

"Yea, whattaya want from us anyway?" Timmy chimed in.

"What do you want from me, bloke?" I asked him. "Did anybody ask you to join this party?"

"Hey, who're you callin' a bloke?" he pointed his chin foreward.

"Oh, cut it out," Danny hissed. "We don't wantta beat you up, we don't wantta do you no harm. We just got orders to takeya outside, walkya up the block, an' make sure you don't come back. So, take a powder, Phil, willya?"

"May I ask who told you to do this?"

"Didn't I tellya?" he grinned spitefully. "Grover told me to. Grover and Florence both. They don't wantta see you no more."

"Did they mention any reason? After all, I've been around a long time . . ."

"Look, don't play innocent with us," Bobby broke into the act, shoving his big feet to within an inch of mine. "We know all about that stuff with Florence. It wasn't any business of mine, I always figured, till Grover caught on, or if he didn't feel like doing anything about it. But seeing that he knows all about it now, and seeing that he does want to do something about it, I'm making it my business. Now, you take this warning, and you leave Florence alone, or I'm going to forget you're a friend of mine and break you in two."

I looked over the whole sad group of them standing in that dark alley, looking very menacing and yet not feeling like beating me up, and I felt like a piece of dung being flung aside.

"And while we're at it," Bobby continued, "Florence said for me to tell you personally not to try to call her or get in touch with her. She said not to come to your corner any more. She said you'd understand where that would be."

That was all I needed. I understood. She sent that message

through Bobby to make sure I realized that she, too, was behind this scene. She was through with me. She didn't want
any part of me any longer.

"You can put that pig-sticker away now, Dan," I said, in
a dry, much deeper voice. "You want to be friends? Here,
shake!"

I stuck out my hand. Bobby was the first to shake it. "Don't
be mad at me, Phil, I'm just doing my duty," he stuttered.
Timmy shook my hand, too. "No hard feelings," he said.
Danny the Rock had been collapsing his switch-blade and
put it back in its hiding place on the inside of his jacket, on
the left side, where he could flash it out in a second. "Take it
easy, kid," he said. "Good luck, and, as the big fellow said, no
hard feelin's." Marve joined in the chorus, and my two little
friends walked me part of the way across the alley to assure
me that they had no part in any of this. Altogether, it was
a remarkable way of "getting the boot."

That should've been the end of the Florence story, except
that it wasn't. She continued to be on my mind, and I pre-
sume that I stayed on hers. Our relationship had been so
intense that no mere break could possibly destroy it. Everything was in favor of our meeting again, because we were
drawn together physically like a pair of magnets. The re-
strictions of society, the bounds of propriety, the limitations
imposed upon us by the lack of money, the desperate straits
of my own struggle for survival—they were all bagatelles in
comparison to that all-consuming, burning fire which we nur-
tured for one another.

The first thing that happened was a telephone call from
Grover, which he timed for my eighteenth birthday. He
sounded as menacing as he could, and under a barrage of

dark threats he sounded worried. Had I ever given Florence anything? he wondered. Had I ever told her that I loved her? Had I ever asked her to elope to South America with me? Of course, the answer to all those questions in reality was yes, but I didn't say anything to him. He answered them for me. "My wife tells me everything!" he exclaimed. If she had really told him everything, he would've strangled her in his nuptial bed! On the other hand, he said to me, she sometimes didn't know what she was saying or doing. That sounded strangely irresponsible for a woman who had the habit of telling her husband everything. But that's how he explained that sometimes people said she told them strange things, he informed me. And I wasn't to misunderstand . . . Oh no, I assured him, I wouldn't misunderstand. In fact, I didn't intend to be around to understand or misunderstand anybody. I had enough of the whole situation. He thought that was good, for if he ever caught me around the neighborhood of his apartment again, he'd break me in two. I thought that was sort of tough, since he lived near a major crossing point of the city streetcar lines. But I agreed to everything. What else was there for me to do?

I held a rather easy part-time job at the time which could be performed during a couple of hours' strenuous efforts in the afternoon. This was supposed to be my way of financing my college education, and my courses were supposed to be at the focus of my attention. But I became a very sloppy student for the next several months. Registration had been in October and I registered for ambitious hours of arduous endeavors. Now, I couldn't understand why I had ever given a damn about an education. What was the use? It wasn't buying me anything. The rickety bookkeeping which kept me alive was something that any twelve-year-old boy could've taken care of if he had been so minded. And I couldn't possibly have cared less than I did about American diplomatic history, the geological formation of the earth's crust, or English literature. I barely managed to get something of a thrill out of my course in Spanish, thinking very seriously of going south of the border to forget it all and start a new life.

In the meantime, I tried to take my hard-earned money to bars and get waited on. Since I wasn't very tall and looked young even for my eighteen years, this provided many a problem. I bought a hat and wore old-fashioned suits with vests, and whenever I could stand them I smoked big cigars. Even so, there were many questions about my being twenty-one years of age.

"What do you mean?" I usually shouted indignantly. "Don't I look it?"

"No, bud," they often answered, "frankly you don't. Do you have a driver's license or an ID card?"

"If I say I'm over twenty-one, then I'm over twenty-one," I'd try to bluff my way through. "If you want to question my word, that's all right too, and I'll take my business elsewhere."

"Okay, okay, I didn't mean nothin' like that," they often gave in.

There were enough bartenders who served drinks without a question or who could be persuaded to close an eye to one's lack of wrinkles around the brow. Besides, one could buy the hooch in a liquor store shortly before closing hours, when the personnel were eager to go home and not too likely to check one's ID cards and create a scene. Or one could buy cartons of beer at some grocery stores with a few items of food, and chances were ten to one that the girl at the cash register wouldn't blink an eyelash. It was only necessary to make oneself as unattractive as possible, because the girls sometimes used the card-angle as a come-on and an introduction when they thought they found a good specimen for breaking through the manpower-shortage. Being ugly was a good idea anyway, for a dirty and tired-looking teenager looks more like a man of twenty-one than does a well-kempt and well-groomed one. There were numerous tricks to master in this game, and the most vital one was never to betray excitement or to show suspense, for they gave the anxious teenager away. A sloppy, sweaty boy, apparently just arrived from the factory, had the best chance of "passing."

Another important question was the little matter of money. The bookkeeping job kept my rent paid and bought me about one meal a day at a hamburger joint. It didn't make any allowances for my gargantuan appetite or the drowning of my romantic sorrows in an artificial Styx of Johnny Barleycorn. That fact was undeniable within five days after payday. And inasmuch as I had decided against a life of crime and my honest labor didn't provide me with the necessities of life, it posed quite a problem.

A partial solution offered itself when I discovered that there were some extra-legal gambling activities not far from town. If I could gain admission to a few gambling dens and establish myself as a known and well-liked customer, I thought I'd be able to practice my system on the roulette wheel and perhaps mooch some drinks from management and the customers. And sure enough, although three of the places in question had me booted out by burly and very unsociable bouncers, there were three others where I managed to be served a glass of beer. Having started on beer, I advanced to the gambling rooms, and the big fellows who watched the entrances for possible detectives and troublemakers decided to be kind and admitted me. And once inside, I could stand around the wheels and watch the heavy gamblers play, occasionally throwing a quarter or half dollar on the field when the odds seemed to be favoring me. Considering all I've learned in the meantime about gambling, it's a minor miracle that this practice didn't wipe out my slender resources altogether. But the miracle may be explained by the fact that I usually had the good sense to bet against the crazy customers who decided they were having a "winning streak" and staked everything they had on it. There isn't any such thing as a "winning streak," of course, and so, such people since times immemorial have been easy marks for the owners of casinos. For the casual bettor of small sums, they also are a near-perfect guide: As long as one isn't betting *with* them, one isn't taking too bad a chance, and one picks up the odds of the house—real and artificial.

Another partial solution was mercifully provided by the racetrack where I managed to clean up some money during the brief turf seasons. But during the critical period of the winter, when I felt most in need of a meat diet, it wasn't in operation, and I couldn't find much application for my skill in outguessing the gamblers whose bets determined the odds. Papa Robeson helped out now and then, as did my rich friend the restauranteur. Otherwise, the pickings were slim. And my appetite and thirst were great.

For about three months, I was usually beclouded by an alcoholic haze, trying to forget what it had been like to make love to Florence. Trying to forget the pressure of her white thighs against my flanks, the throbbing heart-beat under her ribs, the pressure of her flesh against mine, the moment of culmination, when she shrieked like a child discovering the table that bears his Christmas gifts. Trying to forget the magic of her voice softly murmuring in my ears, the ring of her calling my name, the glint in her eyes when I unbuttoned her blouse and found her naked breasts beneath it. But I knew it was a useless attempt. I'd never forget her, no matter how much I reduced my consciousness. Even when I crawled into my bed and could hardly find the switch to turn out the light, I still remembered what she was like. Her image never left me. The torture of knowing she'd sleep that night with Grover, who was "like a dog," made me wish for death.

Toward the end of the semester, I woke up with an aching head one day and realized that the final examinations were around the corner. I hadn't been to my classes very often. Usually, I'd awaken to enjoy a brunch in the afternoon, go to do my shoddy bookkeeping, and then wander straight into the bars or the gambling casino. Only rarely had I been to the university to find out what the class was doing. I certainly hadn't studied much. But I had enough common sense left to understand that I'd have to do something about it now. And I found out when the final exams were going to be and studied my textbooks. Day and night I studied. No more whiskey, just coffee. Occasionally, ham and eggs and doughnuts. More coffee to steady my nerves, so that I'd be able to stay up till four and study. It was like a race with time: my power to absorb information versus the calendar. And the days were passing me by like express trains.

But I managed to win the race. There were a few make-up exams in courses that had mid-terms, and then there were the finals. Nothing but exams for two whole weeks. Never had I thought that I'd be able to work that hard. And when it was all over, I received the best grades that I ever got while in college.

During the tremendous task of doing four months' work in less than one, I had almost stopped grinding my nerves to pieces over Florence. Oh, I still dreamed about her and thought about her whenever there was time, but the nearly impossible job of catching up with my studies saved me from becoming an alcoholic or doing something to end my life over the first case of a broken heart. I began again to have some life of my own, apart from Florence and all that our relationship meant to me.

I was preparing for the last final exam when I got a letter from Florence. She was sorry that she had caused me all that grief, she said, and she'd like to know that I hadn't taken to hating her. She had been up to Chicago to see her mother for a while and had thought things over, and she had to admit that I had been right about being careful, and that there wasn't a solution for our problem. She was lonely and unhappy with Grover. And she had taken a post-office box in a different part of town for the express purpose of communicating with me.

I answered immediately. There wasn't any question in my mind about it. No matter what happened and what the consequences, I had to see her again. In spite of her treachery in betraying me to Grover and leaving me to the tender mercies of Danny the Rock, Bobby, Timmy, and Marve, I couldn't be angry at her.

It was in the late afternoon of the last day before the last final examination. I was sitting by my window overlooking a near-by park and checking over my class notes again. By this time, I'd fairly well recovered from my alcoholic bouts. My skin was no longer swollen around the eyes, my gait had recovered its usual bounce, and I'd cleaned my person and my clothes. Suddenly, I had a strong premonition that I was about to see Florence.

Nonsense, I thought. How could I be about to see her? She hardly dares to write to me because Grover is so jealous of her, and since she dealt me such a low blow she'd never have the effrontery to face me again.

I heard the slamming of car doors below. I leaned out of the window facing the park but couldn't see anything. I had another window facing an alley with a garage. I glanced out of it in all directions. Sure enough, there was a car that looked like Grover's! It was either a strange coincidence, or proved my telepathic powers concerning her once more.

There was a knock at the door. I hurried to open it. I was so excited that my hands trembled and I had difficulty in disentangling the chain. I thought Florence might stand in the hall if I opened it, and I threw the door open so violently that I almost hit myself in the face with it.

The first thing that hit me was that familiar Liederkrantz smell. It was Bobby's feet that I smelled, there was no doubt about it, and they still smelled as if he hadn't washed them since he was baptized. With him was Danny the Rock, who nervously played with a key-chain, and Marve, peering out eagerly and near-sightedly from behind the thick glasses on his nose. The trio hadn't changed one iota since they had bidden me farewell in the dark alley that certain night near Grover's apartment.

"Hi, Phil," Bobby tried to greet me in a casual fashion, and Marve chimed in.

"Nice lay-out you got here," Bobby motioned at the room. "You got some new source for dough?"

I motioned for them to make themselves at home and sit

down, but Danny the Rock didn't give me a chance to extend my hospitality. He was still standing in the door and playing with that key-chain.

"We didn't come here to palaver, we're on an errand," he said out of the corner of his mouth. "Somebody to see you outside. Get your coat and come along."

"Somebody to see me?" I asked, looking at the three of them. I wondered, of course, whether Grover had sent them up to my apartment to get them to bring me down, so that he could beat me up or kill me downstairs. Nevertheless, it didn't make any difference, for with the fellows in the apartment I didn't have a chance of getting away, and Danny the Rock would, I thought, have killed me with the same nonchalance with which he invited me to join them. His new habit of talking out of the corner of his mouth worried me. He was looking more like a gangster and acting more like a hoodlum all the time.

"Okay, what're ya waitin' for? We ain't got all day," he said.

My landlady was out, and her husband wouldn't be back from his business until late in the evening, so that there was no one to see me going out or notice the three boys making off with me. I worried rather pointedly about my chances of getting in touch with any living soul if it should become necessary. But there was no percentage in trying now, and I grabbed my coat and joined them. They were eager to race downstairs. I lagged behind them hesitantly, having carefully locked the door after us. Not until Bobby turned around and grinned at me on the steps did I get the picture. They hadn't come on a sinister errand at all! They were going to do me a favor!

We skipped steps on the way downstairs and went out into

the alley with the garage. The car was parked next to the garage, so that it wouldn't be in anyone's way and would stay out of sight of the people in the building.

"Okay, go to it, lover boy!" Danny the Rock mumbled out of the corner of his mouth. "She's been waitin' for you."

"We'll go take a walk around the block," Marve patted me on the back. "But don't overdo it. We'll give you about twenty minutes."

"Grover is coming back at seven, and she's got to have dinner waiting," Bobby added, joining the others on the sidewalk.

Florence was sitting on the back seat and grinned. My heart was pounding so heavily that I thought she must hear it. She was wearing the dark-brown rayon blouse that I had come to know so well, the one with the little buttons in the middle. And she had on her heavy beige skirt, which I had trampled on in the dark one day and thought I had spoiled for good. Her green eyes shone like cat's, and her voice shook a little with nervousness as she greeted me.

"How have you been?" she asked me.

"Miserable, without you."

"Flatterer! You always were one. And flattery will get you everywhere."

"Cross my heart and hope to die! I was drunk till a couple of weeks ago."

"You shouldn't have taken it to heart like that. It makes me feel all the more ashamed of what I did. But I want you to know that I wasn't happy, either. I left Grover for a while and went home to mother's. Only I couldn't stand it there. My step-father, you know. So, I came back and wrote you a letter."

My left arm had worked its way around her and held her

close. My right hand pulled up her blouse from the skirt and undid the buttons quickly. Florence was up to her old tricks again: nothing underneath the blouse. Her breasts were naked under the brown rayon, and her little nipples invited me by rising above the round bulges of her white skin. She kissed me on the nape of the neck as I pretended not yet to be weaned. A groan rose from her throat, as if she were in pain. But I remembered she always made that noise when she felt a hot desire coming on and she felt within that she was ready to receive me. She always claimed she ached inside when she wanted me that badly. She rubbed her shapely thighs together and gently spread them a hand's width. That had been my signal in the old days.

My left arm gradually let her recline on the back seat while I pushed up her skirt with my right. She wasn't wearing a garter belt and had rolled down her stockings almost to her knees. My hand strayed upwards and felt the fleshy opulence of her thighs quivering with sensitivity to my stimulation. My hand went up inside her thighs to find what else stood in the way, but there was nothing. She wasn't wearing a thing under that skirt. She had come prepared for quick action. A grunt escaped her lips, as if she were carrying a piano across the room. My fingers had caressed the spot which determined all her joys and sorrows. More than any other woman, Florence lived by and for that one nerve cord and now that I had it in my possession she yearned for the ecstasy that we had known before. She crouched ever closer to me as I took her with two fingers, then added a third. She rotated her abdomen as if she were trying to touch every bit of her flesh to every part of my three fingers. We were beginning to make a mess of the seat cover, and I worried for a moment over how she'd ever explain it to her husband, or what she'd do about the ever-growing dark spot on her skirt. But this was no time to think of such banalities. She was obviously ready to enjoy a quick consummation.

She unbuttoned my sport shirt while I attended to my remaining clothes and tried to free myself from the encumberments of civilization. Her tongue moved like a windshield against the hair on my chest. Her eyes were showing just the suggestion of an open slit. Now and then her buttocks moved, trying to establish a comfortable position on the hard, narrow, slanted seat. When I finally came to her and she felt me touch her where she was most sensitive, she sighed and opened her eyes. She was gazing at me with her lids wide apart when I entered her with full force. A piercing little shriek escaped her, and her pupils widened in amazement. Then she reached out and pulled my midriff down upon her, pressing herself closely to me, so that I had to lay all of my weight upon her abdomen. Though she was actually carrying herself and me, too, she engaged in a circular up-and-down motion like a powerful turbine, just as if we were lying in the most luxurious bed. No matter in what direction I approached her or how high I lunged back in order to gain momentum, she followed my every movement. It was as if she were afraid to lose me.

For the climax, she threw her arms around my waist and clasped me so tightly that it seemed I felt the pressure upon the top of my kidneys. Her body hurled itself against mine with such speed that it was impossible for me to follow her. I simply stayed with her and did what I could whenever she gave me a chance. Even more rapidly, she grasped downward and up again, so much so that it felt as if she meant to bury me inside of herself. Finally she charged at me with such a gigantic effort and groaned with such a throaty, broken voice, like an old woman in despair, that it was like a supernatural charge rather than a normal impulse. Something was contracting inside of me from the roots of the spinal cord. An upsurge thronged through me violently, there was the itchy expansion, and the mad release. She breathed all of my being as if it were better air, inhaling and exhaling with lusty regularity. It was as if she meant to pump every last drop of energy out of me. I remained excited and eager even after the climax, and there semed to be no particular reason to quit as one usually does after such an experience on an uncomfortable back seat. Florence sank back to relax, released the hold of her arms around my waist, and panted for air with her eyes closed. I could feel the perspiration growing cold as the air rushed in between us.

It was still afternoon, and the thought occurred to me that it would be embarrassing to have anyone come upon us in the car and catch us right in the act in broad daylight. I bent upward a little to see whether anyone was near us. But the alley seemed deserted. The three boys were still walking. All the good, ambitious citizens were out working or shopping. My back ached a little, my knees felt a bit raw, and my thighs hurt, because I'd had such an inconvenient time of balancing myself on my part of the back seat.

She opened her eyes and smiled at me. When she realized that I wasn't comfortable, she pulled me down to herself and covered my face with kisses.

"Poor darling," she said, "I'll give you a Charley horse. We can't have that! Let's see if we can't do it in a better position for you!"

She raised herself on her elbows to have a look around while moving her thighs carefully so as not to separate us altogether. Naturally, we were separated anyway, and within seconds, she, I, and the back seat were covered with the evidence of our sins. We both tried to move around the spots and remove them from ourselves, but it was a vain endeavor. When she realized the futility of it all, she jumped up, took out a perfumed handkerchief from her purse, and dabbed herself and me to the best of her ability. She smiled at me apologetically and examined my exposed person in the act of seeking comfort. I was slouched forward on the seat in as relaxed a position as I could assume without knocking my knees against the front seat or touching the wet area next to her, which took in a lot of territory. I was still strongly excited from being so close to her.

Her eyes lit up like candles when she saw the possibility of a repetition of the first embrace. She let herself slip down, so that she lay on her right side, with her head on my naked lap and her feet striking the side of the car. Her body was angled, since there wasn't enough room for her to stretch out, and the back of her neck naturally turned toward my stomach. Her skirt was still wrapped around her waist. The sight of her lying like that drove me into a heat of passion once more, and I responded to her kisses with a joy so great that it almost hurt while her right breast lodged itself between my thighs. Her left breast was flapping gaily in the air every time she moved. Her blouse was a tousled mess beneath her feet. Her lips covered me with greedy kisses. She was in anticipation of further erotic ministrations, and it seemed there was no part of her that didn't long for the union to be consummated. She sought out the delicate nerves she knew could send me to the ceiling with excitement. Apparently, she wasn't comfortable now, for she pressed her back against the front seat and supported herself on her arms for a moment, then stretched out her left leg until it could move no farther. She raised her head and smiled at me in a cunning query, as if she meant to obtain permission for what was to follow. With a few well-practiced jerks, she moved over upon me, placed her legs on either side of mine, and pulled me still a bit more off the seat, so that she could bring down her buttocks to the space between my rump and thighs while her feet danced on the floor next to mine. She leaned back against the front seat and tried the spring action.

Before she tried to renew contact, she teased me for a while. This was not her usual habit, for ordinarily she liked to be taken by storm and confined herself to responses to the man's passion. But this time, possibly because we hadn't seen each other for such a long time, she outdid herself in arousing me to equal the febrile heat in which she evidently was. She worked around the delicate points and simulated contact before it was real. Suddenly, she dropped herself with all the precision of an expert marksman. Once more, there was all the thrill of our feel of each other. After all the love-making, she contracted a little, and the second time was better than the first—which it often is. She didn't move much, nor did I. Only now and then did she give a little wiggle, just enough to produce a near-climax and then stand it off at a pitch of delirious bliss. Meanwhile, she leaned forward and touched her lips to mine. She propelled herself forward and threw her arms around my neck, holding on to me, while her tongue sought mine out and caressed it on all sides. She tasted the insides of my lips and licked my face like a cat. Her breasts rubbed against my chest. All that time, she held on to my neck for dear life, lest she were to fall or sever contact between us.

Still without changing anything essential, she leaned over and reached for her blouse. Fortunately it was wrinkle-proof, and it was only a little soiled when she slipped it on. It was just as well that she got dressed, for a second later, there was a rap on the side window.

"Hey, you two in there, hurry it up!" we heard a juvenile voice.

It was Bobby, and he was smiling from ear to ear to hide the embarrassment betrayed by the wrinkles on his forehead. I wondered whether he had peeked in before he knocked and how long he had been standing there. Never had I seen him looking so much like a bewildered child.

In the rear view mirror I saw Danny the Rock standing behind the car, swinging his key-chain around the ring-finger of his right hand and off again. He was chewing gum and looking bored, but studiously so. Near-sighted Marve, standing next to him and following the movement of the keys through his thick lenses as if he were being hypnotized, completed our guard of honor.

There was nothing for me to do but to reach for my under-pants and trousers and get dressed. Florence pulled down her skirt and buttoned up her blouse, and when she wiggled her posterior to straighten out her skirt, she made a wry face. The boys didn't make a move to join us until we gave them the signal. At least they had that much tact. Bobby had joined the others behind the car, and the three of them were talking and laughing.

Florence rolled down the windows and cast a glance around the car. Her face showed silent horror at what she saw.

"Hey, Danny, Bobby, and Marve! Come here!" she shouted at the group. That was her way of letting them know their wait was over.

Bobby was the first to reach us and stick his head through the window. Marve's bespectacled face showed up next to his. Danny stood a pace or so behind them with assumed indifference, wound up his key-chain, stuck it into his pocket, and gave us an amused glance. His jaws were working impatiently on the gum.

"What'll I do about this mess in the back?" Florence asked them. "If Grover finds the car like this, he'll get mighty suspicious of you fellows."

"What do you want us to tell him?" Marve naïvely asked her.

"Nothing, you big lug," she rebuked him. "If you tell him anything, I'll swear you lied in your teeth and you tried to make time with me."

"Do you hear that?" Danny asked them mockingly. "That's gratitude for you! We bring her over to see lover boy here, and if any of us sings she'll turn the heat on. But, fellows, we gotta be big-hearted about this and do our best for young love. I'll tell you what, Florence: I'll take care of your little problem. I got some spot remover the other day. It'll take out anything, from blood to paint, guaranteed. But it's gettin' late, so if you want that spot out of the way and the seat dry before Grover drives this cart home tonight, we'd better step on it."

"You're a friend," Florence looked at him tenderly. "I'll never forget."

"Okay, okay, it ain't nothin' much. Now, Phil, get out o' this car, for we'd better fly low."

"Good-bye!" they all waved to me, as Danny slammed the door behind me.

"Write to me at the mailbox!" Florence shouted while the motor whined under the impact of Danny's push on the gas-pedal.

. . .

I didn't know it then, but that was to be the last time I'd see Florence for several years. At first, there were a few letters telling me that Grover had become suspicious of her and was locking her into the apartment whenever he wasn't at home, that she didn't dare see me again because she didn't know if maybe one of the boys was spying on her, and that she thought the neighbors were clocking her movements whenever she wasn't locked in. Even those letters stopped coming after a couple of months. One of my own letters was returned with the notice that the addressee had moved without leaving a forwarding address. I didn't dare go near that apartment for fear that Grover might see me there and make things worse, or that one of the neighbors might see me, or that one of the boys might detect me and betray us to Grover. And I had a feeling that Florence wasn't in town any longer. I couldn't describe the feeling or account for it any more than I could account for my knowing when she entered the building or when she was lying awake and thinking of me. I just knew that she had gone somewhere else. This suspicion was confirmed when she sent me a couple of postcards without a return address, one of them from back home in Chicago and the other from Mexico City. I managed to call Grover's office just before closing time one day, when I knew he'd be on his way home, and pretended to be a job-seeker in order to talk to his secretary. She confided in me that he hadn't taken a vacation in over a year and that he had just left the office. It was plain to me, then, that he hadn't gone to Mexico. Florence must have left him.

Shortly after I made these discreet inquiries I ran into Marve on the street one day. As soon as we exchanged the usual pleasantries about "Long time no see," I decided to pump him. He was more than willing.

"I quit working for Grover months ago, you know," he explained to me. "I'm a draftsman in an engineering firm now. When I get my diploma next May, I'll be a graduate engineer. After all, I can't afford to be seen walking around and knocking on doors these days. And I can make better money this way."

"Certainly. It's only right that you should. Now, what about Grover and Florence? When did she leave him?"

"Oh, who told you about them?" he challenged me.

"I heard through confidential sources," I played mysterious. "It's a very roundabout way because I don't dare go near him any more."

"That's just as well, for he's got it in for you all right," Marve agreed. "Now, Florence left him almost a year ago to go back to her mother's. You'll remember she never could stand it there very long because of her step-father. Sure enough, after a month or so, she turned up at Grover's place again. Everything seemed to be back to normal."

"That explains the postcard from Chicago," I mused.

"Say, do you have the price of a beer on you?" he wondered.

Marve was the type to not let the opportunity escape him if he thought there was the slightest chance of making a soft touch, even if it was only for a ten-cent beer, and even now that he was almost a full-fledged engineer. As far as I was concerned, I thought that I might need something to drink when I heard what he had to say, and I'd be glad to buy him a couple of beers in exchange for this information. We went to one of my favorite saloons, where they hadn't asked me for my ID card since the first day when I made a great display of anger. The waiter set us up with two beers at a quiet table in the corner. I paid.

"Anyway, she didn't get along with Grover any more," Marve continued, gulping his first glass of beer as if he had been walking through the Sahara without a canteen on his belt. "Say, could we have another round? That sure hit the spot!"

"Sure, drink all you want!" I said.

The waiter brought him another glass of beer. I paid again. Marve emptied the last drop of his first glass and greedily began sipping his second.

"Now, where were we?" I tried to steer the conversation back to the topic of interest again. "Why didn't she get along with Grover?"

"I don't know for sure, but I could make a good guess," he confided in me with a wink of the right eye, accompanying his gesture with a little burp after drinking all that liquid. "He was always pawing her and asking her to be nice to him, even when the fellows were around. It was getting to be a joke with us. He bribed her with pocket money and jewelry. Anything for a piece of that certain something she had to wiggle. He must've got desperate. She took it all and went on making him pay more. I think she came back from her mother's just to take him for everything he was worth. I know this much for sure: when she left, he was hurting for money. He took up with some other babe after a while, but he never had a dime to his name. You know that he used to be pretty generous with us fellows before. Now he often showed up with a sheepish grin on his face and would borrow money from us after he had paid us our weekly commissions. That Florence must've got away with plenty."

"What about her? When did she leave him?" I tried to hurry the story along.

"One day—I don't quite remember when—Bobby was

working late, counting up all the loose change, because Grover's secretary had quit on him in the middle of the week. Then Grover telephoned the office from the apartment house, asking Bobby if he had seen Florence, or if he knew where she was, and wondering whether she was coming to the office to meet him by mistake. Bobby, of course, said she wasn't and there was no mistake, but Grover came back down anyway and asked him all sorts of questions about her and what she had been doing. Bobby said it sounded as if Grover suspected him. As you know, Bobby would've been the last to take up with her, or she with him."

"Yes, him with his big, stinking feet," I laughed. "That would've been a joke."

"Well, he didn't snitch and pretended not to know anything, and actually he didn't know what Grover wanted most to find out. So Grover told him to forget all about their conversation and was especially nice to him after. He's still working for him, and I guess he'll take over Grover's place some day. But whenever we fellows came to Grover's house after that, he was alone. We asked him about Florence a few times, but he always got irritated and said she was at the movies, at a girlfriend's, or something else. At last, he couldn't hide the truth any more that she was gone and said she was visiting her mother. That was a long visit all right, for she never came back. But you said you heard from Chicago."

"Have another beer, Marve," I encouraged him.

"Thanks, I will."

He took off his glasses, which were even thicker now than they used to be, and wiped them with napkins, breathing on them carefully to get just enough moisture. His protruding, near-sighted eyes blinked at me, and he grimaced at the chandelier that hung from the ceiling.

"Funny thing about Florence," he said. "I always used to think she was a real clean kid. Real all-American, the one in a million who could never do anything wrong. The sweet girl who'd always stay a perfect lady. That's the airs she used to give herself. Until we all saw her with you in the car. It sure opened my eyes to a lot of things. And I guess I lost some of my youthful ideals there that day, standing behind the car and seeing you two."

I looked at him, as he sat there, prematurely wrinkled on the brow, with kinky, black hair curling behind his ears, his lips already betraying the loose sag of a middle-aged Mediterranean. He placed his glasses back on his nose and seemed more at ease. With or without them, he didn't look like a chap with youthful ideals to me.

"So, what's she doing in Mexico?" I tried to goad him along.

"Oh, you know about that, too, do you?"

"Not much, just that she was there."

"She got married there. Some Mexican millionaire. His parents own half a province down there, I was told. He was up in the States learning engineering in the office next door to mine. I met him at a party and introduced him to your darling Florence. And click"—he snapped his fingers like castanets— "it went just like that. They took one look at one another, and next thing, Danny the Rock and Timmy found them carrying on in the back seat of Grover's car in the parking lot. Same car you used, same activity."

"They found them together?"

"What do you think? The works! So, they told Florence that night, after our Mexican friend left, that they were thinking of having a talk with Grover unless she decided to give them a little session in the back seat, too. As long as everybody else was getting it, Danny and Timmy didn't see why they should be left out."

"And did she do it?"

"No, she doublecrossed them just like everybody else. She promised them whatever they wanted for another day. But the very next day, when Grover came home at night, she was gone, and so were all her things and her bankbook. This time, she left a note behind, saying she'd never be back and asking him to let her get a Mexican divorce. And if he tried to put a stop to it, she'd get one anyway, for it was easy down there, and he couldn't stop her, no matter what he did. And so, Grover decided not to pour good money after bad and let her go. She had left him so often, and usually he had to drive up to Chicago to her mother's place and get her. Her mother thinks the world of him, you know."

"Yes, I know. She was always soft-soaping him on the phone," I reminisced. "But where did she go with this Mexican? Do you know whether they went to his ranch?"

"I don't know. First, as soon as the Mexican divorce was final, they went to Acapulco for the marriage and honeymoon. That's a big Mexican resort, you know. After that, Grover got a postcard from Mexico City once, saying she was happy and she hoped he was too."

"I got a postcard saying about the same thing."

"Well, that was all. Grover didn't know where she was and didn't care much. He got himself a new girlfriend. Florence's mother called him up once or twice, but he wouldn't have any more to do with the old lady. He has had enough. And you can't really blame him."

"That's right. Do you suppose she and her husband live in Mexico City?"

"I don't think so. His ranch is way south, somewhere near the Pacific coast."

"And what's his name?"

"Gee, I heard it once or twice, but I couldn't remember. Spanish isn't one of my languages. I speak some French and some German, but no Spanish. You know how it is with Spanish names, they're all the same: Lopez, Gutierrez, Hernandez, Gomez, Blanco, and Castro. I never cared for Spaniards, and the Mexicans aren't half as good as the Spaniards, which isn't much. Now, take the French and Germans, they're real people! Those Mexicans are no damned good."

"Sure. Have another beer?"

Marve was getting a little maudlin, but he couldn't turn down another drink. I pumped it into him, hoping that his well-preserved brain would spill out the name, but no matter how much he tanked up at my expense, he couldn't remember which one of those common Spanish names it was, or whether perhaps the man had been so inconsiderate as to have an uncommon name. It hadn't left any impression on him.

"Funny thing, her carrying on like that," he got back on his topic again. "I never would've believed it if I hadn't seen it with my own two eyes. Her always pretending she was a real cleancut girl, and there she was, having affairs all over the place. It sure shocked the pants off me."

"She was in love with me, Marve," I tried to explain. "I certainly was in love with her. I would've done anything in the world for her. I worshiped the ground she trod on. I hated to see her stoop to the tasks of housekeeping. All I wanted to do from morning till night was to make love to her. I believe she felt much the same passion for me. She surely wouldn't have risked letting the three of you in on the secret if she hadn't wanted to be with me pretty desperately."

"Sure, she was in love with you," Marve breathed beer-odor into my face. "With you and a million other guys! Anything in pants! How else do you explain what happened with that Mexican engineer in the parking lot? And I understand that Grover used to have some other Dago stay in the vacant room they had, and he was making out with her too. Do you suppose she was in love with him?"

"Maybe so. Some women fall in love pretty easily."

"Nonsense, she's just a bitch. Just like a million other bitches. That's all she is. She's got hot pants, and she'll screw anything masculine that'll make a play for her. I wouldn't be surprised if she was screwing Danny the Rock and Timmy on the side, and Bobby, too, whenever she got desperate."

"Now you're talking through your hat."

"Before I saw the two of you in that car, I would've taken anybody apart who dared to say a word against her. She struck me as the cleancut type of girl. I thought she really was *it*. But then I found out what type she was. She stinks, that's what she does, she stinks. I'd rather sleep with Bobby's cheesy feet staring me in the face than with her and that wiggling ass of hers."

He was staring into his beer glass. Now and then, he turned it around. He wasn't just playing with it. He used it to twist the shape out of the wet napkin that the waiter had laid underneath. Something was eating him.

"She never made a pass at you, Marve, did she?" I asked.

"Hell no, she never did."

"So that's your trouble, is it? You were in love with her, and she never gave you a whirl, and now you're shooting off sour grapes."

"I guess we were all in love with her," Marve whispered into his beer glass. He addressed his remarks more to himself than to me. "You shook us all up when we saw her straddling you, with her tits flapping in the breeze and her bare behind on you, sitting in the back seat. At first, none of us could say a word. We just stood there, dumbfounded. We had given you twenty minutes, we told you, but Bobby didn't knock on the window till forty-five minutes later. You didn't know what time it was. I'll never forget the expression of pure animal pleasure on Florence's face when we came back from our walk and she was riding you. Not as long as I live. A grin reminding me somehow of the sensuality of a bitch in heat."

"So," I tried to pump him, "what did you say to her when you drove her home?"

"None of us said a word till Danny the Rock broke the silence. She primly sat in the back seat with her legs pressed together, her mouth full of hairpins, combing that long, red hair of hers, as if we had disturbed her in the midst of a little nap rather than surprised her going to town on you as if somebody had slipped her an ounce of Spanish fly. Every one of us three boys probably had the same idea at that moment, and that was, of course, that if you could have her, so could we. And if we'd had any sense, we would've driven her out in the woods somewhere and taken our turns on her till we were all so tired of humping that we couldn't walk a straight line. That's what we should've done if we'd had any sense. If she had put up a fight, two of us could've held her down while the third one gave it to her where she was hot. Not only that, but we could've had her over and over again. She could never have snitched on us, because we could always have told Grover about the two of you."

"But you didn't do it, did you?" I mocked him.

"Hell, no, we didn't. We just sat there, crowded in the front seat, and let her comb her hair and straighten her clothes like a beauty queen, so that she could look Grover in the face that evening and play the loving little wife to him. And he probably laid her that night, too. But we never said a word. Before we took her home, we went to Danny's house and got the spot remover and worked ourselves silly to get the stains off the back seat, so that Grover shouldn't find out what a bitch he had for a wife. Nobody said a word except Danny the Rock."

"So, why didn't you?"

"Because we were all in love with her, that's why. None of us would let the others touch her, so nobody got close to her. And none of us would let the others tell her what she needed to be told, except Danny, of course. When he scrubbed off the gunk that you put on the back seat, he spat out his chewing gum through the window and said he wondered what Grover would say if he found out."

"What did she say to that?" I wondered, and I was afraid to hear the rest of his story for fear of what might be coming next.

"She tried to calm him down and told him to be nice. He said something about not telling anything just yet, unless she did something to make him mad. I don't know exactly what passed between those two. I do know that Danny the Rock was seeing quite a bit of her for a while, and so was Timmy."

"They threatened her, is that it?" I wondered excitedly.

"I suppose so," Marve answered gloomily. "You know Timmy was a funny kid, too. He stayed with Grover only a few more weeks, and that was the time he saw a lot of Florence. Whenever I went to their house he was there, sitting next to her and fussing around her. But all of a sudden, a couple of months later, he quit working and went into the ring. He said he wanted to punch the hell out of everybody. Last I heard of him, he was going to fight some colored punk for the state heavyweight championship. By then, he had cauliflower ears, and occasionally he wasn't quite himself and acted punchy. He had to think a long time before he gave you a simple answer. He's probably gone downhill with a vengeance."

"What about Danny the Rock?" I asked.

"Oh, that guy!" Marve roared disgustedly. "He made believe he was so tough! The day he caught Florence with my Mexican engineer-friend—Joe was his name, by the way, but his friends called him Pepe—Danny broke into a pawnshop and stole a pistol. He carried the thing on his person for a while. One day the police picked him up. He gave up without a fight. When they questioned him, he told them he had stolen the gun only to shoot himself. Wouldn't tell them another thing. There was a trial with all the publicity that goes with it—I'm surprised you didn't read about it in the papers—and Danny never said any more than he had told the police at the first interrogation. Never told them why he meant to kill himself, or why he had waited all this time and not done it. They did find out where he had stolen the gun, and that he hadn't taken the money in the cash drawer. So, the judge gave him the benefit of the doubt, seeing this was his first conviction. He drew a suspended sentence."

"What's he doing now?" I wondered.

"After the business with the gun and the cops leaked out, Grover and Florence wouldn't have any more to do with him, so he drifted out of sight. Last I heard, he went to Havana with some characters who said they were big-time gamblers. Seems to me he'll get into lots of trouble hanging around with people like that. He ought to get wise to himself and go back to school. He could amount to something in this world. He's got a good head."

"He never uses it right if he does," I commented. "Why do you suppose he did those crazy things, Marve? What got into him?"

"I wouldn't know, unless he was in love with Florence. Didn't you tell her you were drunk for three months when you thought the two of you were through?"

I left Marve sitting at the bar, nursing his beer and crying his heart out over the virtues that Florence never had.

As for me, it seemed fairly obvious that she'd remain completely lost to me unless I found out what Pepe's last name was and where she was living. Even so, southern Mexico was a long way and many dollars away.

Her mother had never approved of anything or anybody interfering with her marriage to Grover. As long as Florence was married to him, I didn't dare ask the old lady for help. But now, I thought there might be a chance. I decided against writing her, because people find it much too easy to disregard a letter from a stranger. But as soon as one of my friends drove up to Chicago, I dropped in on the old lady. She lived in a shabby little frame house. We more or less coerced her into telling us Florence's current name and address. We were also shown a picture of Florence and her new husband. Her mother was mighty proud of it. She eyed me with suspicion when we left. I sensed that she'd be an enemy in my next maneuvers, as she had been before.

I wrote several letters to Florence, always making a point of enclosing a photograph of some familiar spot that I knew would make her homesick. It wasn't a very original idea but it was the best I could do. Only once was there a brief answer, and it indicated that she wasn't too happy in her second marriage but resigned to her fate. This knowledge tortured me even more than my previous uncertainty. I was in the process of raising money in order to go to Mexico and persuade her to return with me, when I received a postcard from her, bearing a Chicago postmark, saying that she had returned home. My assistance was no longer needed. All I had to do was catch a train and go. On the first week end that I had to myself, I was on my way.

She received me in the living room of that old frame house. The furniture had been changed, new wallpaper had been hung, and a lawn had been planted, so that it no longer looked quite as dismal as before. Still, it was no palace. But then, I couldn't tell her, as I wished I could, that I'd like to take her out of all that and have her start all over again, turn over a new leaf, and bask in the luxurious sun of wealth and comfort. I was just as poor as before.

Our first meeting after all those years wasn't very successful. I don't know what she expected, but I felt that I let her down. Maybe I should've taken her into my arms, given her a big hug, and slipped my fingers under her dressing-gown to effect a good seduction. But at the moment I was less interested in sex than in finding out what had been happening to her and what her plans were for the future. She had told me just a little about herself when her mother came back from a shopping trip, and from then on there was a thick crust of ice between us.

"Don't forget, Grover is coming over in an hour or so,"

her mother shouted from the kitchen where she listened to every word we spoke.

"Yes, Mother, I'll be prepared for him."

She was embarrassed about it, but it was true. The old lady had pawned her off on Grover once more, and there were plans for her to return to her former routine. In fact, I'd have to go pretty soon, or else Grover would run into me, and that would never do.

I was disgusted and left. I'd thought that she was altogether finished with the old cuckold. But it was Mother Dear who wouldn't let go of him, and Mother Dear drove Daughter back to Hubby Number One time after time, just as she had always done. Now that the old girl's second husband had run out on her and left her to shift for herself again, getting Grover back as a son-in-law and source of support was more important to her than ever. I learned how Grover had done it, too. He always knew how to appeal to the old girl. He gave her presents of all sorts, including cash, without talking much about it. The old dragon didn't like to work. Her three sons had all found her out for the bothersome parasite that she was, and none of them would have the slightest thing to do with her. They were moving up along the ladder of success, and a mother like that could only hold them back. Only Florence had stayed in the nest, and so Mother Dear clung to her for dear life and the weekly grocery bag. Florence was her only hope of escaping work until she reached her sixty-fifth birthday and could draw her old-age pension. That's why she always insisted on Florence's dating no one but the very rich or the very generous—who were just as useful—and that's why she'd never stop throwing Florence at these men as long as Florence would stand for it. And Florence was very easily influenced by her mother. The old bitch had almost hypnotic powers over her. Even after Florence had made up her mind to break away from Mother and lead her own life, as she often did, she never went through with the idea, because Mother always talked her out of it.

For the next several years, I was engaged in a contest for power with Mother Dear. If I could spend as much as half an hour alone with Florence, I'd convince her that she ought to pack her bags, go her own way, and plan on a life with me. But hardly was she back in the clutches of her mother when she'd change her mind again. In this fashion, she was persuaded to return to Grover once more, stayed with him for about six weeks, and again sought refuge at home. She found only Mother's financial needs and requirements and the shabby frame house needing all imaginable sorts of repairs. She moved out into the world, took a job, and used the money to finance a small suite in a hotel. There, she found the company of young people of her own age. But soon they took advantage of her loneliness and generosity, and she found herself paying for the lot of them. She moved back home, but again a few weeks of Mother Dear were all she could stomach.

It was at this point that I made my last attempt. I corresponded with her off and on, but she was a bad correspondent, writing only very sketchy notes. I tried to take time off to see her, but I never had the money for traveling. When I was able to go, I went to see her. But by then it was too late.

I could tell by the smirk that Mother Dear put on when she received me at the door that it was going to be a futile trip. Several times the old dragon had tried to prevent me from talking to Florence on the telephone, saying that she was out when actually she was at home, so that at this point in time the lines of battle were clearly drawn. There wasn't any point in being polite with each other. She said very little, and I observed the bare forms of politeness to please Florence, who would've been shocked at anything less. But I knew damned well that the old woman was a parasite and a liar, and she sensed through my mask of chilly convention that I knew. She sarcastically showed me into the living room, where Florence was painting her toe-nails.

As long as her mother was around, I never felt I could put my arms around Florence and make love to her, which was, no doubt, what she wanted most. The old lady ostentatiously went into the kitchen to grant us greater privacy, but she left the door ajar to listen to what was going on.

"Don't forget, it's almost a quarter to five!" she shouted when I had been there for about an hour and the ice was fianally beginning to thaw.

"Oh, Phil, I've got to tell you sooner or later," Florence burst out. "I'm engaged to be married again. My divorce from Pepe came through a couple of months ago, and I'm a free agent again. I'm going to remarry Grover!"

"No, you can't!" I shouted. "Not after all we've been through together. Not after all the scenes, and the cheating and the lying, and his locking you in, and the years that you've wasted on him and that it's cost me. You can't."

"Nonetheless, I'm going to."

The old dragon had won. Triumphantly, she came out of the kitchen, wearing a grease-stained apron and a tight black dress, like an old hussy in a third-rate whorehouse. She wiped her dirty hands on her apron, crossed her withered legs, and sat down opposite me.

"You've got to start doing your hair, dear," she said to Florence, casting a side-glance at me.

"Florence, I'm staying at the Bourbon Plaza Hotel. If you change your mind, call me there. I'll be there for another two days," I said. And without another word I left.

"Good-bye, Phil," Mother crowed after me. "Have a good time while you're in town."

I've occasionally had reason to hate people. Sometimes I've even wanted to hurt them. But never have I been so close to killing a human being as I was on several occasions to killing Mother Dear. She needed killing worse than any of the more horrible monsters I've had the misfortune to know.

On the next day, Florence called me up at the Bourbon Plaza, but she only wanted to apologize for what she intended to do.

"Nothing will ever change between us," she assured me. "We'll always be the same. You just don't give me a choice, because I need so much and you can't give it to me. Yes, I love you, too. I'll always love you. But I've got to be realistic about things. I can't go on like this, and I don't want to. Mother can't work any more, she's too frail."

"Nonsense, she's frail like you're a heavyweight boxer."

"Oh, Phil, you just don't understand about women. She's entitled to lead a quiet life now that she's getting to be sixty years old. And she's given the world enough of herself. Now we ought to do something for her."

"What? What did she ever do for you? Did she ever help you out when you really needed it? Did she ever do anything except push you off on the nearest millionaire and hope that he'd support her in style?"

"You can't talk that way about my mother!"

"Somebody has to tell you the truth, if you don't see it."

I don't know what more she said or I replied, because all

we had was a stupid quarrel about the old dragon, and I could see that Florence's affections had been thoroughly alienated from me. Oh, how I hated that old woman!

"Look, there's no point in arguing, Florence. I can't support your mother, and I wouldn't even if I could. Now, for the last time, be sensible and pack your bags, will you?"

"I'll send you an invitation to the wedding," she said. "I'm sorry, but that's how things are."

"When you decide you've had enough, you know where to find me."

"I'll make a go of it this time."

"As I said, when you want to leave Grover, just give me a ring."

She hung up on me with a bang. We'd had our last quarrel, and over another man, to boot, and about Grover! It seemed like the absolute end.

But just as I had predicted, her second marriage to Grover didn't last as long as the first one. I had given it about a year. Actually, I received my letter in six months. It said that Grover would be gone next Friday afternoon, and she'd be walking through the front door of the apartment building where she lived at two-thirty in the afternoon. She didn't bother about an inquiry about my health, she never questioned that I'd be there when she needed me, she had no doubt that I'd be at her beck and call. And she was right: I was there.

She was on time. The taxi had barely pulled up in front of the building when she came out, carrying a huge suitcase. She noticed me immediately—perhaps the telepathy was still working. After she placed the suitcase in the trunk compartment and let herself drop in the back seat, she just looked at me, as if she meant to ask me, Aren't you going to beat me up?

She was afraid of going to one of the larger hotels and we had to settle for a small one, somewhat out of the way. I knew the owners, and they often were accommodating to people who didn't care to fill out a registration blank. They were very courteous to us and gave us a huge old-fashioned room and a Victorian bath.

When we received our baggage and could be certain that the bellboys wouldn't be back, she collapsed on the bed. Her entire body shook with convulsive sobs. She cried like a little girl. I was quite lost, as men usually are when a woman breaks out into hysterical tears. I tried to tell her that it was all over now, that everything would be all right as long as she was in the hands of the man who adored her. But nothing I could say would do any good. Her tears stained the coverlets, and the makeup on her face came off. It went on and on, and I became quite disturbed. What if she suffered a nervous collapse? Had it been too much for her delicate system? Had Grover said or done something that had left irreparable scars upon her? What could I do?

Our love had always been strongest in its physical bonds, and so that's what I decided to use for a remedy. She and I had enjoyed each other's bodies to an extent that I believed few other people could. If that didn't help, I decided, nothing would, and she'd have to see a psychiatrist. I moved up close to her and started removing the outer garments that separated her from my touch.

She wouldn't permit me to undress her as I had always done but went into the bathroom and changed into a horrible pink balloon masquerading as a nightshirt, which probably was the latest thing in night fashions but left me absolutely cold. I've always reacted most strongly to women in pristine nudity—a barbaric taste, I'm told, but nevertheless it's mine. She snuggled up to me under the blanket and gently stroked me, waiting for the ceremonies of Eros which so far I'd always performed so religiously when we were together.

It was one of those awful things that shouldn't happen to a dog, but it happened all the same—and to me. No matter how hard I tried or what I did, I was unable to make love to her. I don't know whether it was because of that silly nightgown, because of the excitement of getting her out of her house and into that third-rate hotel, because of something I had eaten, or what the reason was. But try as I might, I couldn't summon an once of strength into that member which otherwise was my strongest part. We spent hours waiting for me to become my usual erotic self, but we waited in vain. I shoved the blanket aside and worked my way up the pink balloon, and finally I even persuaded her to pull the garment all the way up to her neck, so that I could feast my eyes upon her beauty. In the years before, the very sight of her had invariably stimulated me to a point where it was embarrassing before other people. But now, the naked nearness of her flesh couldn't evoke one ripple of masculinity out of me.

She became disgusted at this failure, turned her back on me, and left me to my own devices. We didn't speak a word when we turned the light out. She couldn't forgive me for what she thought was an insult. She attempted speaking to me in a civil fashion, but she couldn't sustain even a light conversation without becoming enraged. I suggested making love to her in the inimitable French fashion, but she wouldn't hear of it. She was going to receive her lover in true-blue style, with the traditional confrontation, or not at all. And since I had no more to offer her than an ancient squirrel on his last fling, she determined there wasn't going to be any love-play at all. Maybe she thought that I had exhausted myself with another girl the previous night. Maybe she thought that I didn't love her any more the way that I used to do. Maybe she thought that her beauty was fading. Maybe she didn't think at all and merely reacted in animal fashion to a frustrating situation. But it was our first unpleasant scene.

The next morning, she wanted to take a bus to Chicago. I don't know if she intended to go home to Mother Dear because she was so decidedly disappointed in me or whether it was just a reaction of helplessness, since she no longer seemed to have anybody. At any rate, I took her to the bus and bought her a ticket. I couldn't stay to see her off, because I was due at work, and since we were barely parting friends I saw no reason to lose a morning's pay just to see her rolling out of a bus depot. I've never liked the protracted scenes of farewell and premature nostalgia at train stations and curbs that seem to entertain most people to their weeping heart's delight.

After that, she cut a wide swath across Cook County, Illinois. Chicago was so brim-full of her antics that some of the information even leaked southward to Kansas City, where musicians and gamblers knew about her. I heard them talking about the goings-on in Chicago, asked them if they knew some of the people I knew there, and casually dropped her name in connection with the others. It raised an amused eyebrow on more than just a few occasions.

"Oh, sure, that chick with the red hair," they'd say with a

twinkle in their eyes. "What a looker! She's got at least a dozen guys crazy for her all the time. More energy than a rabbit at a hunting party. Nobody understands how she does it. You can see her at all times of the day and night, and always bright and chipper. Runs around in the fastest circles. Some of the real big-time operators. Any other babe running around with that crowd would've been in trouble. But not that one. She's too smart."

I went to see her twice. The first time, after she had written to me that she needed to see me. It turned out that she wanted to get married right away. She kept me occupied with small talk at Mother Dear's shabby house, and then we went to have a couple of drinks at a cocktail lounge where one of her friends was working. He kept coming over and bothering us with his own conversation, obviously thinking that we came over to keep him entertained. Maybe she came over for that reason, but I had made a trip of several hundred miles to see her, and her conversations with other men weren't my idea of fun. All that I got out of her was that she suddenly had a strong urge to get married again.

"But why again for the fourth time, when you fell so badly three times before?"

"Oh, it's no good living alone."

We played cat-and-mouse during most of the evening. The only conclusion that I could draw was that she must be pregnant and needed a father for a child of unknown origin. I still think that's what was the trouble, though there wasn't any talk of this incident ever again. I told her to wait three months, until I had my master's degree and I could go to work with better chances of making good in business. I had gone back to school to better myself, and I was determined to follow through. There wasn't any reason why we absolutely had to get married at that particular moment. We'd known each other for years, and the three additional months couldn't possibly mean a thing—unless they were three of the nine months it takes for a young one to hatch.

No matter what the true circumstances were—and I'll never know—she lost interest in me immediately when she perceived that I wasn't interested in a quick wedding right then and there. In fact, she "remembered" that she had agreed to meet some people later that day, and I had no choice but to take her home and spend the night on my own.

"I'll let you go out by yourself and paint the town red," she smiled.

"But I don't want to paint the town red. I want to be with you," I protested.

That didn't make any difference. She was sorry but she couldn't spare the time. She wanted to keep her promise to these people.

Later on, I ascertained that she went bowling with a gang of young fellows that night. My company must've bored or embarrassed her a good deal to make her prefer their society.

I was angry with her and waited for her to make the next move before I went to see her again. It came in the form of a letter. She explained that she had had an operation for cancer of the tube. She was all by herself in the hospital, and the only friend had turned out to be a childhood sweetheart who was helping her along and, incidentally, was taking care of Mother Dear.

The childhood sweetheart seemed as much of a threat as her letter was a surprise, and I wished that I could've got away to stand by her in her hour of need, but my job wasn't in Chicago, and leaves were difficult to obtain. Now that I'd started working seriously and my schooling was at last paying off in something of a career, I couldn't take time off any longer to dash about the country to please my personal whims. I'd begun to sell my time to my employers.

By the time I got away again to see her in Chicago, it was too late. First of all, she was taking some kind of narcotics in small quantities, which she purchased from shady characters who were furtive pests around her house. Secondly, she had made friends with other people who were deeper in the quagmire of the extra-legal and downright illegal worlds. Finally, her new habits of life required so much of a regular expenditure that I couldn't possibly think of making her my mistress or my wife and setting up housekeeping with her. And the operation hadn't been entirely successful. She was still having pains, which were responsible for her addiction to dope. Doctors' bills were only one of many items on ever-growing debts which she accumulated. The only answer for her was her childhood sweetheart, who owned a textile factory and didn't care about a few thousand more or less.

For a few brief days, it seemed that I still might have a chance. I managed to see her several times in the afternoon, before the textile man was expected to call.

"Florence, dear, it's nearly a quarter to five!" Mother Dear yelled from the kitchen, just as she had done before when she was hawking her daughter to Grover. "Remember, he's always on time!"

And away I went, off to the corner drugstore to telephone for a taxi. Again, I'd gladly have strangled the old dragon, if I could have hit upon a way to do it without being caught. Older, uglier, and more parasitical than ever, Mother Dear deserved killing more than before. Why couldn't she have done everybody a favor and died? No truer words were ever spoken than the ancient proverb: Only the good die young.

In spite of it all, and with Mother Dear denying Florence on the telephone as usual, I managed to dissuade Florence from her plans. Whispering so that Mother Dear shouldn't hear us, and talking now and then in cocktail lounges, we drafted plans for her to pack her bags one day and skip out on Mother Dear and all plans for the wedding, to join me at my hotel, and for the two of us to leave for my house where we might live as man and wife. I was fairly sure by that time that she was a very sick woman, and I wanted very much to have her live out the rest of her life with me and not be used as a means for her mother's support. Cancer doesn't hurt badly until it's spread throughout the body, and then it's usually too late for operations to do much good. Since the first operation was only partly effective, I presumed that I'd be marrying a long doctor's bill. But I loved her still, and I didn't mind. I thought I'd rather spend the few remaining months of her life with her, even under those conditions, than learn from mutual friends some day that she had died in the arms of another man. Time, I thought, didn't matter, as long as one knew what one wanted. At worst, the knowledge that it must all end inside of a year or two would intensify the feelings I had for her.

I grew increasingly nervous as I waited at my hotel all night long where she was supposed to come with her belongings. She didn't put in an appearance. I smoked cigarettes all evening and stayed awake all night, but there was no trace of Florence. I knew that it wouldn't do any good to telephone her. I'd have to wait until she contacted me.

It was Mother Dear who gave me a ring rather than her daughter.

"I hope you feel proud of yourself, young man," she began to berate me. "I just hope it's worth it to you. Florence had another attack yesterday afternoon. She's in the hospital now."

"That's terrible," I replied. "But why accuse me? Did I give her cancer?"

"I just hope you're proud of yourself," the old lady insisted. "She was packing all her things to leave with you. Behind my back, too. Hadn't told me a thing. And I'm supposed to be her mother! First thing I found about it was when she asked me to call you. She was over the worst of it then and I was allowed into the room. She asked me to call you and tell you that she was all packed and ready to elope with you, but that it wasn't meant to be. It'll be a long time before she's ready to go anywhere now, and it won't be with you."

"That's telling me!" I barely squeezed the words out of my mouth. Tears were welling up within me. Was it to be so soon? Would she die before we could get married?

"Oh, it wasn't my idea to call, young man, I assure you of that," she said.

"For once I believe you," I said.

"After you cause her a relapse like that, you ought to be ashamed of yourself, sassing me like that!" she shouted indignantly.

"Me? Did I cause her to have a relapse?" I almost choked with anger. "Now, listen, you old fool, if anyone deserves to be blamed, it's you! Decking her out for millionaire suitors like an old panderer, just so you could sit on easy street! Cutting us short when we wanted to talk, so we wouldn't annoy the sources of your old-age pension! Pushing her from one unhappy marriage into another from the age of consent to the eve of her death! It's just too bad, isn't it, that she can't support you any more, if she dies! She's letting you down by dying, isn't she? You might have to go to work! That's the only thing you'll grieve about, isn't it?"

"I don't have to listen to vile stuff like that!" she weakly rejoined.

"No, but you're listening. And it's the first time anybody has told you the truth for a long time, isn't it? How does it feel?"

She hung up the receiver as a reply. Apparently, it didn't feel too good. Probably no one had spoken to her like that since her sons had left her, who also had understood the story about her. Maybe they had been too well mannered to speak their minds. In that case, I was possibly the first one.

I went to Chicago a few months later, mostly to check up on Florence. I learned from the friend in the cocktail lounge that she was about to get married. It was to the textile manufacturer. I tried several times to telephone her, but I heard her mother's voice and hung up. Finally, I got her.

"I'm sorry, Phil, but that's how it is," Florence said. There was a new kind of determination in her voice. "I'm marrying this man. He's the kindest man I've ever met, and we've known each other since we were kids together. He helped me when I needed it most. He's paid all the hospital bills. He's taken care of Mother and me as if we were already part of his family."

"Aha, so that's it," I said. "He's free and easy with the dollar."

"Phil, there's no sense in talking about it," she tried to evade the issue. "I'm going to marry him, and I'm never going to do anything to hurt him. So, please, don't ask me.

I can't go away with you. We can't get married. Maybe, once in a while we could meet, as we've always done. There'll always be a bond between us, stronger than marriage and everything else.

"No, Florence, if you marry this character, the bond is torn."

"Sorry, if that's how you feel . . ."

I didn't hear the rest of what she had to say to me. My hand mechanically replaced the receiver on its hook. Like a robot, I stalked out into the lobby of my hotel. I walked and walked and walked, until I got to the South Side, where the sailors and the tourists throw their dollars away on cheap women and cheaper whiskey, both of which are sold to them at fancy prices. I walked into Tony Bocelli's place, where I often dropped in to while away an idle hour.

"Phil, nice to see you again." Tony came out from behind the bar and stretched out his hand. "My God, Phil, you look like death warmed over. What's the matter boy? You been sick? Have you seen ghosts?"

"No, I just talked to one," I said. "The ghost of almost seven years of my life. She's getting married to another guy. She's dying and doesn't know it."

He didn't say another word. He went back behind the bar and poured me a double bourbon with very little soda. He didn't let the bartender touch it. The bartender wanted to ring it up on the cash register, but Tony held his pudgy paw over the machine.

"Here, Phil, you need this," he said, placing the glass in front of me. "You'd better drink it quick or you'll be a goner."

I emptied it with one swallow. It burned my insides, though it was good bourbon. It felt like just the right medicine. When a body has a wound, it needs a disinfectant. That's what liquor can be on occasions.

It was nine months later when I ran into one of the musicians I used to pump for information about Florence and her life in Chicago. He was playing in a small band that had just arrived in one of my favorite clubs.

"You know that redhead you used to be so crazy about?" He bored a finger into my chest. "You know the one I mean?"

"Florence. She got married to a manufacturer."

"Yea, that she did," he said. "They painted the town red when they came back from their honeymoon. She was cutting up like crazy, too. Everybody knew she was dying except for her. Maybe she knew, too, or at least suspected it. Anyway, they were living it up, having a grand time, until she took sick again."

I could sense the rest. My brain turned inside out. The world swiveled madly around me, and I felt violently sick to my stomach. There happened to be a glass of ice-water in front of me. I grabbed it and emptied it to steady my digestion. It helped a little but not much. I needed something stronger.

"Next thing I knew, they carried her out to the cemetery, a few days before I left the Windy City," he continued. "Big funeral, with all the works."

I had to hold on to the table to steady myself. My feet wouldn't carry me when I attempted to get up, because I had to go to the bathroom to vomit. All of my innermost being looked at the people around me and wanted to retch.

"Are you all right?" the musician asked, with worry, wonderment, and kindly concern in his voice.

"Yes, I'll be all right," I managed to gulp. "Thanks for telling me."

"Sorry, kid, I didn't know you'd take it so hard," he said. "Have a drink on me. Have two or three." His hand, accustomed to beating the drums, gently placed itself upon my back. He patted me several times and withdrew it considerately. The drinks arrived, and we drank a toast to "Memories." Soon his recess was over, and he had to return to the stage to entertain the public. It was just as well.

For the first time, I was feeling old as well as forlorn. While the music and the young couples performed the latest steps and the stereotyped rites of love on the dance floor in a mass of perspiring confusion, my mind raced through the seven years that had been dominated, if not enthralled, by Florence. My eyes wandered through the smoke-filled room and saw nothing of what was there. They saw her flashing green eyes, sparkling with mirth, her red hair shining in the sun, and her naked lithe figure stripping for the love-act with the speed of enthusiasm. My ears didn't hear the beating of the drums, the wailing of the saxophone, or the din of happy voices. They strained only to hear the ringing echo of her speech and the quaint little chuckle that was all the laughing she ever could produce. My fingers clasped a paper napkin but felt the white softness of her luscious flesh, rippling with ecstatic passion under my touch. I underwent a blissful torture, and when it was all over, I felt as if I'd been through a clothes wringer.

Up to and including the deaths of my parents, no death has ever affected me as strongly as Florence's. Although she's been dead for nearly a decade, I've never spent a day on which I haven't wished that I could be Orpheus and she Eurydice, so that I might bring her back from Hades. Somehow, I've known ever since I was told she was dead that my life will never be complete without her. . . .

V Laura: Virginal Passion

During the years when I racked my brains over Florence, I acquired another problem named Laura. It happened without my really knowing that it did, because I never took the initiative in connection with her. Any other man exposed to the same treatment, I'm sure, would've been trapped, manacled, bundled off, carted before an altar, sworn, and safely married in the process. But not me: Florence excepted, I was and am marriage-proof. If I've ever believed in conventional morality, I don't know about it. I'll leave the pleasures of marriage to the gentlemen who enjoy being bossed by a withering female, just because, at one time, many years ago, they felt they couldn't get along without a daily round of sex with her body. As for me, I can dispense with any one person's body; there are so many bodies around! I'm not going to be one of those people who buy a cow just because they like to drink milk.

We met in the back room of a little music shop where I used to drop in to use the instruments and keep in practice. I liked to dash off the old numbers that my despairing teachers had taught me when I was ten, twelve, or fourteen. Now I could play them as loudly and as slowly as I wanted, without having some jerk disturb me by shouting, *"Crescendo! Pianissimo! Dulce!"* And I could give vent to all my melancholy without having someone rap me on the knuckles and tell me that I wasn't following Schubert's and Chopin's sense. As far as I've been able to ascertain, neither Schubert's nor Chopin's original instructions were extant anyway, and these comments between the bars were the work of some poor hack hired by the music editor, so why should I bother following them? Whatever Schubert or Chopin were thinking of when they played their instruments—and those instruments sounded different from ours, too—was something I'd probably never know. And I doubted whether they themselves always played their own pieces with the same expression, like automatons reciting from a pre-stamped roll of paper. If they had the stuff to write great music, they probably had sense enough to vary their expressions to fit their moods. And that's what I was doing. But never could I do it with impunity, until I got rid of teachers and started playing for my own enjoyment rather than for their sense of duty.

There was something else I enjoyed doing. Sitting in that back room, I could let my hands roam freely over the keyboard and improvise. I could make up a melody of a few bars and convert it into a droning, orchestral suite, or into the thin warblings of a string quartet, or into a simple exercise of the type that every litle boy and girl must go through before he or she is allowed to play anything he or she might enjoy. I could compose whole suites, to be forgotten as soon as they had seen their first performance, or songs that were sung but once, or brilliant virtuoso pieces with which no virtuoso would ever shine. As long as I sat in that little back room, I was the king of the keyboard and the czar of music.

When people like me dropped in at the music shop and practiced, we had to tolerate occasional visitors. That was the point of letting us play. It was supposed to be advertising. The reason behind it was rather flattering to those of us who couldn't afford to buy a piano: People would hear us play from afar and, attracted by an irresistible impulse, would drop in to sit and listen to us in wide-eyed enchantment. At last, having convinced themselves that the piano was a wonderful invention, they'd buy one.

Most of the people who came to listen to us budding geniuses were women. There was nothing wrong with that. More than than half of all the people on earth are females, and the owner of the store knew, no doubt, that women owned or controlled more than three-fourths of all property in the United States. Sales appeals were always pitched to women, for women were many times more likely to buy pianos than were men. And if they wanted to come in and listen to the long-haired, bright-eyed young men pour out their artistic souls, they were welcome. The more, the better.

The only trouble with this line of reasoning was that not all those who came in to listen to the long-haired, bright-eyed young men were actual prospective piano purchasers. Some of them were far more interested in the acquisition of a long-haired, bright-eyed young man. And that statistic includes both middle-aged and young women, who made up a substantial part of the visiting clientele. They sat on their hard chairs with enraptured eyes and unabashedly stared at the young man going through enraptured melodic contortions. Ah! They spotted, behind all that exertion of euphonious energy, the lonely male calling for his female! Behind every creative man, they reasoned, there's always a woman, The Woman, in fact, to whom all this beauty emanating from the strings was dedicated and constituted an appeal. It was a kind of courtship, they imagined: the unfulfilled, unredeemed artist's soul in search of love and recognition, and they themselves, oozing out motherly kindness, ready to bestow the crowning glory of womanly charms as a reward for the warblings of the lonely son of the Muses. And so, what if the music became a little loud now and then, resounded with the beats of the war-drums or echoed the titanic struggles of great souls wrestling with the inadequacies of human potentialities? The course of true love, they thought, is seldom smooth, and the young man was portraying a lover's quarrel. Wasn't it touching? But what he really needed was *their* sympathy, *their* love, *their* support. All these weighty and thunderous conflicts would be smoothed like a soaring surf under the benevolent smothering of a flow of oil. That was it, there was no doubt about it! The kindly hand of a woman and her love would soften the sharp edges of the young man's immaturity that still tugged away at his wounded ego. And soon he'd be just as round, smooth, and well-adjusted a member of society as all the other poor saps who've been subjugated by the ever-loving, beneficent matriarchy.

Laura was sitting there one day when I finished an improvisation that had lasted some forty-five minutes. She had sneaked in and sat down quietly and not made one sound or the slightest attempt to call attention to herself. This circumstance was altogether in her favor, since some of the young matrons used to rustle their skirts, clear their throats, stumble in with bundles all over their arms, come in twos and whisper, move their creaking chairs, shake the pebbles out of their shoes, and go through any other motions that might possibly be disturbing to the person playing the piano. Naturally, they always disclaimed the slightest intention of disturbing or interrupting. "Go on, please," they'd invariably beg, with exaggerated pleading. "I hope I'm not distracting you. I so want to listen. You sure know how to handle that piano!" And they'd be quiet for a few minutes. Soon they'd be restless again, finding themselves outside the center of attraction, and think of some other objectionable noises. Worst of all, they'd make silly requests. They'd either want me to play Tchaikovski's piano concerto, without knowing which one, or they'd ask me please to play an opera, which is manifestly impossible on a mere piano, or they'd request semi-classical pieces with which the nightclub virtuosos make their living: Malagueña, Claire de Lune, Chopin's Military Polonaise, and the like— all pieces which one must practice for day after day, week after week, and month after month in order to perform them at all decently and which don't mean much if one does. Some of them even had the gall to tell me that I was playing too loud or too fast, hoping that I'd lull them to sleep in a sort of dreamy world made of syrup, marshmallows, and chocolate milkshakes, and topped by a movie hero whispering sweet nothings into their ears.

But not this girl. She'd sit in that easy chair, one leg bent under her posterior and the other stretched out, with her head leaning sideways on one of her hands and the other hand leaning on the armrest or inoffensively keeping time with the music. She had the tact not to make extravagant compliments, which would have put me on my guard right away, or to make childish requests, or even to chatter on any topic. It was a lot if she acknowledged the end of a composition by an appreciative nod or raised an eyebrow at a particularly long concert piece that I was trying to memorize. She returned several times without even asking the usual stupid questions which are the last resort of the would-be music-lover's shrunken kind: "What was that? Have you been playing long? Are you giving any concerts? Do you like my favorite composer —— (fill in blank)?" No, she waited for me, and yet there was something suggestive about her attitude that invited me to become a friend. It wasn't just sex. The floozy who dropped in occasionally to pick up a young man to satisfy her wore tight clothes, short skirts, precarious toothpick-heel shoes, and the customary mask of makeup. Not Laura. She didn't exactly hide her sex. Her breasts always showed to good advantage in her blouses and dresses, and she managed to cross her legs during the intervals when I was resting. But it wasn't the obvious come-on.

She was taking business courses at the local university, so that she had more time than she knew what to do with. This undoubtedly was one of the reasons for the fact that she took time to cultivate me. Gradually, cultivating me became a habit, and in the beginning she probably didn't know the ultimate way station to which this road was bound to lead. Then, she fell in love with me and couldn't let go. And that's where the birth of tragedy lay in her case. I liked her as a human being and came to enjoy the pleasure of her body, but the electric spark which I had known from the first mo-

ment with Florence simply wasn't there. Whenever I had a
chance to see Florence, I'd happily board the next train or
bus and leave, and the few chances I had to spend a few hours
making love to Florence, I certainly let no one and nothing
stand in my way—even when I was eating on Laura's money.

It was the fifth or sixth time that she came to listen to my
playing when I asked her to accompany me to have a beer. She
didn't want beer and said she'd prefer a gin-rickey. I said
that I couldn't afford to pay for anything but beer. That
fixed things up in a perfect way. It got her into the habit of
paying her own way. If I bought her anything at all, which
happened very infrequently, she was surprised. It was far
more common for her to foot my expenses. From beer to
beer, and gin-rickey to rickey, we proceeded, and then we
started sitting on the grass and admiring the great outdoors.
My attention was frankly far more concentrated on Laura
than on the great outdoors, but I gathered soon that she
hadn't had much experience with men, and in order not to
frighten her out of her wits, I pretended to love the green
grass, the brown earth, the creeping worms, and the blue,
blue sky. I'm not averse to appreciating nature at any time,
and so it wasn't too difficult, even though the part of nature
that fascinates me most is sex, or specifically, my own possi-
bilities of enjoying sex, of which Laura obviously was going
to be one. The question was when.

Our little idyl was about two months old, when the serious
struggle began between us. Its object was clearly Laura's
body. It was a struggle as bitter, determined, purposeful, and
often as violent as a wrestling match. After every round that
I lost, I took her home, always expecting her to assure me
with tears and a cracking voice that this would absolutely

have to be the last time we met, that she was sick and tired of having me try to seduce her, and that she never wanted to see my face again. But instead, she regularly melted toward the end, and when we were opposite the door to her house, and she expected to have to explain to her mother why she was coming home at one o'clock in the morning in the middle of the week, with her skirt grass-stained and her hair all tousled, she gave me a brave smile, paid me some jocular compliments, thanked me for my company, and asked when she might have the pleasure again. And then I knew that, even though I had lost another battle, I was going to win the war.

That was the first stage of the struggle. It was the hand-holding, neck-kissing, breast-fondling stage, with occasional long kisses on the mouth, to be followed later by little wrestling-matches conducted with the tongues in our mouths, in a kind of match within a match. We also had staring contests and thigh-feeling sessions, but she always stopped my hand from wandering too far up those fleshy columns of pink, and she couldn't stand my looking at her very long until we were long beyond this innocent prelude to our relations.

The next stage was that of the intimate caresses, which must've created quite a laundry problem for her and cost me a lot of sleep. Once I pushed my hand into her kingdom of heaven and felt the warm and plentiful response upon me like honey dripping out of a dispenser under the gentle pressure of the thumb. She couldn't get enough of that sensation and begged me not to stop. Ordinarily, we had to wait until it was dark outside and we could sit in the park and fondle each other, because neither of us had enough money to go anywhere else. But sometimes, she'd feel especially passionate and pay both of our admission fees to a movie. She never sat anywhere except in the balcony seats, and no sooner had we sat down than she grabbed my hand and placed it between her legs, where I could already sense that she was longing for the contact for which she didn't have the courage. My fingers played a regular musical symphony upon her and practiced rhythmical beats at the entrance, where her most sensitive spots lay. The moisture sometimes caused us to produce certain smacking sounds, so that frequently people turned around to give us indignant stares, probably surmising that we were snapping bubble-gum. Those people would never have believed that I was appeasing the ravenous appetite of a virgin, even if I'd drawn them a picture. They thought, no doubt, that we ought to learn how to chew gum. And yet, I knew that I was exploring the end of nerve centers that were waiting for my touch, preparing my virgin for the big night, when all caution would be flung to the winds and she'd throw herself upon me, ready to receive me.

She fought a valiant, if futile, war. Whenever I readied myself for action and she saw me approach her, she pushed me back, even though she was flushed with sexual longing and panted with yearning. I tried to hold her down and force myself on her, but she wouldn't be subdued that way. She was strong enough that I couldn't hold down both of her arms with one of mine, and if I used both arms to hold hers, she'd close her legs and wriggle away altogether and try to rise from the ground. Opening her thighs with my knee was a possibility, but she writhed and clawed like a tigress, and on some occasions she threatened to scream. Her skirt sullied from her own reactions, her blouse torn, her shoes battered, and her panties crushed, she still held out against me and time and again struggled to an unwanted and a bothersome virginity. Finally, she'd decide to go home, and I'd accom-

pany her to her front door and expect her to sulk or slap me.
But she always kissed me good night and made another date.
It was tantalizing.

I had just about made up my mind to give her up as an
impossible task, when she became a bit more affectionate.
Instead of lying and struggling on the ground, she'd undress
me and kiss and pet me in order to give me some satisfaction.
I suppose she needed to acquaint herself with the idea and
aspect of a man and accustom herself to the thought of contact with me. It required only two acquaintances for her to
fall in love with the aspect of my masculinity and press
some kisses all over me. She seemed to enjoy the feeling of
intimacy it gave her, while I fell into action and excited her
private parts to a boiling point of mad frenzy. At this stage
she began to make inchoate and hysterical sounds of surprise
and well-being which used to worry me sick for fear that
some overly zealous policeman or a casual passer-by might
come hurrying to see what we were doing and discover us in
such a position of embarrassing intertwinement. It didn't
seem to bother her at all that we were in a public park. She
was losing her sense of shame which, I suppose, was a sure
indication that she was shedding that hard shell of Puritanism
with which her bigoted family had surrounded her. Though
it sometimes made me quake with fear of discovery, I still
continued to let her ignore the rest of the world, because it
could be considered as progress toward her education.

When it finally happened, it was—like all events that have
had too much of an advance preparation—a distinct letdown.
I've always maintained that a pound of beefsteak can make
a pretty good meal, but if you're forced to starve yourself
for three days before enjoying it, and every stimulus is applied to make you hunger for meat, you not only fail to savor

its full flavor, but you tend to have built up in your mind an image of "beefsteak" that vastly exaggerates its true good qualities and you almost necessarily must be disappointed. That's one of the things which continually spoil the relationship between men and women in Puritanical America and comprise the wholesale load of disillusionment composing the average human life. The virginity that the woman can give the man is over-priced, over-valued, over-advertised, over-suggested, over-stimulated, over-discussed, and over-regulated. More than any other country, America bases its moral code upon the ethics of sex, and so the various churches concentrate upon their function of withholding, granting, distributing, and regulating it. The prelates, having no other merchandise in their inventories, concentrate their publicity campaigns upon it. The preachers, not daring to talk about little things such as cut-throat competition and charity— there might be wealthy clients in those expensive front-row pews—talk about "sin" as if there were only one kind, the kind for which many of their church-goers are too old. This is about as sensible as refusing to acknowledge the existence of anything but apples when talking about fruit, but when apples are the only safe topic, it tends to be profitable. Moreover, as long as sex is recognized as the predominant factor in people's mentality, and as long as it is as much discussed and advertised as it is in America, its predominance must remain unchallengeable. That's the best manner of holding people's attention and making sure of that annual contribution to the church coffers. Laura, as a perfect illustration, had her mind made up that religious principles were all wrapped up in that certain nervous area between her legs, where she carried her honor, and she clearly anticipated the tortures of Hell in the eventuality that she yielded to my temptations. Yet she wanted the stimulation and the pulsations within her worse than anything else in the world. And so, one night she forgot to struggle and snuggled up to me a little tighter instead, turning her head aside and squealing like a tickled baby.

The setting wasn't exactly the best. We were in the city's largest park, where young couples usually went to perform such necessary and desirable operations, but which also was the hangout for bums, juvenile delinquents, fugitives from justice, and other undesirables. In the last days of spring, as we were, the small insects that make life difficult in parks were out in force, creeping and crawling over such discarded items as Laura's panties and brassiere, my jacket and newspaper, and a shopping bag which she had brought along for some obscure reason. Now and then, a stray dog approached us, with its tongue hanging out, attracted by the strong odor of the genitals of two humans in heat. In fact, I had to administer a solid kick to one cur that insisted upon rubbing its mouth against my crotch and licking the exposed portions of both our bodies. It was all quite elemental, and my enjoyment of her defloration was also dampened by some strange noises in the bushes nearby, where I saw the contours of a dark something moving about, and by the happy cries of some teenagers under the trees on the other side, some sixty feet away from us, where they were roughnecking it and staging mock fights, which might at any moment draw nearer to us, so that their curious eyes would discover our amatory exploits. I suspected that they were the sort of "nice" boys who might beat me to a pulp and take turns in enjoying Laura's newly-initiated charms, and I drew a sigh of relief when they finally decided it was too dark and nothing was happening, so that they'd rather be elsewhere. The shape

on the other side seemed not to be stirring at all, and I
gathered from its actions—or lack thereof—that it must be
one of those Peeping Toms who used to frequent the parks
in hopes of meeting up with precisely the sort of situation
that I created: watching two young lovers ploughing away
and catching glimpses of their naked bodies in the moonlight. I became so curious about it that, when we finally
went home, I threw a rock in the general direction in which
I believed him to be and remarked something about old
men who didn't have the guts to go out and get a woman
on their own, and there was a distinct unfriendly grunt in
return. Apparently he had been watching us all that time
and wasn't strong, sober, or ambitious enough to come out
and fight—either for the preservation of his dubious honor
or for possession of the female whom I had introduced
into the society of Venus.

It had been pretty good regardless of the unpleasant circumstances, and I kept exploring all the mysteries of the
body with her for several hours, before I tired and noticed
the chill of night sweeping through my haunches and the
ants crawling into my shoes. She didn't have much to say
except that she had decided the previous day that she'd
never be able to hold me unless she gave me what I wanted,
and that she had come to the conclusion that she'd rather
risk that than lose me. And so, I took her home once more,
certain that from now on I had a steady thing.

Laura was a little older than I was, about twenty-two when
it all happened. Her stupid parents had brought her up in
that odd belief that a man ought to have marital intentions
if he wants to engage in sex-play with a woman, that one's
first love must be one's last, and that there wasn't any benefit in love without the benefit of clergy. Now she was in love,

and she knew that I could never marry her in my then state
of poverty, and that I probably wouldn't at all. And she still
was willing to have sex with me three or four times a week
and loved it. She looked forward to it with heart and soul.
For the truth is, she loved sex for itself in addition to loving
me. She never could get enough.

A few weeks after I had introduced her to the secrets of
love, I enjoyed her on what seemed like a perfectly innocent
patch of greens in the park. Unfortunately, she started itching
fairly soon. It turned out that in my haste to merge our feverish bodies into a perfect union, I had flattened her on some
poison ivy. And since I normally stripped her of every patch
of clothing, she had a red rash all over her body. The poor
girl suffered horribly.

We met again during her days of torture, and all she
could think of was sex. I was mortally afraid that I'd get
rashes too, and so I wouldn't have anything to do with her.
She was quite upset at this cowardly attitude of mine. She was
of the opinion that if I liked to engage in the act, I ought to
risk getting poison ivy without hesitation. Several times, she
attempted to seduce me by rubbing herself against me and
stroking the part of me that she wanted to excite, but I was
most adamant in my refusal and felt somewhat like Joseph
with Potiphar's wife. Finally, she lost patience with me. Her
parents were on vacation for a couple of weeks, and except
for an ancient grandmother, she had the house to herself.
And so, she set the perfect trap.

Knowing how fond I was and always have been of good
food, she offered to feed me a big steak dinner if I came to
her house. Naturally, I gave in. She had some excellent soup,
a bit of fowl, and the huge Porterhouse steaks, with potatoes
and broccoli, a tomato salad, and garlic bread, followed by

fruit and ice cream. The whole meal was washed down with gargantuan potions of red wine and followed by some genuine French cognac. It was absolutely delicious. When it was all over, I was invited to sit on the sofa and rid myself of my slight intoxication with some coffee and listen to Liszt's Hungarian rhapsodies. It was perfect.

Having got me into a good mood, she then sat down next to me and pulled her skirt up to her lap. Her hands went caressing all over my body, and her lips smothered me with kisses. She gently took off my necktie and unbuttoned my shirt. Her tongue licked the hair on my chest and described tiny circles at the base of my neck, while her arms wound around me and her weight gradually pulled me down on the couch, so that I had to support myself on my own arms in order not to slip. Her naked thighs quivered upon my legs while now and then she pressed her mouth on mine and let her tongue circulate around mine, so that her saliva ran into my mouth with a hungry and suggestive abandon. And when all of these tricks wouldn't work, she unbuttoned her blouse and let me see the bare beauty beneath it. The female breast always had a great fascination for me and she knew that this would tip the balance in her favor. I became so excited that my trousers wouldn't hold me, and she had some difficulty in unzipping me without doing me injury. She went into raptures when she saw how monstrously excited she had made me.

Her grandmother sat in her little room. The old lady never came out except to go to the bathroom, and then she had to be helped. We were fairly safe on that account, but we still were a bit worried that perhaps the old cripple might come to the living room door to ask Laura to walk her the rest of the way. And so, we went out into the kitchen. Laura with one determined pull stripped off her panties, which showed evidence of her violent desire, and lay down on the kitchen linoleum to accommodate me. I kneeled on the linoleum before her, trembling with impatience to savor a desire for me that was so noticeably strong. Before I knew it, she closed around me like a vise and pulled me tightly toward herself. She performed this maneuver so quickly and so forcefully that I hadn't had time to complete my undressing, and I almost missed connections with her the first time. I had barely started giving her some satisfaction, when she went into convulsive throbs and I felt evidences of her passion all over me. Before long, we were locked in a union that sounded and felt as if it couldn't but result in fertilization. She went through at least four spells of ecstasy in the first half hour, and I couldn't hold back any longer and gave way to the boiling, pent-up passions rising within me. Laura wouldn't think of stopping. It was like getting caught in a machine and not finding the lever to turn off the action. Her big cheeks kept throwing themselves at me, and her abdomen went through greedy, concentric contortions with increasing speed. Sometimes she balanced her entire weight upon her head and shoulders, because she wished to fling the rest of herself at me. Her breasts, usually very firm, were bouncing down upon her chest, as if they were threatening to fly off into space. When finally we both sank down exhaustedly upon the linoleum, we were dead tired. Laura was just wiping up the pools of evidence we had created, and cleaning herself, when we heard a scratch at the door, like that of a dog wanting to come into the house. It was Grandmother. She was rapping on the living room door to summon Laura to her duty. I certainly was glad that we were in the kitchen, because I was too tired to dress in a hurry, and I just lay on the floor, with my clothes upon a chair and my skin breathing in the summer air, trying to absorb all the oxygen it could for a speedy recovery of strength. Grandmother would've deemed me extremely indecent.

When the old lady had relieved her kidneys and bladder, Laura returned to the kitchen, poured some more wine into my well-filled and much-exercised stomach, licked my breast, and finally decided to take a rest by reclining upon me, mouth to mouth, navel to navel, and knee to knee, hoping to revive me to give her some more of that special bliss of which she was so very fond. She had to wait for an hour before I could accommodate her. By then, my strength had returned, and I kneeled on the linoleum floor, ready to deflower a regiment of virgins, if given the opportunity. She was willing, ready, and able to comply with all requests. And henceforth, every hour on the hour, all through the night, we kept it up. Laura finally felt sore and started bleeding, but she wouldn't stop. As long as it was only the linoleum that got dirty, she didn't care. As long as there was an ounce of strength left within me, she wouldn't let me go home with it. Her skin strained against me, her arms reached out for me, she writhed voluptuously to let me enjoy every fiber of her. When I wanted to go home at five o'clock in the morning, she cried. I looked into the mirror: A stranger was looking at me with beady eyes, sunk into a balloon of a bloated face. I knew that this sort of thing couldn't last.

Shortly after this exhausting night, the streetcar and bus conductors decided all over our city that they wanted more money and went out on strike. For about six weeks, there was no public transportation. I hitchhiked to and from work, but I figured I could use the strike as a convenient excuse to get a little rest from Laura whose passionate desires and

requirements were sapping my strength and consuming en
tirely too much of my time. But there was no rest in store
for me. Laura walked the five miles to my house, three times
a week! She was just like an obedient slave. And what was
more, when we had joined our loins and left enough of a
remembrance upon the city's park lawns, she walked all the
way back to her home, whereas I had only a two-minute
walk to my abode. At about that time, I developed a truly
tender spot in my heart for her and resolved to be kind to
her if I could. Those self-sacrifices three times a week, just
to enjoy the pleasure of mating with me, did something to
my toughened mind. For some months, I think I actually
loved Laura. It's hard not to love a person like her.

But the seasons wore on, and the weather soon got cold.
Laura and I had started going out to a golf course by streetcar, when the public system of transportation functioned
once more. The golf course was infinitely preferable to the
park, since it was far removed from the city so that the bums
and juvenile delinquents didn't frequent it, and we had more
privacy. Moreover, the grass was kept better and there weren't
so many insects. And if we could manage to straighten out
our clothes sufficiently, we could sometimes walk into the
club house, pretend that we belonged there, and act like
members, ordering drinks and food to recover from the
strains and stresses of our embraces. When it grew colder,
Laura brought a blanket to spread below us and wrap around
us, once our bodies were safely joined. It meant that she
couldn't wiggle and wriggle as much, but it kept us warm.
And when it grew colder still, she brought two blankets
along, and I brought my overcoat. With all that equipment,
we braved the elements like Eskimos in the spring, until there
were near-freezing temperatures outside. After that, we were

at a loss about what to do. My aged landlady would never have tolerated my bringing a girl to my room, and her parents would as soon have seen her dead as seen me squire her in her bedroom.

We found a temporary solution in the good nature of Vassilyi, an exiled Ukrainian, who maintained a modest office for the purpose of conspiracy and soliciting funds from other exiled Ukranians and former denizens of the Red world. I haven't too much of an idea what they did, whether they threw bombs, printed propaganda literature, assassinated Soviet dignitaries, operated a white slave ring, or what; and furthermore, I didn't care. Laura introduced me to Vassilyi one evening over a friendly glass of vodka, and we became fast friends. He offered to let us use his conspiratorial headquarters in our desperate plight. And so, we began to meet in a café around the corner from the exiled Ukrainians' organization and sneaked into their business office after dark, after the janitors had gone home. There were no couches or sofas in the Ukranian office—revolutionaries must either stand to keep in training or squat on the floor. It was a bare little affair, with only a desk and a swivel-chair, an overstuffed armchair that was losing its stuffing, and huge file cabinets labeled in Cyrillic letters. Next door, there was another office with more file cabinets labeled in Cyrillic letters but no desk. We had no choice but to lie on the floor. Since Laura usually lay beneath me and supported most of my weight, it wasn't hard on me except on my knees. For the first time I found out what it was to get knee burns without the sun shining.

It seemed like the answer to every maiden's prayer, until a complication threw a monkey wrench into our amatory exploits. Vassilyi found himself a girl, a buxom, red-cheeked,

big-hipped Ukrainian waitress, whom he wanted to lay in his
office, too. He gave us what seemed like a reasonable amount
of time: an hour or two. Then he arrived with his specimen
of Slavic beauty and claimed his proprietary rights as man of
the house, while we were ploughing away happily, trying to
placate our insatiable desires. For Laura's fleshly appetites
clearly exceeded my own, and I've usually been regarded as
something in the order of a satyr. After an hour or two, we
were usually just getting started on our second or third
round, looking forward to two or three more, depending on
how well I'd been eating the last few days. We never were in
a mood to quit that early in the game. Now, we couldn't
very well disappoint the hopes of our Ukrainian host, and so
we were more or less forced to get dressed in a hurry and
make room for the next actors to appear on the stage. We
carefully wiped the floor to obviate any embarrassment.
Sometimes, on our way out of the building, we heard weird
shrieks of Slavic delight.

Clearly, our welcome in the Ukrainian emigrants' headquarters had almost been worn out, and we had to find another solution to the shelter problem. It was difficult, for
we didn't have much money between us, and we could barely
afford one cheap hotel a week if we pooled our resources and
I ate nothing but sandwiches. Some of our friends owned cars,
and we approached them from time to time for permission
to amuse ourselves in the back seat, but that, too, was manifestly unsatisfactory for a couple of people who loved to take
their time. There simply wasn't a good solution.

We were both much happier when spring came and we
could venture out into the golf course with those blankets
again. For a week or two, we met every day in order to make
up for lost time. It was like going on a honeymoon, only

better, for it didn't entail any of the obligations that follow most of those.

The honeymoon was broken up briefly by one of those re-emergences of Florence upon the scene. It never occurred to me to hesitate. When I received the message from Florence, I called Laura and told her I couldn't see her for a few days, refused to answer any and all questions, and dashed off to see my true love. It was selfish and cruel of me, and I couldn't offer a single excuse except for the real one, which was that I had a compulsive feeling about the situation. I didn't doubt or waver. I simply acted, as if inspired by a higher law.

Laura had always been unreasonably jealous. Whenever I so much as looked at another woman, she became indignant. She hated to see me speak to other women, and she was slow to accept the simplest business contacts between them and me. All women, of all ages and all varieties of looks, were potential competitors for my affections, as far as she was concerned. She had no understanding of what made some attractive and others repulsive, some attainable and others beyond my reach. Any woman with whom I was in the same room was her natural enemy, whether it was a hotel room or a crowded motion picture lobby. She speculated on the maternal affections of the older, the companionship and beauty of the younger, the innocent airs of the youngest girls. Perhaps the fact that she was a couple of years older than I had something to do with her attitude. Our disparity in age made no difference whatsoever to me, and it was too little to matter one way or the other, but she harped on it quite often. A more serious fact was the undeniable circumstance that there were many women of greater beauty than her own. She didn't realize that the way to hold my affections was to realize the truth and compensate for it with affection and tenderness.

Instead, like most women I've known, Laura, too, waxed hysterical and tried to put me through little rites of "proof" to reassure her when she was plagued by notions of inferiority, as one would put a horse through its paces to prove one's mastery. In my case, at least, such behavior always results in reactions of revulsion and final disgust. I can accept a woman as long as she tries to hold me, and most likely she can hold me as long as she works at it. But when she makes me undergo tests and long arguments regarding loyalty and monogamous inclinations, the relationship becomes tedious. A man has enough troubles of his own without adding the self-doubts of a hysterical female to them. It's possible that I'd never have listened to Florence's siren calls if I hadn't been subjected to these screenings by Laura. As it was, Florence's return to my life happened at just the right moment.

I never pretended or lied to Laura. She knew all about Florence, and when I informed her that I was going to see Florence again, she accepted this fact with a cold yes. I didn't know for sure whether she'd ever see me again or not, but it didn't influence my decision one iota.

And when those few, mad days with Florence were over, and I was alone with my tortured feelings again, I telephoned Laura and asked her for a date. It was one of the few times when I had to take the initiative. She consented immediately and showed up well dressed and friendly. I tried to explain it to her, and she listened to me with deep understanding. I could tell from her attitude that she had already made up her mind to accept the situation for what it was. That's precisely what she did. She carried on the affair with me as if nothing had happened and forgave me for my vagaries.

Well, almost as if nothing had happened. One couldn't quite blot out the memories of the hurt I had done her, and she began to become ever more morose after my first open infidelity. She worried even more about my contacts with other women, though she must've been able to count the hours on her fingers that I had to myself, since she spent almost all of my free time with me. We met for meals, for movies, and for walks. We talked and fondled each other and laid each other on lawns. She stripped for action with the practiced skill of a strip-tease dancer, without wasting a single glance on her garments, and she moved herself into the most comfortable position for me with all the perfect mastery of repetition. She knew every movement that I could contribute to the love-act, and I knew every one of hers. We were, so to speak, a perfect team, of the type which I imagined married people must be when they're happily married. Neither our bodies nor our minds had any secrets from each other. We could predict each other's reactions to every stimulus, psychological and physical. We could communicate without speaking a single word.

In this fashion, we managed somehow to last through another winter. The cold came late that year, so that we were able to take our blankets to the golf course until the end of November. Then suddenly, cold temperatures and snow were upon us. We sat out Christmas Eve in a bar, because the cheap hotels were all booked up with happy revelers and we couldn't afford the expensive ones. We managed to obtain a room on New Year's Day, but only after swilling beer in another bar all New Year's Eve. Her hands seeking out the parts of me that she loved best, my fingers caressing her breasts, we sat in booths and hoped that the waitresses wouldn't pay any attention to what we were doing. We went to the lonely back entrances of old buildings and sat on the decaying stairs, my fingers following the lure of her passions and stirring her up to the point of orgasm, with her moaning and groaning as if she meant to alert the whole city police force to our activities. The miracle is that no one ever discovered our doings and that nothing happened to us.

The best session that winter was in a streetcar which we found open in a city streetcar park. We rode out to the yard where the streetcars were parked for the night, and the conductors made everybody get off. We intended to go to a small business building which usually left the back entrance open and to enjoy a good petting session on the stairs, but on that day we found the door locked. Much to our disappointment, we couldn't locate another suitable place. And so, we returned to the streetcar yard, more in order to find the next car going downtown than to accomplish the business for which we had ridden out that far. But there were so many cars that one couldn't possibly know which one was going out next. I tried to open the front door on one or two. They were difficult to open, but I pried one of them ajar. After that, it was easy. I waved to Laura to come over and see what I had done. She climbed in without saying a word.

At first, she was rather worried that someone might come and discover us. There were some Negroes sweeping up inside the hall in the entrance of which our streetcar was standing. But they weren't paying any attention. And so, we placed ourselves on the back seat, where there wasn't a telltale side window to give us away. There were some stains on the upholstery: Perhaps it had been used for these purposes before. She stripped with her usual agility, leaving only her open blouse and her loose skirt on, just in case someone came. Her blouse, falling back over her shoulders, didn't hide her breasts, on which I feasted merrily, and her skirt was all the way up to her hips, with her thighs gleaming in the near-darkness as if they were phosphorescent. Our preparations were the work of moments. We were getting to be masters at adjusting to the trying situations of a hostile environment. My trousers were draped over the seat next to me, with my shorts in the breast pocket of my jacket. Her panties and brassiere, garter-belt and jewelry lay neatly arranged on the other seat, so that they'd be easy to grab. All I needed to do was to approach her and press her panting warmness against the smooth velvet of the dirty seat, which I did with the usual alacrity. And after that, we carried on for hours, hardly pausing to catch our breath and to stop the climax from occurring too soon. Not a word was spoken. Nothing but animal noises. It was like a mechanical, pre-arranged ceremony. Outside, we heard the Negroes talking and an occasional streetcar going out or coming in. They arrived twenty minutes before another one moved out. We heard six of them, so that we must've busied ourselves with each other for three solid hours.

When finally we became tired and I grew worried about catching enough sleep for the night, we dressed as best we could in the near-perfect darkness that surrounded us and scurried away to make good our escape. A solitary Negro, almost invisible in the darkness, was walking along with a shovel near the main gate which we had to pass, but he pretended not to notice us, studiously ignored us, whistled a little tune through his teeth, and walked on with measured steps. No doubt, he knew what young lovers were doing around the streetcar yards at that hour of the night and wished us well.

Somehow, that winter passed, too, and spring came. There was another incident when Florence called again and I had to perform a few errands for her and saw her briefly. Naturally, Laura suspected that I was carrying on with both of them at the same time, although she should've known that I was spending my sexual energies on her. But she was always ready to believe me capable of the most amazing feats of prowess when it came to erotic matters, especially if it strengthened her jealous suspicions. There were scenes and recriminations, and I almost decided to break with Laura right then and there, but I didn't have the heart to do it. It would've felt like turning on a faithful domestic servant or like administering an undeserved beating to a loving child. And so, I listened to her complaints and to her professions of misery. I didn't bother to defend myself because there was no defense I knew against what really ailed her: the fact that she was a little older than I and the fact that I was still in love with Florence. Both of these facts were perfectly clear to me, and I was as helpless to change one as the other. To me, the small age factor of two years was unimportant, as the love I cherished for Florence was all-pervasive, and Florence was only a few weeks younger than Laura. But Laura's "woman's intuition" somehow connected these two factors that stood against her and developed the "intuitive" theory that, if she were only those few years younger she'd drive Florence entirely out of my mind and take complete possession of me. Nothing could possibly have been further removed from the truth. Laura was at the stage of sexual development when a woman's body is at its most desirable apex of sexual excitability. Women, in their interminable brooding, are prone to develop such quaint biological theories about circumstances which displease them, so that they shall not have to admit that they could, in any manner of degree, be inferior to other women in attraction. Laura would enunciate her "intuitive wisdom" on the situation with the air of the Eternal Mother handing down an unalterable decision and with the sad comment, "A woman knows." Actually, she didn't know a damned thing. She didn't comprehend that I was very fond of her and loved Florence at the same time, and she couldn't or wouldn't understand that I could've gone to bed with half a dozen other women on my off-nights and felt emotionally involved with them, too, without its having the slightest effect upon my feelings for her. But she wanted my complete, exclusive, and unexceptional love, which I couldn't give her. When it came right down to a matter of choice, I always would choose Florence without thinking about it for as long as a second. The only thing Laura could have done was to accept me as a lover and companion, or to break with me altogether. But she wouldn't do either. She wanted me as a doting lover and probably as a future husband, and although I wasn't either one, she couldn't break away. She was going to convert me step by step. And if there's anything absolutely impossible in this world of ours, it's for a woman to convert a man.

Therefore, I greeted it as more than an economic blessing when I obtained a position in another town upon completion of my university studies. Now I made a little more money and lived at some distance from Laura. I still wasn't wealthy, but I was able to manage now, if I watched my step. As for Laura and Florence, they were both within arm's reach: Laura lived at the end of a four-hour bus ride in one direction and Florence four hours away in the other. Florence had just returned to that ogre, her mother, and was thinking of remarrying Grover, while I tried my darndest to dissuade her from that silly notion and persuade her to live with me as my mistress. I maintained an active correspondence with the two of them and burned up the telephone wires with sizzling conversations. Often there was a telegram waiting for me when I came home from work.

During the last few months that we lived in the same city, Laura had carried her jealousy to such an undesirable point that I had to consider ways and means of dropping her. She was insanely jealous of all my friends, even of men, because they occupied some of my time and interest. Whenever I mentioned that I was going to see one of these people, some of whom I had know for years, she always nagged me about it until I consented to take her along. It's true that she tried to cultivate them as friends, too, and she did her best to get along with them, no matter how obtuse or degenerate some of them must've seemed to her, but she placed herself in the way, no matter how hard she tried not to. Men have a sort of intimacy that they can't share with women. They enjoy a camaraderie and an unrestrained exchange of ideas which evaporates as soon as there's a woman present, because the presence of a woman immediately introduces the rigamarole of etiquette and courtesy, the taboos, the unmentionable subjects, and the question of what sort of an impression every word and gesture is going to make upon "the lady." I'd go so far as to say that there can't be any real male companionship when there's a woman around, because—no matter how much everyone may deny it—the element of competition for her feminine charms and favors enters the scene as soon as she appears, and if all the males should, by some magic collusion, agree not to place themselves into a status of candidacy at all, the woman will wreck the party because she'll feel insulted. It's always bad manners on that account for a woman to force her way into a circle of male friends. If that woman also happens to be unreasonably jealous and watches for every possible opening to attract the attentions of her lover, she's about as useful as a preacher in a whorehouse.

Not content with wrecking all my friendships with other people, she also proceeded to push herself into every sphere of life which I had enjoyed since childhood. I'm not saying that it isn't fun to share experiences with the woman of one's affections to some degree. Someone wisely defined the mysterious feeling which we call love as experiences shared and remembered together. But even this process must have its limits. When the woman insists upon studying every book that one reads or has read, delves into every composer to whose music one likes to listen, and enters into the phases of business in which one happens to earn a living, it becomes tedious, no matter how flattering it may seem. In our case, I couldn't read a newspaper without telling her what was in it, couldn't pick up a magazine without reading its contents to her, and couldn't take a walk without telling her where I had been and what I was thinking while on the street. I never lived in such close intimacy with anyone, and it began to make a neurotic out of me. I felt that she was penetrating me, permeating every phase of my existence, entering the darkest recesses of my mind which a kind Mother Nature had gracefully permitted me to veil in oblivion. She saw to it that there could be nothing in my life but her: Laura in bed, Laura at breakfast, Laura at work, Laura at lunch, Laura at dinner, Laura at the movies, Laura at the concert, Laura at the theater, Laura when I read, Laura when I thought, Laura when I walked, Laura when I spoke, Laura whenever I breathed. I felt constrained, and it became only a matter of time when I'd burst out of my straitjacket. She killed our relationship by trying too hard to make it permanent.

Her manifestations of insecurity wrecked the visits we had

after I moved away. Whenever I returned for the week end, I was greeted with tears and that special aura of self-sacrifice which can make a bitch out of the nicest woman. When I asked her what was the matter, it was always the same story. She worried about whether I was still faithful to her, how long I'd continue to be faithful to her, whether I'd get tired of her body, whether I had already tired of her companionship. She borrowed trouble by making a point of crossing imaginary bridges before she could come to real ones. There was always the future to heap imprecation upon, even if she couldn't detect a flaw in the present. She felt nothing but uncertainty about me all the time that I wasn't with her, when she couldn't watch over me to make sure that I wasn't trotting off with some floozy to sweep her off her feet and into my bed.

"What the hell is the difference?" I finally yelled at her. "Why worry about what may happen tomorrow, or what might've happened three days ago, when we weren't together? Am I supposed to hire a private detective to follow me around and hand you a notarized certificate that I've been a good boy? What are you worried about? I wish you'd quit wasting time with these senseless scenes! It's now that counts, this moment, this fraction of a second, this part of our lives that we're going to spend today and that'll never come back! So, quit giving me a hard time with the phantasmagoria of your jealous imagination! I've got troubles enough of my own!"

"Yes, that's all very well, until Sunday night, when you leave again," she'd answer to all statements of this sort. "But then you're leaving again, and I'm alone, and I'm plagued by doubts. How can I be sure?"

"Hell, you'll never be sure!" I shouted at her many a time.

"You wouldn't believe me even if you watched me every second, because you're so set on proving to yourself that I'm untrustworthy!"

"It isn't that . . ." she'd begin, but I realized fully well that this was precisely the point that was at issue.

And she was right. Although I didn't play the field, I had been unfaithful in my mind many a time. And when Florence wrote or called, nothing could hold me. In fact, the more Laura argued, the more I was tempted to try everything in the story books and then some, to separate the princess Florence from the claws of that old dragon, her mother. It seemed clear to me that the worst thing I could do would be to chain myself to a nagging woman, and that Laura was such a nagging woman to whom I must avoid getting chained.

It was easy to devise a scheme to make her break with me. She was so vulnerable that it pained me to hurt her, but there was this question: Wouldn't it be much kinder to hurt her a little now than to hurt her more afterwards? What if she remodeled her entire life after me? What if she should quit her job and decide to devote herself entirely to me? Wouldn't it be much worse to effect the inevitable break when there was no more out for her than to do it in time, when she still had some life of her own upon which to fall back?

I still owed her some money when one day I announced on the telephone that I wasn't coming to see her but going to Chicago to see Florence. It really was true that I wanted to see Florence, who despite all of her adventures and unfaithful conduct was better company than Laura, whose suspicions and insecure maneuvers communicated themselves to me in the guise of an uncomfortable premonition of disaster, a kind of permanent contemplation of the sword of Damocles. And so, I decided to hop a bus for Chicago.

During the last several week ends, Laura had come up to see me. Laura was a good girl that way. She never avoided efforts or pains to be near me. Her trouble wasn't that she was unwilling to give, but that she was too demanding in return. And since she knew she could no longer garner in as much emotionally as she once had, she apparently tried to make do with sex. Each time she visited me, we went through the same ritual. I met her at the bus depot, helped her catch a taxi, and sent her off to her hotel. I went to a drugstore and waited there until she called me to tell me which room she occupied. As soon as I knew, I walked to the hotel and went to her room. Silently I opened the door. She'd be lying in bed already, her legs playing with the blanket, a vague haze over her eyes, a tired expression on her face. I'd throw my clothes on a chair and jump into bed with her. The sight of her lying there almost motionlessly, expecting me, would excite me enough to start with the business upon which I had come without further ado or preparations. Neither of us would speak one word until we had spent hours in silent and violent contortions, designed to let us derive a maximum of enjoyment from the wrestling match in which we engaged like enemies scheming to punish each other for their corporeal differences. We always worked at it until the early hours of the morning. Our bodies squeezed each other and strained in order not to miss a single thrill to the nerves. Each pushed unmercifully toward the other body, each withdrawing as much of the other's energies as he dared. Our arms fondled each other's bodies as though in a trance, as if they were impersonal objects. Our faces drank one another like travelers who have crossed a desert. We panted and groaned uninhibitedly. Neither paid any attention to indications of the other's exhaustion. Never did we quit until we were both all but paralyzed from muscular weakness. She always cried in the end. Silent, bitter, unforgiving tears that had already been explained too often, tears of a disconsolate agony which I was powerless to end. Her soul tortured itself with the images of misfortunes that were totally unrealistic. She lived in a private hell of her own which I was incapable of reaching. Whatever her salvation was, or whoever might bring it to her —I wasn't the right man. And though she loved me, she must've realized that we didn't belong together. Maybe that was why she cried.

We met for a cup of coffee on that last week end, after I had seen Florence and found out that Florence wasn't going to join me. Laura would never have believed that I hadn't touched Florence that previous week end, and so I didn't try to tell her. In her sick imagination, every woman I met was a bed-partner whom I might find more desirable than her. Laura said that she was now convinced of my utter immorality and that she couldn't take it any more. I was prepared for the incident, since I had provoked it, and shrugged my shoulders. She asked me if I didn't care. And I told her that even though I cared I wasn't going to force her into anything she didn't want. She wouldn't believe that I cared, but I was equally convinced that that was what had been our trouble all along. She never believed me. And as long as that was the way it was going to be, she was quite right in calling it quits. People should have relationships to make each other happy, not to make each other miserable. And apparently I made her very unhappy, and I certainly hadn't been happy myself these last few months.

"We've had a wonderful affair, Phil, but it's over," she said.

"I guess so," I replied, wondering at her unusually mature reaction.

I walked her to the streetcar stop and kissed her goodby. It was a cold kiss on the mouth, and she didn't even look at me. There was no response. We had nothing more to say. I walked away, feeling that I had just dropped the greatest treasure I'd ever possessed or might ever possess: a pure heart. Since then, I've learned from bitter experience that my feeling was true.

Only once did I contrive to see her again. I was on my way from the United States to Canada, when a friend of mine arranged for us to meet at a cocktail lounge. I approached the meeting with some trepidation. The friend had always wanted me to marry Laura, and I felt that this was some kind of a last trap, possibly engineered with her connivance.

The woman who arrived there some fifteen minutes late was Laura and yet she wasn't the same girl. She had aged, grown more slender, and acquired a determined look about her that she had never had before. We said "Hello" without much ceremony, and the waiter took our order for drinks.

She told me her story after a little encouragement. At first, after our separation, she refused to accept our parting as final and expected me to come back and try to restore things to their former state. When it turned out that I meant what I said and never returned, she had a nervous breakdown. For some six months, she was unable to do anything but stay in a room under a doctor's care. But she recovered. She'd taken up music and painting, was playing the piano at concerts and entering exhibitions, besides holding down a job as a business executive. Things were going along as well as they possibly could with a solitary spinster. She was still living with her parents, and her savings amounted to a considerable bank balance. She'd had a few affairs with marriageable young businessmen, a German baron, and a ski instructor of undetermined nationality.

"Why haven't you ever married?" I asked her point-blank.

"Don't you know?" she asked me back, looking me straight in the eye.

I walked her to the streetcar stop for the last time. It was a stronger and more cheerful Laura who now walked beside me, a successful person, a woman with a career. She had proved herself strong enough to withstand more storms than most young girls can endure.

"Could I see you when I pass through town again?" I asked her. "I won't be leaving the country for some time."

"No, not again," she said simply. "I couldn't go through it any more."

That was all the answer I needed. I knew now that she wasn't vulnerable any longer. And I was glad of it. Although I knew I could never have made a go of marriage with her, I didn't want to see some grinning idiot weaseling his way into a woman who was basically my creature, whom I had taught how to confront life's problem situations. And if I couldn't talk her into it again, she'd be strong enough to have an affair and break it off when she wanted—and carry few if any battle-scars away from it.

"Goodby, Laura," I said. "I wish you luck."

Never had I meant those oft-repeated words so sincerely.

VI Marsha: Pure Sex

Las Vegas was its own, fascinating self. The Strip was re-
splendent with shiny, new, block-long cars flashing past one
at breakneck speed, neon lights dancing before the eye of
the curious tourist, and the hulks of the newly constructed
hotels sprawling behind vast parking lots. A well-dressed
crowd, amazingly quiet for the type of entertainment preva-
lent there, which it had come to seek out, trundled in at this
hotel or that, dug into its pockets for vast amounts of money,
fed the one-armed bandits, placed bets of whole stacks of
chips on the numbers on the crap tables, scattered more chips
on the roulette tables, and looked sagely into the poker

cards. Everywhere there was testimony of the presence of money: the well-tailored men's suits, the mink and Persian lamb coats of the women, the expensive gowns under the furs, the glittering jewelry on their ears and fingers, around their necks, and occasionally on their dresses. Money floated across the counters and was changed into chips, to be lost even more quickly to the men with the little boxes, who made the rounds now and then to centralize the winnings of the house and put them into a locked safe. Money flowed across the bars to pay for the drinks, money flew into the pockets of the waiters in the restaurants, where it jingled and bulged amiably, when the man evened up his accounts and surrendered his tables to his relief. Money was stacked high in the change booths, where one could obtain coins to stick into the slot machines. Money fairly spoke to one out of the faces of the numerous elderly gentlemen, most of whom were vacationing in Las Vegas with young women; it spoke to one out of the faces of wives searching for a quick manner of disposing of their husband's earnings. Money was everywhere. In Las Vegas, money is king.

I walked into my favorite nightclub, the Casbar, located in one of the new hotels with the gambling lobbies. One of the old-style jazz kings who's sold millions of records was holding his daily jam session on stage with his boys, and they made the 1920's live for us again, as they had for countless thousands. The bandleader and I were speaking acquaintances, for he appreciated my regular patronage and the fact that I knew a great artist when I saw one. He was dancing up and down with his saxophone squeezed tightly in his fists and his mouth moving back and forth at the mouthpiece—an exhibition that ought to be seen to be fully understood. I sat down at the bar, which describes a semi-circle in front of the stage, turning my back to those tables where every woman might've been a contestant in the Miss Universe race. There had only been one seat vacant, between an elderly gray-haired woman with a mink-coat and a young red-head, whom I'd seen only from the back when I entered.

That was Marsha. I knew right at the beginning that this would be the prologue to a long story, as soon as I laid eyes upon her beautiful face, her ivory skin, her shiny, blue eyes, her extremely full bosom, and her slender waistline. I knew it even before we exchanged a single word. Sometimes those moments have occurred when I "just knew" future events. They've always come true for me, either because I made them come true or because of some deep magic. And in her case, I knew just as well as I knew my own name that she and I would mean a lot to each other, that we'd probably hurt each other before we were through, and that for me, life would never again be the same without her. I knew all these things instinctively and wished they weren't so. For to tell the truth, I've always felt a certain reluctance to enter into intimate relations of the soul, as distinct from purely physical affairs. Perhaps I've been afraid of making myself vulnerable to a woman's caprice. Perhaps I've simply treasured my privacy too much. Casual affairs are so much less complicated and so much less demanding! Yet I've usually not been so fortunate as to develop much interest in superficial relationships. I've usually been emotionally involved, and I've been stung regularly. It may be that my life has been richer for it, that the pains are worth the suffering, and that the memories are sweeter because of the scars. Yet I've often envied men who could simply take a woman and discard her again like an old overcoat. Their lives are indescribably less involved and less tense.

Having obtained my cognac from the bartender—in Las Vegas one can order premium-brand French cognacs and get them without anyone's blinking an eyelash—I concentrated my attention upon the music, waved hello to my friend the bandleader, and gazed absent-mindedly at the mink coat on my neighbor on my left. It was a very exquisite fur.

"Quit drooling over that old lady!" were the first words Marsha ever spoke to me. Her eyes said something like, Let's find out what he's like when he squirms.

"I was just admiring her mink," I replied in great amazement.

"You shouldn't go around picking up nice old ladies like that," she continued. "Why don't you pick me up? I'm quite pick-up-able."

It was an interesting introduction, but it wasn't followed by much conversation. She had a girlfriend along, a long-legged, black-haired beauty, who had already succeeded in attracting the attention of a couple of fellows, and they were standing on the other side from Marsha and doing their best to keep the two girls occupied. Marsha's conversation, I noticed, was bright at all times, and sometimes even brilliant. She sallied out at one person, delivered a satirical little blow here and there, parried every thrust made at her, launched dashing little sorties, doubled back when caught in an inaccuracy, and went right back to the attack. In my mind, I wished that she could fence, because it would've been a pleasure to see her in action. She could shift ground and feint well enough to catch the other person unawares, and when she had him where she wanted him, she finished him off, only to laugh at the whole performance and play the *coquette* once more. It was first-rate entertainment just to watch her.

One of the two suitors finally departed and the other one

became engrossed totally in the statuesque, black-haired beauty, and so Marsha turned back to me. She wasn't surprised that I was still there and picked up the conversation where it had left off almost an hour ago. I bought drinks for her and her girlfriend, we listened to the music, and I paid even closer attention to the workings of her conversational efforts. After a few glasses had been emptied, I felt at liberty to stroke her hand and we exchanged kisses. She kissed voraciously, so that it was almost as much work as it was enjoyment. All of her contours sinuously followed the motions of her tongue. It was teasing to the sensations to partake of such preparations for the most intimate contact in front of hundreds of people. The bandleader winked an eye at me, nobody else paid attention to us.

"You've been in France," she said. "I understand the language."

"That means, 'Come home with me,'" I said.

"Go on, you couldn't afford me," she countered.

"Who said anything about money?" I inquired.

She looked at me quizzically. Her whole face lit up for a brief instant. "Okay, you'll do," she said. "I'll go with you."

"Let's go."

"Not yet," she nagged. "Let's have another drink."

That we did. Another and another and another. It was getting late.

"Let's go home," I said.

"Keep your shirt on. If you don't want to wait for me, you don't have to. There'll always be another man along."

She deliberately turned around and began to talk to her girlfriend. The former admirer had given up on the raven-haired beauty, and three new ones had appeared who swapped double entendre remarks with her. She was doing all right by herself, and when Marsha joined them, it sounded like something out of a movie script. I sat and watched my friend the bandleader, and when he took his intermission and another band played for their forty-five minute period, I took an intentionally long time to stay away from my seat in order to converse with the boys. When I returned, Marsha was watching me. Her eyes seemed to say, Well, I knew he'd come back. Nobody leaves little Marsha when he still has a chance.

"May I have another drink?" she asked me. Not a word about going home.

"Might as well," I said. "The Germans say, 'A drunken woman is an angel in bed.' "

"Not me," she replied. "I like to be aware of what I'm doing."

"You can be aware and still carry quite a load."

"And you'd like to be the load I carry?"

"Nothing else."

The drinks came, and we exchanged a few more remarks. Then we were disturbed by a bull-necked Mexican, who turned out to be a Las Vegas policeman. Marsha put up a show of great interest in him, with the obvious intention of getting my gall. I sat between the Mexican and her, and she conversed with him as if I weren't present at all. He seemed quite surprised at the situation. One time, she turned aside and asked me, "Are you still here?"

"I was buying the drinks a minute ago, remember?"

"And you'll continue to buy them as long as I want," she said. "And if you won't, there's always someone around to take me home."

"You said that."

"It's still true."

"And I'm still here."

Before I knew what was happening, she grabbed me by the hair and pulled me over toward herself to kiss me with the passion of a woman in bed. I almost fell off my bar stool. She kept at it and wouldn't stop. The Mexican policeman watched us and laughed. The bartender watched us and laughed. The whole band was looking at us, as she balanced the two of us between our stools and kept on kissing. Her whole face was a part of the kiss. We must've made quite an exhibition of ourselves. And yet, when she was finished, she pushed me back and went on to talk to the policeman as if nothing had happened, resuming the conversation where she had left off. It made me think of a cat, now playful, now vicious, but above all, assertive of her independence. Laura was to make me think of cats throughout our relationship.

It took her two hours to wear out the patience of the Mexican. He finally offered her a marijuana cigarette, provided she came out to smoke it in his car with him. For a minute, I gasped at the possibility of her accepting the offer. But in spite of all the liquor with which everyone had plied her, she still retained enough sense to stay where she was. The Mexican wished me *"Buena suerte,"* patted her on her rump, and left us.

"Are you still here?" she asked me.

"I was buying the drinks a minute ago," I replied.

"You said that."

"And you."

"Let's have another round, and then you can take me home," she suggested.

"Let's."

"You needn't make it sound like a conquest. I'm merely going with you because my car is being fixed. I need a ride home."

"Whatever the reason, more power to it," I toasted.

When we discovered my car in that sea of automobiles found everywhere in Las Vegas even at four o'clock in the morning, I thought again I'd lose her. In the last minute, she had second thoughts.

"You were better-looking on the bar stool than you are outside," she began to pick a quarrel. "People always look better where the light is bad."

"It doesn't seem to do you any harm," I tried to compliment her out of her mood.

"Go on, you're not for me. I'll take a taxi."

There seemed to be only one thing to do under the circumstances, and that was to stimulate the same desires in her that she felt when she kissed me. The best way to do that was to repeat the performance. I walked up to her, put my arms around her, and tried to find her lips. She was taller than I in her high heels, and she resisted me until I took her head between both hands and forced her mouth upon mine. Then she snapped back into the mood again. Her tongue caressed mine and wiggled in a gay mambo-rhythm.

"Take me home," she said, when we finished. "I'll tell you how to get there."

"Can I go there with you?"

"Certainly not. My mother is very old-fashioned."

"Then come home with me."

This precipitated another crisis with doubts and arguments, finished again in the same fashion. By the time I argued her out of her second thoughts, I had run my fingers up her stockings and found the warmth that breathed above them. She clasped both hands around my neck when she felt me petting her. Her body reacted more quickly than her mind. It was up to me to seize hold of her and convince her that it was best to do what she wanted. But since she wouldn't permit my hands any greater intimacies, I had to it all with the organs of speech, which I employed for kissing rather than for speaking. It was an approach to which she was far more susceptible.

"Okay, I'll go with you," she finally said, snuggling up into the opposite corner of the front seat, as if she wanted me to keep my mind on my driving.

Once we obtained a motel room in a nice, discreet place, Marsha wasn't going simply to let me make love to her and enjoy it. By no means. This is where the real fight began. She probably didn't want to be considered "easy." I don't know why it is that women never want to have anyone think that they're "easy." Ordinarily, when you ask them, they comment that it's a matter of pride, and that the men wouldn't really like them unless there were a show of initial resistance, a struggle, and the triumph of the union of the flesh achieved in a heat of fury. Personally, I don't have the faintest idea of why a person would be any prouder if she has a wrestling match before the assignation takes place rather than going to bed and meaning it. On the contrary, I'd judge it to be humiliating for both the man and the woman for her to put herself into the situation where she's obviously going to have intercourse, first to resist as if she weren't going to, and finally to succumb to the combination of the man's strength and her own instinctive desire. If a woman goes to bed with me, I want her to realize fully that she's going to get laid, and unless she wants to bestow her favors upon me I don't see for the life of me why she should enter my bedroom in the first place. Furthermore, I can't say I enjoy wrestling matches with either males or females. A show of loving tenderness, or better still, of an eager welcome for my ardent embrace, is infinitely more stimulating to me than the sight of a shrew that first must be tamed. After all, the love act, in order to be properly enjoyed, must be a mutual caress rather than the violation of one person's privacy by another. If a man didn't want the woman to react with tender caresses and abdominal co-operation, he might as well make love to a dummy with raw liver inside. In fact, it's the reciprocity of the love act that gives it its most enjoyable facets. But Marsha, no doubt, had been corrupted by the centuries of Puritanical tradition which still holds that the sex act is a sacrificial concession that the poor, pursued female must make to that greedy animal which is man. Hence the assumption in the Puritan "mind" always is that the pitiable woman must lie under the man with the docile submission of a well-ironed handkerchief, and that this awful compromise with divine virtue must be made only with the blessing of the sky pilots and no more than required for conceiving one's wanted children. Sex for the sake of enjoying sex is an anti-Puritanical pursuit of happiness. Even though Marsha wasn't a believer in Puritanism and realized that all that bunch of fairytales was poppycock, the after-effects of the tradition lived on in her instinctive reactions. She struggled.

"I agreed to come in with you, but not to take off my clothes," she argued.

I unbuttoned her dress and tried to strip it off her. She clutched it with both her fists, so that the seams began to crack.

"You'll ruin my dress!" she shouted.

In answer, I held her mouth against mine and kissed her. She responded as she had in the car, while I gently raised her skirt to the level of the belt. She helped me unbutton the belt and raised her arms so that I might pull the dress up over her head. When the thing was all on top of her, and she stood there with her arms up in the air, struggling to free her shoulders from the tight garment, I jerked off her brassiere and kissed her breasts. She had large, bulbous orbs like a woman in her late twenties if she's had a lot of sexual experience, though Marsha was only twenty-two. She whined, groaned, and produced some muffled grunts of protest against the liberties which I was taking. By the time she freed her head and brushed the sleeves off her arms, I crowded her, step by step, against the bed. It required only a brief struggle to throw her down upon it, with her legs far enough apart to permit me to slip my hand in between and begin with the final preparations to stimulate her desire to the heights of my own. She was wearing expensive, black lace panties of the type that is definitely made to be seen rather than to be worn. It seemed a pity to ruin them, and so I tried to take them off her, but she decided upon a last-ditch stand. Unfortunately, it requires two hands to take panties off a woman who wiggles and won't help. Far removed from helping, she held on to those panties for dear life. And so, to throw her off the track, I undid her stockings and rolled them off her feet.

"You do that well," she grinned. "You must've had practice."

To apprise me of her better mood, she took off her garterbelt. She raised her midriff from the bed for only the fraction of a second to strip the thing off, but I seized the opportunity to catch her panties and pull them part of the way across her widest latitude before she lay flat upon the blanket again. She bent over in pain, because she lay down on my knuckles, and that gave me enough time to pull the flimsy black garment farther down. Just a little more, over the end of her torso, and the hardest part of my task would be finished. To me, the removal of the panties has always been the hardest part. Sure enough, she decided to fight another round and fought against me with savage ferocity. She wriggled and slinked out of my grasp and pulled those black lace panties back up.

"Aren't you ashamed of yourself, lying there stark naked?" she taunted me.

"Aren't you ashamed, coming dressed to a bout of love?"

"I let you undress me this far, but that's all. A few minutes more, and I'll go home. Mother will be worried about me."

Seeing that it was past four o'clock, her remembering her mother wasn't too cogent a reason, and I realized she was merely tantalizing me a bit more. On the other hand, I gained the impression that she might very well go home and leave me frustrated, just to show me that it could be done. I could tell by the glint in her eyes that she wanted me as much as I did her, but that she enjoyed herself too much in denying herself to me for her to give in too easily. I wondered whether it was Puritanism or pure contrariness.

With a gigantic effort, I brought all of her under me. She tried to get away, but I flung both arms around her and crushed my ribs against hers. This was bound to hurt her a little, but I didn't care. I felt a strange mixture of desire for the enjoyment of her body and the penalization of her person for the resistance which she placed in my way. More important than hurting her, my squeezing stunned her long enough for me to slip both of my hands into the last remaining obstacle in the path of my erotic advances and push the black lace down without tearing it. The question now was whether she'd spread her thighs to prevent me from slipping it off, or possibly roll sideways to free herself from my weight long enough to pull it back on. But she did neither. She placed her hands on her hips and looked me in the eyes with an expression of great surprise. Within a second, she was naked beside me. She was rigid like a corpse.

Rigid, that is, until I threw that black lace up into the air. As soon as I placed my hands upon her again, the next round of the wrestling match began. She was a hefty girl, though not fat. Her thighs were very muscular, as were her arms. She had a waistline of only twenty-four inches, but her breasts were large, so that her measurement there was thirty-eight, the same as the line around her hips. There wasn't a badly-placed pound on her entire body. It was one of the most nearly perfect works of art I had ever seen. Naturally, it excited me tremendously. She took note of this fact, which she could obviously see, but she never brought her abdomen within the range of danger. If I placed her beneath me, she rolled sideways or wiggled out of the hold. If I lined her up sideways, she made an obstacle out of the mattress by lying on her stomach. If I tried to mount her from the rear, she raised her hips and bucked forward like a bronco, so that she again withdrew from me. If I flipped her down again, she pushed me away with both of her hands. It was worse than trying to mount an unbroken mustang. Apparently, she wouldn't even entertain the notion that I might swing into the saddle. She pushed me back by the face, hammered on my stomach, and kicked her sturdy knees against me without watching where she hit me. Once I thought I had her, when she slapped me. I told her never to do that again. She slapped me a second time. Thereupon I held both of her hands with my left and gave her a sound slap with my right.

"I'll tame you yet," I hissed at her angrily.

"You might at that," she breathed and pulled me down above her.

Her lips sought mine and gave me a kiss like those with which she had trapped me at the bar. Her body rubbed against mine. She deliberately propped her breasts against me while her hands groped their way along my lap. Yet when I tried to consummate the act, she shrugged back once more.

That's when I gave up. I felt sore all over my body, and I was exhausted. I had been ready to take her on during most of the struggle. Now I doubted that I could muster the strength. Her body, in the realm of sensations, turned into just another stranger's body, pink, warm, and now somewhat covered with sweat. It was all over for me. I didn't even feel frustrated. Just tired. If she had turned out the light and curled up in the blanket, I might've gone to sleep. I lay back and glanced at the ceiling.

Before I knew what was happening, I felt the pressure of her breasts against my side. Her hair brushed against my chest.

"Would you like to make love to me?" she asked.

"If you like," I answered, as if it didn't matter.

She lay back and watched me approach her. I noticed that she must've been aroused as long as I had been ready, even though she made a game of resisting. Her hands wandered up and down my spinal column, while her breath became strangely heavy. The color of her eyes turned into a shiny velvet, though little more than the pupils was showing. Her entire luscious figure rippled with anticipatory delight. She adjusted her legs so that she'd be comfortable during the act. When she felt that it had actually started, she emitted a sigh halfway between a grunt and a squeak, and her whole body went into convulsions. She raised her legs straight into the air and placed her arms in an iron hold around me, while her buttocks vibrated up and down and toward me with such speed that it was impossible to do anything but relax and let her do the work. She must've kept this up for five or ten minutes—it didn't matter what the time element involved, for it was so delectable—and then resumed a more regular and slower movement to take advantage of every move I made. Now and then, her lips pouted for a kiss. Between times, she offered me now this breast, now that, always intent on keeping me fully occupied. When I finally increased the pace for the last effort, she gently gave in, opened her eyes, and kept looking at me, as if she wanted to read the language of my eyes.

What it was she wanted to read was something I found out soon. Her decision to take me on had been quick; her decision to push me away was even quicker.

"Out!" she shouted. "Get out!" and wiggled free of me. Eagerly she trundled off to the bathroom.

"What's the matter?" I asked her, when she came back. "Did I do something to hurt you? Let me apologize . . ."

"Have you ever had an abortion?" she interrupted me. "It's very painful. I've had two of them in the last three years. I'm just like a rabbit. If I don't watch it, I'll get pregnant from every man who goes to bed with me."

We lay side by side for at least an hour, simply caressing each other's naked bodies. There wasn't much to say. I thought she had been silly about the struggle before the act, but I believed then and I believe now that she had the most beautiful body I've ever seen. A man can forgive a lot if the guilty mind dwells in such an adorable shell. She must've thought me brutal and rude, and I hadn't played the game her way, so that she may have been partially dissatisfied even though I was sure she was physically satiated even the first time. We were strangers, and as such we made each other happy and failed each other.

The passage of time restored my strength, and I ran my fingers all over her curvaceous body to prepare her for the second round. This time, she was more accessible, and her lips reciprocated my compliments while her hands reached out to find the sensitive spots on my physique. She was meek now, almost tame. Her eyes filled with tenderness at my impatience, and she willingly abandoned her body to me a part at a time. When it was about time for me to join the two of us together, she looked down to watch. My glance followed hers, and we watched ourselves uniting into a whole with speechless ravishment. A knowing smile passed over her face when she realized that I saw her enjoyment of this ceremony. Then she went wild. Like a cat, she rubbed every part of herself against my skin. Her head turned from side to side, like that of a patient in insufferable pain, while her throat emitted a brand of shrieks that sometimes rose to a piercing height which I feared would alarm the neighbors. Her posterior moved alternately toward right and left but also dipped forward and backward. The thought struck me that this motion must be the ancestor of most Afro-Cuban dances and must account for their primitive appeal, for she moved almost entirely in the same way that I had seen the natives dance in Cuba. She bit my lips when she was tired of kissing me and used my tongue like an ice cream stick. Occasionally, she seemed to try for an even greater contact and she swung the bottom of her rump upward like the punch of a powerful boxer. Each time she reached a climax—and it happened four or five times that I could tell—her fingernails dug deep into my shoulderblades and scratched my skin all along the spine, and the second time she bit me in the throat just above the collar-bone. Strangely enough, I didn't feel the pain until later, when I took my shower. For she kept me so enthralled during the act that I was insensitive to anything but the delights of the union. Finally, she closed her muscular thighs around me and vibrated me through the passion of ecstasy, biting again to leave the marks of her teeth all over my chest. And then came the ending as before. She jerked herself aside to escape from me in the penultimate moment and turned over on the side away from me.

When I came back from the bathroom, I tried to kiss her.

"Don't!" she cried, still turning her back toward me. "I'm sore all over. My sex is sore, my breasts are sore, my lips are sore. Now leave me alone."

"Are you mad at me?"

"No, I love you."

Not having anything else within my reach, I kissed her on the shapely back of her thighs. She trembled at the touch of my lips even there.

"I guess I love you as much as I'll ever love anyone," she whispered.

She remained in the bathroom a long time, and when she re-emerged, she had an odd, school-girlish expression on her face, her hair done up neatly, and her skin radiant with cleanliness. She modestly climbed into bed on the other side from me and approached me coyly, as if she was actually bashful. When I reached out for her, she warded me off. She wouldn't let me lay a finger on her for the rest of the night, but she pressed herself against me and ran her fingers and her tongue over every square inch of me like a mother cat over its kittens. There was something quaintly feline about her, as there is about many passionate red-heads I've known. She moved with the primitive grace of a leopard, and she clawed like one when she was aroused.

"I've got to go home," she finally broke it up.

"What for? It's almost seven, and we haven't had any sleep. Now, stay here and have breakfast with me at noon."

"No, I've got to get home. Mother will expect to find me in when she gets up."

"When do I see you again? Tomorrow?"

"No. Never."

"But you just got through telling me that you loved me."

"That was five minutes ago."

"And now it isn't true?"

"Never mind. I never go back for seconds."

"But it gets better every time."

"No, it's never like the first time."

"Give it a try."

Silently she threw her clothes on. It looked as though she'd had ample practice, for she was dressed in ten minutes, which is about ten times as fast as any other woman I've known. She sat down in front of the dresser to comb her hair.

"Why can't people be as pretty when they get up in the morning as they were at night?" she wondered. "In the morning, all the charm of the night evaporates."

"You're as pretty now as before."

"No, I look pooped out. So do you."

I didn't comment, for she obviously was right. She was still a lot better-looking than most other women, but it was true that she'd lost something of the luster she had when I met her. As for me, my face was the color of unbaked bread and my eyes the size of baby oysters.

"Where did you learn to love like that?" she asked, when she adjusted her belt.

"The school of hard knocks and bumps."

"Me too," she smiled. "You want to see me again?"

"Today. Where do you work? I'll come and pick you up."

She named one of the finer women's cosmetics stores in town. "I'll meet you at the front entrance about six."

"Is that where you work?"

"No." She was finished dressing and sat on the chair, waiting for me. "Actually I don't see why I should lie to you. I'm the complaints department of the men's store down the street from there. When someone comes in to raise a ruckus, they send him in to my office. I sit there with my back turned. He starts bitching. And when he's started well in, I turn around. That usually stops them cold."

I looked at her to gather from her expression whether it was true or not. She was smiling proudly. She had obviously related exactly what happened at her office every day.

"I'd bet you make a lot of interesting contacts there."

"That's where I meet most of the men I go out with. Before they're quite finished talking, they've always asked me for a date."

"And then you go with them?"

"Yes. It costs them at least fifty dollars. A good many give me more."

I didn't comment but merely marched to the door to open it for her.

"Are you disappointed?" she asked.

"No, why should I be?"

"Because I told you what I am?"

"No, I'm not disappointed. You are what I need. As long as you don't try to bring your outside life into your relationship with me, it doesn't matter."

We sat down in the car. It was slow in starting in the

chilly morning air. I felt a shiver run down my back.

"Then I'll pay you," she said. "I believe that, whenever people screw around, somebody ought to get paid. One way or another, that's the way it is, anyway. If you won't pay me, I'll pay you."

"I don't take money from women. The only thing I want from you is your love."

"I don't believe in love. It's all monetary in this world. I've bought men before, I'll admit it. And usually they buy me. If I buy them, I give them ten dollars. If they buy me, they pay at least fifty. That's fair, isn't it?"

"I'll be the exception that confirms the rule. With me, all you'll give is yourself and all you'll get is me. We've just started having an affair, you know."

"Have we?" she looked at me sideways.

"That we have. A long one."

We arrived at her house. The sun rose over the roof-tops. The neighborhood was slowly coming to life. The milkman was carrying out his bottles. Here and there, a pale light could be seen behind closed curtains.

"I'll go in and change and go to work. You go home and sleep, so you'll be big and strong tonight. Will you?" she smiled.

"At six."

Naturally, I couldn't sleep much that night, or rather, that day. Before I could unwind my nerves from the thrill of Marsha, the cleaning woman was scurrying about with a bucket and broom, trucks were pulling up and leaving with their motors in low gear, and children were playing in the swimming pool in front of the motel. I tried to relax by taking a walk around the city. People of all ages, in all kinds of dress and costume, and of all nationalities were downtown,

putting their money into slot machines, placing it on numbers on crap tables, betting it on roulette wheels, or backing
up their opinions at cards with it. Millions were floating in
the air, and here and there, an empty face stared at the
passers-by in front of the gambling casinos, where the people
usually stand and gape after they've lost all their money and
they wish they had some more to brave it out till that lucky
streak came their way again. Old men chewed cold cigars and
bet their pension money on horses at bookie offices. Here and
there, an optimist tried to sell his "winning system" to people
on the street or collect a tip for a hard-luck story. Luck was
just around the corner for everyone, for the people strolling
into the casinos, for the tourists playing in them, for the ones
waiting for their money to catch up with them from home,
for the old people awaiting their support checks from their
children and the government so that they could try once more
to get rich quickly. Luck was the elusive cloud that floated
just beyond the horizon, where the eye almost caught it before it disappeared.

Food and a few hours of sleep restored me to my usual state
of good health, and at six o'clock that evening I sat in my car
and waited for Marsha to come out of the shop. She wended
her way with slinking hips and looked both ways up the street
to see whether I was there. When she discovered me, a satisfied smile passed over her face like that of the proverbial cat
that swallowed the canary.

"Where would you like to go first?" I asked her.

"Home. To bed," she replied. Her voice was huskier than
the night before, and I could tell that she felt passionate even
then.

My car roared out of the downtown area and up the Strip
toward my motel. In Las Vegas, the police aren't much con-

cerned about speeders, as long as the driver seems to be careful and the car is of a late model. Only when one of those inane young jalopy drivers comes up from southern California do they watch that he doesn't get himself and a number of other people killed, and of course, when a car starts swerving and giving other indications that the driver has been drinking too much too fast. As for me, I couldn't complain. They watched me barreling down their streets with benevolent eyes.

"I've been thinking of you all day," I made conversation. "Even when I was sleeping, I dreamed of you." It was true.

"I've been thinking of you, too. All day long, people wondered why I was running around with a big smile on my face, and I was cheerful with everybody. Usually, I'm not that way, you know. Sometimes I give them a hard time just for the heck of it. And I thought about you, how you were probably lying in bed and snoozing, while I had to work for a living. I was wishing that I could've been there with you. You wouldn't have snoozed so much."

"There would've been no snoozing at all if you had."

She smiled. It was about as much of an indication of amusement as she ever gave. No matter how often I saw her or how carefully I listened, I never heard her burst out into loud laughter. When she told me jokes, she always kept a straight face, and when I told her one, she barely condescended to show me her teeth. She told me often that she liked me because I laughed and tried to make her cheerful, but she never seemed to share my state of hilarity. There was too much passion within her to grant her that measure of emotional relief. For laughter is the way of the soul to break through its tensions and shake off the compulsions and strains of reality and experience, an overthrow of the necessity to react scientifically to stimuli that have been digested. Laughter topples the walls of serious endeavor with which our business environment surrounds us and relaxes the grip of control with which we force ourselves to conform to the requirements of our equally compelled fellow-humans. But if there's too much compulsion necessary, or if our emotions run too deep, or if the tensions are too taut, the gift of laughter is denied us. That's why the most passionate women, the ones whose sexual desires rule over every particle of their being, the ones for whom the cult of the body is everything and who would formerly have made a god out of a phallus, never are the ones to guffaw with laughter. On the motion-picture screen, on the stage, and in stereotyped fiction, the archetype of the loose woman is one who emits shrill yells of laughter, giggles, cackles, and pipes with mirth. And whenever one enters a bar or a club where many women customers hang out, one can actually hear their happy yells of merriment. But the men who fall for their giggles let themselves in for a grave disappointment. A woman who shouts and screams with laughter is like a wet dish-rag in bed. Her imagination is exhausted with the act of lying still and tolerating the man's gymnastics. She doesn't have enough brains to figure out that movements conducted in common will intensify the enjoyment. She'll probably stick her thumb into her mouth and close her eyes and make believe she's a baby again, as I've seen some of those cackling hens do. Her energies have been exhausted in her exhibitions of amusement. Her body doesn't have a bit more sense than her vacant mind. And when she's finished laughing, she's like a hyena that's been in the desert too long and can't do another thing but loaf around an oasis, with all the howling laughter gone. No, the laughing girls aren't the good humping girls. The most delirious bliss always has a faint aroma of melancholy about it. That's why, when a man is looking for a good prospect, he ought to steer clear of the laughing hyenas and hunt up the lithe tigress who can't do much better than a friendly growl. She'll sap every last delicious ounce of energy out of him. She'll mangle him and chew him. But he'll be satisfied.

That was Marsha all over. Never a cackle, never a yodel, never a yelp, never a giggle, never a squeal. Her passions had so intensive a possession of her soul that all she could do was to restrain them for the best of her health and for the sake of social acceptability. She had a beautiful body with desires so strong that there rarely was a time when a single man could've satisfied her. That's why she never went back for seconds. She believed that only the first time could the male stir up enough enthusiasm within himself to exhaust her. She spoke of second assignations as "warmed-up rolls." I don't know if she meant the pun.

In spite of the fact that I had slept during the day and she hadn't, she was extremely passionate again that second night. She walked into my room and stripped within five minutes. She was finished so soon that she helped me undo my necktie —an occasion she used to rub her big bulbs against my chest. Her hips undulated against mine when I undressed. We plunged into bed like thirsty travelers into a desert pond. Our hands wandered up and down our bodies deliriously, while our tongues danced around each other. It was all so effortless, so divinely natural, almost compulsive, that I had a sensation of preordination. We were performing a rite that had sketched itself in our minds long before it took place, carrying out movements that were meant to be, reacting with motor sureness to stimuli that belonged where they were. Never had I considered myself so supremely mated, matched with such perfection, married—so to speak—to a twin soul in the eyes of Aphrodite. Every bounce was a thrill, every push a delight, every moment of rest a suspension in a cloud of bliss. It was as if we were now reaching a culmination for which we had been too tired that morning.

No matter how often I threw myself upon her that evening, how long I stayed with her, or how often she came, I couldn't give her enough. Between acts, she lay back upon the pillow with her legs spread far apart, her nipples standing erect, her hips continuing a slight wavy motion, as if she were in communication with a lover who never ceased. Her eyes remained open most of the evening, but she had a glassy, almost opium-drunken expression in them, as if she were half asleep or intoxicated with her eyes wide open. Her mouth was half-open for hours, and she gave off rasping noises, like someone reaching too far but yet unable quite to grasp what he wanted.

"Please, don't leave me like this!" she managed to say now and then. "Make love to me! Pierce me! Burn me! Consume me!"

One might've thought, on listening to her, that I had refused to give her any satisfaction, and I was sure that she came at least four times. But that evening she couldn't get enough. She wanted a succession of orgasms all through the night. With an unwilling gesture, she led my hand toward herself and showed me her sensitive spots for me to caress. While she stared at me with that doped expression, with her hands behind her head, I strained every muscle of my two hands to reach all of her fine points contemporaneously. She went on groaning and rasping, until finally she shrieked like a child pierced by a needle. And then she settled back limply and gently removed my hands. She was satiated with sex. She pulled the covers over her head, turned over away from me, and relaxed. Within less than two minutes, I heard a regular breath entering and leaving her nostrils. She slept motionlessly for over six hours.

I had to leave Las Vegas the next day. When I took her home, she said that we ought to say goodby and never see each other again. She was pleasant about it and didn't name a reason, except that it would never work out on a permanent basis for us. She was convinced that our affair, like every other, would "get old." Yet when I suggested that it had been pretty good for us that night, she told me "Shut up" and smiled. The glossy stare was entirely gone out of her eyes, the shiny, dark-blue color wasn't there any longer, and she seemed like any other pretty girl going out for an afternoon cup of coffee, only prettier. I told her I'd write to her, and if she didn't want to see me again she didn't have to answer, but that I'd be hoping to hear from her and eager to return every week end. She wrote down her address and left it in that uncertain stage until I kissed her goodby.

"I'll answer," she promised. "I think I love you." And then she slammed the car door and dashed into her house.

It wasn't till two weeks later that she answered my letter. She wrote me only a brief note, saying that she'd be at the Casbar Friday night, and if I wasn't there, she'd find herself another boyfriend. No more and no less.

The Casbar was crowded that night. Fridays, the weekenders arrive and spend their money in a vast hurry on their get-rich-quick schemes, which ordinarily end in great profits —to the owners of the casinos. The usual array of distinguished elderly gentlemen with platinum blondes and big-chested brunettes sat at the tables, and my friend the bandleader was bouncing up and down with his saxophone while

his singer made soft, moaning noises into the microphone
and swung her hips in time with the music. Minks and dia-
monds were represented in quantity. Here and there, a celebrity or a would-be celebrity elucidated fine points to a crowd
of eager listeners, who were probably mooching drinks from
him while deploring his lack of good manners. In short, it
was Las Vegas at its usual nighttime self, with its thousands
of tourists carrying millions of dollars to the amusement
capital of the United States, and all the wonderful things that
the money of the rich will concentrate in a resort city.

Marsha appeared with the long-stemmed, raven-haired
beauty from out of nowhere. The two of them sat down on
vacant bar stools on either side of me and looked at each
other. Three Air Force officers, probably from the nearby
proving grounds, were following the black-haired one and
monopolized her attention before I could say "Good evening" to her. The Air Force has always been good at closing
in on the kill. These fellows must've been rocket experts.

"Look at that little old fool over there," Marsha pointed
toward the other end of the large room. "See the little fool?
He's trying to impress me."

Indeed, there was a little man in an immaculate gray suit
at a dice table, rolling the dice in their cup with great gusto
each time he made a pass, and shouting and praying to the
dice as if they were saints able to intervene with God Almighty for the outcome of the game. He was surrounded by
a crowd of onlookers, who watched him operate with his
stacks of $25-chips in front of him. Only a few of them both-
ered to place bets along with him or picked up the odds of
the house by betting against him. Most of them watched. And
that was obviously the purpose of this performance. The little
man occasionally shook his white mane and looked around

himself imperiously, as if he meant to say, You see how much money I can afford to lose? You see how much I'm winning? You see me in action? You have the impression that I can buy and sell people like you by the dozens? And he succeeded utterly in conveying this impression, except that people didn't look very favorably impressed. In Las Vegas, they see people like him every day, and they're far more inclined to sympathize with a skillful player than with an obvious fourflusher like that.

"He went to the crap table to make an impression on me," Marsha explained, when the first round of drinks came. "I watched him for a while. Then I got tired of him and his big act. I don't care if he can drop a million bucks over there. The question in my mind is how much he can afford to drop on me, not in a gambling hall. Anyway, now that he's got so interested in the game, he's forgotten all about me. Now and then, he still looks up to see if I'm still there. Won't he be surprised to find that I'm gone?!"

"Let's cuckold the old bastard!" I suggested.

"Wait till I finish my drink."

"Drink up fast."

She clenched my hand in hers. The little man from across the hall saw her with me and motioned to her, pointing emphatically to all his chips. He had lost the dice and was betting with another player. But though he saw her sitting at the bar, he couldn't shake himself loose from the game. He pointed to her and to the crap table, to his chips, and to another drink, which probably was hers, standing there and doing nothing. She didn't even bother to return the gesture. All she did was grin and raise her glass toward him. At the table, the croupiers were taking bets, and the little old man eagerly placed a new stack of bright $25-chips worth $500 on the "Come" line. He'd made up his mind that he was in his proper environment. I guess at his age gambling is more fun than sex.

We drove to my motel room without saying much of anything. I tried to tell Marsha that I had been thinking of her night and day, but she tuned in a jazz program on the radio, which made me angry, for I hadn't driven all the way to Las Vegas to listen to jazz. She crossed and uncrossed her legs and fumbled around. Her passion was obviously stirring within her. When we arrived at my place, she didn't wait for me to open her door but jumped right out. We dashed rather than walked into the room. Undressing was a mere matter of minutes. We barely took the time to remove the cover from the bed before we sank into each other's arms.

The night was one of those odd ones when nothing has any reality except sex. I sensed it right at the beginning that it was going to be a marathon. She didn't emit the usual groans when we first joined, but began with her noises only when I did some moving around. She adopted a slow, rolling motion, and she must've been in good form, for she kept it up most of the night. It went on and on, interrupted only by those convulsions of the climax. But we never stopped for that or anything else. Whenever she tried to withdraw, I followed her motions and held her clasped to me, and whenever I tried to raise myself away from her, she embraced me with arms and legs and pulled me down toward her so that I wouldn't get away. It was a long, continuous ecstasy. Though not as intense as the initial meetings I had with her, it was a prolonged debauch, more extended than getting drunk, because getting drunk never lasts. First you become a little tipsy, then you have that pleasant feeling of glow, and pretty soon you're lost and want to go home, sometimes even getting sick and wishing that you had joined Alcoholics Anonymous the night before. But a long, drawnout night of love gives you that feeling of pleasant intoxication all the time, and you can't possibly upset your stomach on it. You just steel yourself, and as the hours pass by, you stay with it, moving less and less and enjoying more and more delicious feeling for your trouble. Of course, the bed soon showed more signs of strain than we did, and I rather hated the thought of having to spend the night in it, but it didn't really matter. Silently, we labored on and on, neither of us wanting to quit.

"All right, that's enough," she said finally.

Obediently, I lay down beside her and allowed her to go to the bathroom. Pretty soon, I heard the shower splashing. Marsha hummed a happy little tune. It was a peculiar feeling to be joined this way in a relaxed boudoir atmosphere. I imagined that a happy marriage must be like that every day. But how many happily married people did I know? There were precious few. Most of my married friends spent all of their lifetimes pecking on each other in a sort of sustained guerrilla war, and I couldn't imagine their making love till five in the morning and then singing a flighty tune in the shower.

"Hurry up and wash," she urged me, when she came back out of the bathroom, all clean and brushed like a well-scrubbed schoolgirl. "I've got to get home before Mother wakes up."

"Can you sleep tomorrow?"

"Yes, and then I've got a date."

"With me."

"No, with a big spender from the East."

"Break the damned date."

"I can't. I like to keep those goodies coming in. Or can you afford to pay me a hundred dollars tomorrow? Fifty a night?"

"I'm sorry, but that leaves me out."

"That's the story in a nutshell. I'll be thinking of you when I'm sleeping with him. He's almost sixty, fat, and very bald."

"Thanks. That reminds you of me, I suppose?"

"Nonsense, you know very well what I mean."

"What about Sunday?"

"I go to church with Mother."

"That's in the morning. What about the evening?"

"Do you want me this way?"

"I want you, any old way."

"Phil, you'll drive me out of my mind!" She kissed me on the forehead, as if she wanted to consecrate me. "Okay, Sunday night I'll come here and sleep with you. And don't you dare get yourself another girl."

That's the way it always was with us. She liked what I gave her, but there wasn't any money in it, and she also liked money. There was a cohort of sugar daddies surrounding her like bees around a honey jar. She specialized in elderly gentlemen, because they were more generous, more dependent, and less demanding. That meant, however, that she was usually frustrated sexually, even though she might have several men fawning over her at any one time. For these kindly grandfathers had seen their physical apex a long time ago, and what they now had to offer was affection rather than potency, not to mention money, of course. What little energy they could muster served barely to whet Marsha's appetite rather than to satisfy her desire. And so, she'd taken to the habit of picking out beautiful boys in their late teens and offering them money to go to bed with her. That was one manner of quenching the ever-present fire that seemed to burn within her, but it wasn't the final answer either. She reveled in the fact that she could summon them and throw them out again when she felt she was through with them, for it gave her a feeling of power, and she enjoyed the exercise of power over men almost as much as their physical possession. But she also wanted someone to respect her, perhaps even to love her, and those boys whom she bought didn't offer her anything except what she paid for: pure sex. They had no respect for a female who bought her love with ten dollar bills. For a while, out of pure fear of further pregnancies, she took up with a Mexican girl who came to visit her every day to put out the fire, but that wasn't the answer either. What Marsha craved was a man, a real, live, lascivious male who'd love her physically and spiritually. And the ones who could afford her expensive tastes couldn't satisfy her, while those who satisfied her couldn't afford the things she wanted. It wasn't a new problem for a woman, yet it was expressed more succinctly in Marsha than in anyone else I've ever known, for she was such an extreme in all things: extremely passionate, extremely beautiful, extremely demanding in her requirements from life, and extremely contemptuous of whoever and whatever displeased her. As for me, I filled a kind of need in her life that arose from the discrepancies of her expectations and hungers. I was the instrument of her satisfaction and temporarily gave her a reason to focus her emotions. I was the necessary exception that confirmed all the rules she had created for herself to live by. I neither paid nor would be paid. I just wanted her for what she was, and she wanted me for myself.

But not for long. With women like Marsha, absence is the worst of all possible crimes. In physical love, that's almost the cardinal principle. For sexual relations, the partner must be present. When he's unable to attend to his duties, his importance rapidly recedes, until he soon is disestablished.

She was a bad correspondent. She couldn't be bothered writing to a man who wasn't with her. In the beginning, there were greeting cards, and each time I'd jump into my car on Friday and rush to Las Vegas to embrace her. Each time, it was passion galore, and each time, we had trouble in meeting even for the brief days I spent there, because she couldn't forego the compensation she derived from her sugar daddies. She always wound up giving in, as long as I was with her. But by mail, such arguments were impossible, because I wasn't there. She could simply discard a letter and join the man who was in town, calling for her. It was so much simpler. And any amount of trouble was too much for her. The men who'd fussed and fought over her ever since she was in high school had so thoroughly spoiled her that she was unaccustomed to putting forth any effort or initiative herself. All she had to do was to plunk herself down on a bar stool or a park bench, stretch once or twice to show off those big breasts of hers, and wait for the future to take care of itself. There was always someone near her in Las Vegas who'd gladly part with a fortune to enjoy the pleasures of her company, sometimes on a purely Platonic basis. Why should she write letters?

One day, when I hadn't heard from her in several weeks, I went to Las Vegas uncalled. She'd just had a telephone installed when I last saw her, and I called her up, but she wasn't at home. At night, I walked the round of the casinos and the bars and restaurants. I drove and drove and walked and walked, feeling a premonition that I'd see her that evening. It was one of those "just knowing" cases which always pan out. I spent most of the night on these rounds. Las Vegas isn't so large that one couldn't cover it in one long night, especially since the places of amusement never close, and I calculated that I had at least until four or five in the morning to find her.

At The Dunes I saw her coming toward the entrance when I arrived. The raven-haired beauty was with her, but there were no men. She was wearing dark glasses and a simple, white dress. The Beauty was eyeing me with a spark of recognition and gave Marsha a fleeting glance.

"Hello, Marsha," I shouted at her, when they passed me.

She barely turned around to look at me. Then the two of them walked on with brisk steps, leaving me standing agape.

Then I knew. I had just seen a stranger. The stranger had the same face, the same figure, the same walk, and the same name as Marsha. But she was a stranger, nevertheless. In the fast life she led, she'd changed so much that she'd left me far behind. There would be no more nights of passion.

VII Anne: Young Mother

When I lived in St. Louis, I was walking through a department store one day, when I was atracted by a gorgeous woman behind the nylon stocking counter. I used to take slow walks through all the department stores with precisely this sort of aim in mind. There were always some unattached young women working behind the counters, and quite a few of them fairly good-looking, at least potentially so. The best-looking girls, I noticed, usually worked behind the cosmetics and ladies' lingerie counters, obviously intended to be living advertisements of what the merchandise could do for a woman. Usually there also were some very pretty ones behind the candy counter, which is an easy job and is often given to the very young girls or to the dumb-but-beautiful types. In the men's garments department, they often had more mature, hard-boiled types who'd know how to deal with customers who wanted to pinch them on the posterior every time they spent a five-dollar bill. The real bags were in the household goods department. Nobody but housewives ever shopped there, and they weren't interested in the looks of the salesgirls. Children's and teenagers' departments also were senseless for me to patrol, because the saleswomen there almost always had faces that even a mother could barely love. I had, then, regular beats that I used to pound to investigate what novelties were offered on the local flesh market in the big department stores. Sometimes, I even made a small purchase, just to throw the floorwalkers off the track. Floorwalkers have a very unreasonable attitude toward young men who patronize their stores only to keep warm and to pick up their better-looking salesgirls.

It was really one of those floorwalkers, following me about the store with all the tact and demeanor of a pack of hounds chasing a deer, who gave me the idea for the approach. His fishy eyes stared at me while he followed me doggedly around the ground floor. I don't know whether he thought I was a shoplifter or a pickpocket, or whether he guessed my true intentions, but no matter how that may be, he never lifted an eye from me. He was an annoying bastard of some forty years of age, overdressed like the best man at a wedding, with a faint aroma of perfume, and an aura of importance which only an officious busybody can possibly develop. I walked over to the nylon stockings just to escape from his clutches and looked over the merchandise. The girl behind the counter had turned her back to me when I came toward her. I didn't realize what a good looker she was until she suddenly turned around.

"I'd like a pair of stockings for a girl just about your size," I said.

"What size?"

"I dont' know. What size do you wear?"

She smiled. Her hair was jet-black like the feathery coat of a raven, her skin a pinkish white like alabaster, and her gray eyes like menacing clouds. She had a narrow, pointed nose and a rather narrow pair of lips, which were parted to reveal a perfect set of teeth. Her chin was pronounced without being prominent and sat on top of a longish neck. She had a well shaped tall figure. She stood well in her high-heeled shoes and was somewhat taller than I. Her whole being radiated health and good grooming.

"What color?" she asked.

"I don't know. What color do you wear?"

"Dark brown. Is that what your wife wears?"

"I haven't got a wife. But that's the right color."

"What about the gage?"

"Make it all the same that you prefer. I'm sure you have very good taste."

"But maybe your friend won't approve of my taste."

"I'm sure she will."

The floorwalker was gone, satisfied that I was a bonafide customer. There were some people passing by, but fortunately nobody stopped.

"How many pairs?" she wondered.

"Just one will do," I replied.

I handed her a five-dollar bill, and she gave me back my

change. Her hand was long, white and a little moist. Obviously, she had never done any heavy labor. By the way she looked at me, I could tell that she knew I liked her.

"Shall I gift-wrap them?" she asked.

"Never mind, they're for you."

She looked at me with a raised eyebrow. Her mouth opened to say something, but whatever it was it didn't come out. She looked in the direction of the floorwalker, but he was being bothered by a fat old woman in the corset department.

"I can't take that," she protested. "I never take gifts from strangers."

"But I'm not a stranger. Consider it my calling card."

"And what would this gift cost me?"

"Meet me for lunch tomorrow. What time do you go to lunch? At twelve?"

"Impossible. I can't."

"Nothing is impossible. You've already accepted a pair of stockings from me, now surely lunch won't hurt you either. No strings attached."

"Honest?" she looked at me penetratingly. "Meet me at the back entrance tomorrow at one o'clock. But if you think this is going to get you anywhere or persuade me to do anything—"

"One o'clock sharp," I cut her off, motioning to the door. "The floorwalker is coming this way again in his own prissy little way. See you tomorrow."

I really didn't expect to see her on the next day but went there more or less on the slight chance that a long shot might pay off. It did. She wasn't just there, but she was on time, a quality which I always liked in people. Punctuality is the courtesy of kings. Maybe she was just hungry. We walked a few blocks to the Mayfair Hotel, which has the reputation of having one of the best cuisines in the United States. It's always crowded for lunch. We were very lucky to get the quick attention of the head-waiter, who showed us to our table and sent another waiter to take our order. The girl was obviously impressed. When I held my lighter in front of her to light her cigarette, she held my hand steady with both of hers. For a brief moment, her cigarette trembled in her mouth.

"I'm Phil," I raised my glass to her. "Here's to you."

"I'm Anne," she responded, and clinked her glass on mine. "Here's to us."

We hit it off perfectly that first day. She was a friendly and co-operative girl and could hold her own in a conversation, which is a quality I've always admired in women. After all, you can't engage in erotics with them all the time, and especially when you're still in the getting-acquainted stage, there isn't too much chance of that anyway, so you're always better off being with a woman who can talk. Not only that, but later on you'd feel easier in introducing her to your friends, for if she can occupy them with conversation there's less chance of her going to bed with them during your first trip out of town. The important thing about an ability like that is whether you can switch it off as easily as on. For at certain times, there's nothing more exasperating than to hear the other person babbling along, when all you want is a kiss and quietude. Anne, it turned out, had both talents. She not only knew when and how to talk, but she also knew when and how to shut up. In fact, the woman consisted of little else but virtues.

We had lunch one more time, before she consented to go out with me at night. I think she knew what was coming all along, but she didn't want to bring it on any more quickly than it had to come, and she was a little afraid of me. As it was, we went to have dinner, and then we sat and talked for five hours without moving. I took her to one of my hangouts on the Illinois side, where they stay open till all hours of the morning, and where we could sit in a big armchair, with her sprawled out over me, running her hands through my hair and rubbing her thighs against me.

"Let's go to your house," I finally suggested.

"We can't. You know what's waiting for me there?"

"A husband?" I ventured to guess.

"Nonsense. I'd never have gone out with you if I still had a husband. But I did have one. And I still have his two children. They're at home with the maid, waiting for me."

"Then let's go to a hotel."

"No. Thanks for the compliment, but I've got to go home."

I think she meant what she said. At least, I thought so at the time, didn't feel dejected, and only blamed myself for not suggesting our assignation a little earlier. Perhaps, though, it wasn't a loss. With a woman like Anne, conversation itself was a pleasure, and I'm sure she'd never have considered going to bed with me until she thought she knew me quite well.

"Disappointed?" she asked. "Then you'd better go to a bar and get yourself one of those unattached females there. It isn't that easy with me."

"Let's go," I said and helped her into her coat. "You're a complex person, and you mustn't judge me as if I were a simple one."

She stroked my hair and looked at me as if she wished that she could do what she refused to do.

"What about tomorrow night?" I whispered, squeezing her narrow waist.

"Sorry, but that's impossible."

"Why impossible? Are you put out with me because I asked you?"

"No, I'm flattered that you asked, but it's still impossible. I've got a date."

"Aha, then you do go out on dates."

"I never said that I didn't."

"The night after?"

"Busy. What about Sunday, Phil? I'm not doing anything then."

"Where would you like to go? I'll get tickets."

"Don't get any tickets. I'll fix steaks. Do you like steaks? And I'll play housewife. You can sit in an armchair and talk to the children, if you like. I want you to meet them and like them."

"If they're yours, I'll be crazy about them."

"And then, I've got to tell you about me. You don't know me very well. And I think you ought to know more about me before you take me so seriously."

We parted with a kiss, and I rode the same taxi home. My mind busied itself with questions regarding Anne, with recollections of how she smiled, of her charming ways with me, and of her consummate skills of entertaining without yielding an inch of her ladylike qualities. I wondered what dark secrets she had to reveal, what strange tales of woe her gorgeous visage withheld from view. All women, it seemed, had stories, or at least I had a knack for finding those with stories of woe and violence. Almost every woman I've ever known had enough material for several novels in her repertoire, and usually the girls weren't telling all they knew. I often wondered how come I never met a quiet, simple, uncomplicated girl who hadn't committed any deeds more daring than rob the family piggybank and whose only boyfriend had been her childhood sweetheart. I was sure there were plenty of those girls left in the United States of America, but I only heard about them from other people.

I bought presents for the children, a boy of four and a girl of three. We took our meal together, that is, I ate a huge steak dinner while Anne sliced up some of her steak for the children and fed them, forcing them to eat the vegetables and potatoes, and generally having a difficult time with them. She was preparing dessert for us, when I noticed that she hardly found time to touch a bite of her own. I called out to her to come back and finish her plate herself, just as she had made the children do. She came back with cake and ice cream and I forced her to sit down and finish eating the main course before she bothered with the children again. The boy emptied his plate in a hurry and drank his milk, but the girl played with her food.

"Go on, eat it up, then you can go play," I told her.

The little one looked at me as incredulously as her mother.

"I said, eat up your food and then you can go and play," I repeated. "Look at your brother! He's finished and just waiting for you."

Her features trembled a little, as if she wanted to cry.

"It's all right, darling, he doesn't mean you any harm," Anne said, fondling and petting her.

"Anne, sit down. We'll see if you can't finish your dinner in peace."

Obediently, Anne sat down and finished her steak. The little girl, not knowing what else to do, stuffed the rest of her food into her mouth. I took the empty plate away from her and handed her the cake with the ice cream. She eagerly

gulped it down, too. Anne eyed me with frank amazement.
"Have you been around children before?" she asked me.

"Not much," I admitted. "But I know nobody believes
you, unless you look as if you meant what you're saying.
Children are no exception."

"What's your name?" the boy asked me.

"That's Uncle Phil," Anne introduced me.

"I'm Billy," the little boy said.

"Never mind that 'uncle' stuff," I corrected her. "We're
going to be friends from now on. I'm not anybody's uncle.
Just call me Phil."

"You're my friend, Phil," Billy said.

"Go play with your sister," Anne sent him packing. And,
after a while, turning toward me, "You seem to have made
an impression on the children."

"I'd rather make an impression on the mother."

"You have."

She sat down in my lap and kissed me. It wasn't one of
those experienced whore's kisses, one of those tongue-baths
that make you wonder how many people's saliva the girl has
swallowed, but rather an innocent, somewhat bashful kiss,
as from a virgin, a kiss on the cheek below the cheekbone,
where she wouldn't have to look me in the eye. I pulled
her down a little farther and tried to reach her lips, but she
only proffered her other cheek. I kissed her on the neck, behind the ears, and on the forehead. She didn't offer me her
mouth but rather got up with a little effort and began to carry
out the dishes. In the kitchen, I heard her talk to the children. I picked up a newspaper and read for a while. It was a
scene of quiet domesticity to which a professional bachelor
like myself was quite unaccustomed.

"Excuse me for a while longer," she came back to say, "but I have to put the little one to bed. Only a little while longer. Think I'm worth waiting for?"

"Longer than that."

When she was finally finished with the little one and with the kitchen, Billy wandered in to keep us company. I wanted to see Billy about as much as I wanted to have a hole in my head, but remembering that the road to a mother's heart leads through her children, I put up with as much from him as I could. She must've noticed that it became pretty hard on my nerves, for Billy and I were just crawling around on the carpet when she took him by the hand and said, "That's enough now, Billy. Get your pajamas on and get ready for bed."

"Aw, mom, Phil and I were just having such a good time."

"He'll be back again to play with you some other time. Get your pajamas on now like a good boy."

He stalked ut to the hall with tears in his eyes.

"Well, you've made quite a hit with the children," Anne said. "The little one wondered if you'd be here in the morning, and the boy can't get enough of you."

"What about the mother?"

"She likes you too."

I put my arms around her. She was standing in the middle of the room, and in her slippers she was just as tall as I was. I pressed her to myself and tried to kiss her on the mouth. She drew back, but I craned my neck to follow her and found her lips. A shudder went through her shapely body, and she rubbed herself against me. I could feel her heartbeat through her sweater. We stood there, kissing again and again, when Billy came back in his pajamas. She released her hold upon me and turned to her son.

"Say good night to Phil, dear."

I shook hands with Billy man-fashion, saying, "Good night, partner." She picked him up and carried him into his bedroom, which was a tiny little affair next to that of his sister. Anne and he whispered a bit before they kissed good night, and the two of us then retreated from his room.

"Good night, Phil," he shouted after us. "You come back soon, won't you?"

"Sure," I said. "Just tell your mom you want to see me. She'll tell me."

Anne squeezed my hand in appreciation when I closed the door behind her. We walked into the living room, released at last from the supervision of the children. She turned out all the lights but one. I wondered whether that was my cue. Just to ascertain where we stood, I slipped my right hand under her sweater and began to massage her right breast. But she pushed my hand away. That wasn't what she had in mind.

"No, Phil, take it easy with me. I have to talk to you."

She beckoned to me to sit down on the sofa, cuddled up beside me, and lit a cigarette for me, which she took out of her lips to place into my mouth. Not until then did she light one for herself.

"I've got to tell you something about myself," she commenced. "Do you think you'll understand if I tell you something awful about myself?"

"I'll understand, unless you're going to tell me that I can't have you."

"Don't insist on it, please. There are too many others who have. Maybe you won't want me after you know about me."

"Don't keep me in suspense. Come on and tell me."

"Well, you see the apartment I have, and the way I take care of my children. I also told you I had a maid in the daytime and when I'm not at home. Where do you think it all comes from?"

"I suppose you make good money where you work."

"That's peanuts. Nobody makes any money working in a store behind a counter."

"So then, do you get it from alimony?"

"No, from men. Nice, kindly, elderly, generous, amorous, and often impotent men, that's where. Husbands whose wives don't understand them. Bachelors cheating on their girlfriends. Fathers who can't get married again for fear of disillusioning their growing children. Grandfathers who have a horror of looking ridiculous before their families and who still like to enjoy a girl now and then, that's where. Men, mostly old enough to be my fathers, and sometimes my grandfathers, that's where. Now, do you understand why I don't want to go to bed with you right away? I've had too much of that already. I don't want you that way. I want you for what you've been for me so far, for a friend and nice person to have around. I've had the other up to my ears."

She pulled out a handkerchief and wiped her nose. There were tears in her eyes. Her beautiful body shook with tremors of emotion. She sobbed violently.

"I debated with myself whether I ought to tell you," she cried. "I thought I'd like you to go on thinking I was the sort of woman that you thought I was. But I simply couldn't deceive you any further. The truth has to come out sooner or later, and it's better this way."

She went on crying. She bent over sideways and rested her head on her arm. I didn't know what to do, because she'd be as likely to reject any indication of tenderness on my part as not. After all, I was a man, and when she told me that she was sick and tired of men, I was at a loss as to what to do. I didn't know any way of consoling a crying woman except to make love to her. I had observed that the love act at least sidetracked women from any other emotions they might be experiencing. But here was a woman who didn't want it. What was I to do? I hated to see her cry, and I was afraid of making the wrong gesture. Yet wasn't it as wrong sometimes to make no move at all? I decided to chance it rather than be obtrusive. I let her calm herself in her own way. I lit a cigarette and let my thoughts follow the smoke as it disintegrated in mid-air.

That was a distinctly good idea. When Anne had composed herself a little, she bent over, changing her weight to the side next to me, and put her head in my lap. My left hand held a cigarette. She took my right hand and placed it to her mouth to smother it with kisses. Now and then, her curvaceous torso still shook with sobs. I didn't know what to say to her, and so I preferred to sit in silence.

"Now that you know, you can get up and leave," she said, but made no motion to let me go. "If you don't like me any more, I wouldn't blame you."

"Let him who is without blame throw the first stone," I replied.

"Do you still want me?"

"More than ever."

"Show me."

She used her arms to raise herself up against me and closed her arms around me, then pulled herself into my lap. Her lips opened upon mine and let her tongue slip out to insert itself into my mouth, where it explored every spot in my gums. She squeezed herself against my chest so hard that I could feel her crushing her breasts against my ribs. Her head moved back and forth to permit her tongue further exploratory operations within my mouth, without her arms being relaxed from their grip around my neck. During this maneuver, her sweater became dislodged to reveal her bare, pink flesh around the waistline. Her skirt slipped up on her thighs. I used both hands to pull it even higher and grabbed the rounded flesh of her posterior. It didn't take me long to ascertain that she didn't believe in wearing lingerie when she was entertaining her beaux. She willingly co-operated with the movement of my fingers. When I reached the target on both sides at the same moment, she gasped and gurgled and bored her tongue even farther into my throat. She pressed against me voraciously.

"Take me, burn me, consume me, do with me whatever you want," she breathed into my ears, "only don't let me go before I'm ready!"

I unbuttoned her sweater. There wasn't a stitch of clothing beneath it either. Her breasts stood up like good grenadiers at attention. They had a shape resembling spiked helmets, with abnormally large nipples for spikes, standing up almost like pointed thimbles. The texture of their skin was remarkably firm for a woman who had two children. I took that part of her eagerly as a new-born babe and let my hands gently caress her willing skin. Her long, black hair fell down over her shoulders to make an exciting contrast. She helped me pull the skirt over the equatorial circle of her buttocks and stood up momentarily to complete the job. As soon as she had placed the skirt on a chair, she sat down on the sofa beside me and raised her legs on the seat. Her arms around my neck pulled me down with her. My hands mechanically undid my belt buckle and performed the most necessary work on the rest of the clothing that twisted and dragged all out of shape because it was being used as a pajama. Anne let her fingers

stroke various parts of my body until she found the part that
excited her most. We were both at a high pitch of erotic
expectation, and she could hardly bear to await my taking
complete possession of her. When she felt that the union had
been consummated, she arched herself up on her feet and
shoulders and held herself in position that way to make it
easier for me. Her hands lay clenched into tight fists beside
her. When I looked at her face, it was bent backward above
the black cloud of her hair, and she was biting her lips to
avoid making any noises that might awaken the children.
Now and then, a desperate gasp escaped her. When it did,
she held her own mouth with one of her hands. Her arched
body must've been tremendously strong and her muscles well
trained to sustain that much effort, but even so she finally
collapsed and lay there flat, with her legs bent sideways. I
waited for her eyes to blink and then to open before I let
myself go. By then, the effort of it all had made me powerless
anyway to go on. She was pumping me inside of her, with a
strong, billowing wave that seemed to reach every nerve
center deep inside of me. She'd obviously had some practice in
this exercise. There was a smile on her face, and a quizzical
look, as if she meant to ask, You didn't expect this, did you?
How do you like me now?

I kissed her when we separated. She let me wash up in
the bathroom and told me to stay and wait for her to go to
bed. After a few minutes, she joined me there. Our heads lay
side by side on the pillow.

I wanted to kiss as before, but she was crying again. She
lay upon the coverlet, naked as nature had designed her, and
shook convulsively. Tears streamed out of her, into the handkerchief with which she tried to dry herself, and upon the
pillow next to my head. Tears of bitterness, anguish, and tor-

ture. Her shoulders arched above her, her head buried deep in the pillow, she let herself go into quakes of mourning.

When she stopped shaking and her tears flowed more quietly, I asked her, "Why are you crying? Are you sorry you let me make love to you?"

"No, that's not it," she sobbed. "I wish to God I'd been a virgin the first time that I slept with you!"

"But I knew you had children," I suggested uncomprehendingly.

"Of course you did," she said, "but just the same, I wish I had been a virgin the first time with you. I wish that I could've given myself to you pure and unsullied. I'm so ashamed of myself!"

"Don't be ashamed of yourself," I tried to console her. "I want you the way you are, and if it took two children to make you what you are, then I accept them just as cheerfully as all the rest."

"The rest, as you call it, is what I was thinking about," she went on sobbing. "All those men. I'm unclean. I don't know why you even bother with me. I've played the lover to dozens of men in the last two years, maybe three. My husband didn't take care of us. What was I going to do? I hadn't learned anything. I was attractive to men, and I liked men. They offered me everything. They promised me heaven on earth. I was only thinking of the children . . ."

She started crying heavily again. Her hair was a tangled mess, her body seemed whiter somehow than it had been before, and a wrinkle showed on her neck.

"It never turns out to be heaven on earth," she continued, "just passion. Nothing but passion, and even that gets stale after a while. That isn't heaven. That's closer to hell. Anyway, my husband left me because I wasn't faithful. He was going to divorce me for adultery, but I had already put in a divorce suit against him for non-support. I got my divorce, but he's never paid me any of the alimony he's supposed to send. I don't dare ask for it for fear of the stink he'll cause. So it's more passion for me, and the men come and go, and I have to smile at them and be nice to them and listen sympathetically to their troubles. I'm a little something that they take along with the expense account, or they introduce their business friends to me, give me a hundred bucks, and tell me to show them a good time. I'm the garbage pail of the business world and the late hours entertainment of a lonely sixty-year-old straw widower who wants a little fun while his wife is vacationing in Florida. I'm daddy's last fling before he goes to his son's wedding, and the boss's nerve tonic before he assembles the office employes for their regular admonitions and pep talk. I'm the persuader that clinches the argument with the assessment specialists of the tax-revenue offices not to change the evaluation of the business property, and I'm the final reason for a sale that nets somebody a million dollars. All for a hundred bucks a night, breasts, lips, and hips, sold, wrapped, delivered, and used, to be discarded after a full night's wear. Isn't that quite an existence? What do you think of me now?"

"Don't talk like that," I stroked her. "You're also my sweetheart, and I won't have you malign yourself in my presence."

"I wish I could've come to you a virgin," she started in again.

"But I don't care. I never liked virgins anyway."

We lay there a long time while the room turned cold and her tears dried on the pillow. We had to creep under the blanket to be comfortable. Finally, toward morning, she made me go home so that the children shouldn't find me there when they got up to go to school. She explained that usually when she had dates, she went to the man's apartment or to a hotel, and the children had hardly ever seen her with a man, let alone a man in her bedroom. The children, she said, were going to have a "good upbringing." They were never going to learn what their mother was. I could've told her about those things. About children who always find out what their mothers are, about ten-year-old boys who run away from home because they find out from the other kids that their mothers are nothing but whores, about little girls who are raped by their classmates because it's assumed that "like mother, like daughter" entitles them to this privilege. About the awful moment of truth that comes to everyone some time, when lies are no longer long or wide enough to cover up the shame, about the agony of women whose children avoid them because they hate them for not having maintained those standards of virtue which they taught them. But who appointed me Jesus Christ? I didn't tell her about any of it. I wasn't going to save her soul. Men never convert women. If a woman wants to be converted, she has to do the job herself. Why should I lose a perfectly good bed partner and burn my fingers, when chances were a hundred to one that I couldn't do her an ounce of good? I kissed her gently on the forehead and got up to dress. I didn't let her turn on the light, because I could see sufficiently in the dark to take care of my preparations for facing the world.

"How about tomorrow?"

"Nope, I've got a date," she said. "And the next day and the next. It just isn't any good with us. You might as well forget me."

"Meet me at the back door the day after tomorrow. When do you get off?"

"That's our late night. I get off at nine. But I've promised somebody that I'll go out with him.

"Tell him to go to hell and go with me instead."

"Phil, please, don't ask me. You know why I'm doing this—"

"I'm asking you. Now, tell that man you'll make it some other day. Day after tomorrow. Please."

"Wait for me. If I don't show up, you'll know why."

We left it at that. I didn't have any idea whether she'd be there or not. For two days I walked around in utter uncertainty. It bothered me not to know where I stood, and it bothered me to know that she was with some elderly tycoon or other almost every night. At nine o'clock that appointed night, I stood at the door, wondering whom she had chosen. Nine o'clock, nine-ten, nine-fifteen. Had she decided to stand me up? I watched all the other girls coming out and was about to give up on her, when I saw her hurrying toward me.

"I was afraid you weren't coming," I said and grabbed her by both shoulders to look her in the eyes. "I've missed you terribly."

"You're lucky I'm here at all," she said, her voice creaking a bit. Tears rose to her eyes, when she bowed down to kiss me gently on the mouth. She was wearing her high heels again.

"Let's go out on the town and celebrate," I suggested.

"Let's not," she threw cold blankets on the fire. "Let's go home."

"What's the hurry?"

"I'll tell you all about it. Grab a taxi for us, will you?"

In the taxi, she sat practically on top of me but didn't look at me. She played with my fingers and bit her lips. There was obviously something on her mind. I thought of asking her.

but decided against it. If she wanted to tell me, she would, and if she didn't want to, she'd only lie to me. And so, we didn't say much in the taxi. I paid the driver, and we walked upstairs to her apartment.

The colored maid opened the door for us. "I put the children to bed early, as you said on the phone," she said. "Whatssa matter, Miss Anne, don't you feel good?"

"I feel fine, Mable, it's something else."

Mable gave me a long, hostile glance.

"No, it's not this gentleman either," Anne guessed her thoughts. "It's something highly personal. Now, are you finished?"

"Yes, ma'am, I's finished," Mable replied dutifully. She gathered up her hat and coat and rushed out, as Anne obviously wanted her to do. We stood and waited in the kitchen until she left.

"Oh, Phil, I'm so miserable," Anne cried, throwing her arms around me. "I don't know how to tell you. It's all so complicated."

"Suppose you fix us a nice, tall drink and start at the beginning."

She removed her shoes, her overcoat, her jacket, and her belt, and took out two glasses from the pantry. Our drinks were ready in a jiffy.

"Let's go in the bedroom, we can talk there," she suggested.

I never turn down a lady's invitation to enter her bedroom. Before she was ready to talk, she went into her little daughter's room and looked at her. We then tiptoed into Billy's room. Billy awoke and gave me a big hello. He was all for getting up for a while and keeping us company. But Anne explained that it was too late and that he must go back to sleep. She closed the door behind herself with tears in her eyes. Then she took me by the hand and led me to her bed, tears flowing down her cheeks. She kissed my hand, laid her head in my lap, and stared at the ceiling to avoid my eyes.

"Sometimes circumstances and events grow to be bigger than people," she mused. "Sometimes, we just can't help ourselves, and we're swept along with the crowd. That's what happened to me. I'm helpless when it comes to other people. Anybody can make a fool of me. They often have . . . So, I have to take care of myself. You can see that, can't you? If I don't support the children and give them a good home, the juvenile authorities will come and take them away from me. Maybe they'd put them in a home, or maybe they'd put them out for adoption, or maybe they'd give them to their father, which would be the worst thing of all for them. I'll never let him have those kids, never. I'd rather do anything, steal, kill, even this . . ." She cried again. Her sobs shook the mattress springs. I was helpless. I've never been much good around women who cried.

"So, what are you trying to tell me?" I asked her, when she seemed to have calmed herself a little. "Is there anything you want me to do?"

"Nothing, Phil, darling, just make love to me. We haven't much time. I've reserved the first hour of the evening for you. At eleven, someone will come to pick me up for a late show and midnight supper. Will you ever forgive me?"

"Then let's make the best of the time we have," I said.

"A little over an hour," she said. "Maybe he'll be a few minutes late."

"Don't you want to go with him?"

"I want to stay with you. But I'm doing it for the children."

It was a cold-blooded act, purely for the physical satisfaction of it. She started us off by engaging in intimacies for which women usually have no stomach until several hours after the start, so that I was one mad mass of throbbing masculinity. Then she sat down next to me suggestively and looked at me expectantly. I rolled over on her vehemently, like an alligator-wrestler on an alligator, not leaving a spare molecule of air between us. We squeezed each other so tight that both of us had some trouble breathing. Everything immediately sat tightly in place, without the help of the hands. All we did was roll the solid unity that was composed of the two of us. Each followed the other hungrily. We never separated. Our skins clung together as if they were glued. We tried various movements with no more hint than the necessary pressure involved, and we always remained together. It was like perfect teamwork, though completely unrehearsed. We fit each other perfectly, so that there appeared to be something preordained about the desperate and exhaustive enjoyment of which we partook. She increased her pace twice and started shrieking shortly afterwards, but I stayed with her to the end. Finally, when I figured my time was about up, I permitted the climax to happen. It was like drowning a well-ordered machine with lubricating oil: The parts kept moving, but they were out of time with each other and the viscosity was too high for the necessary friction to move the wheels. Like all machines that are overgreased, it had to stop.

"What time is it?" I asked her, when she got up to wash.

"A quarter to eleven. We'd better hurry."

At eleven o'clock, I was as immaculate as a male fashion model and ran, rather than walked, downstairs. As I was leaving the building, a sleek, long Cadillac pulled up in front of the door, with a white-haired, distingué type behind the steering wheel. I didn't have to wonder who that would be. . . .

• • •

Anne and I came to an understanding about these matters. Obviously, I wasn't going to break her of the habit of "receiving" all those men. She needed money, and I actually didn't know a better and quicker way to get it. I reasoned with her that this would deprive her of her good figure sooner or later, that it would wear out her capacity to enjoy the sex act at all, and that it would age her prematurely, but she wouldn't listen to me. All these arguments might be true or not, as far as she was concerned, but they didn't eliminate the all-pervasive reason for her to follow her occupation. She needed enough money to keep the children, and she wasn't going to part with them, come hell or high water. And so, I acknowledged the fact that she was going to date a large and wealthy clientele of middle-aged and older gentlemen, and she gave me what she could of her body and her free time. I never gave her anything except my love, and she never asked for anything more.

Her free time usually was after the old fellows had delivered her home. That might be at midnight or at four in the morning, depending upon the mood and the finances of the client. He might be eager to get away himself, wanting to enjoy a good game of poker with the boys from his hometown, or he might want to feast all night by looking at her beautiful body, or he might want to diddle her the way he always wanted to diddle his wife but never dared, because his old lady would get very angry if he approached her with anything but the old-fashioned, true-blue, frontal assault. Napoleon never failed to attack the center, and old-fashioned American women seem to think that these tactics certainly aren't outmoded, or at least not in bed. If the husband wants it any other way, he has to find himself an Anne with whom to engage in the experiment. Some of the old boys couldn't get enough of what they had been missing, and she'd be worn to a frazzle when she had to go to work in the morning.

Our agreement was that she'd call me up on my telephone if she managed to bid her admirer farewell before two in the morning. Sometimes, if she anticipated that it might be after twelve, we agreed that I'd be waiting at the Rio Bar downtown or at the Playdium in East St. Louis, to get the call. Occasionally, I also waited in a hallway across the street from her apartment for her to show up, but that was cold and very boring. Usually, after the first few phone calls, I'd wait at one of the bars.

"Well, I finally got rid of the old codger," she'd say, or, "Hurry over, before I get cold."

I was surprised to hear from her that many of the old fellows never even touched her. They paid her fifty dollars a night just for being nice to them, listening to their success stories over the dinner table, and kissing them now and then in front of their friends and acquaintances. This kissing ceremony was very important, it seems. Businessmen really felt their oats if they could tell their friends that Anne was a girlfriend who waited for them to hit St. Louis now and then and put them up. It made them feel young again. And if she ran her hands over their trouserlegs under the table, so that occasionally someone could watch her on the sly, and if she always agreed with them in starry-eyed adulation, they might double the fee without asking for another act of kindness. Her main job was simply to be that stately, raven-haired girl fawning over them. At least that's what Anne kept telling me. I calculated that maybe it didn't pay to pry too closely into these "Platonic" affairs. Whenever a man sticks his hands into a woman's private life, he finds a lot of muck that he's better off not knowing. And she wasn't dishonest with me in principle, it was just these occasional hard-to-believe stories that she slipped in which made me suspect her. I had nothing to complain of. I was the man who was summoned to her bed when the fruit was ripe for the picking. Whether the others did or didn't avail themselves of the merchandise for which they'd paid was strictly none of my business. Why should I spoil their fun, or they mine?

I thought of them sometimes as I sat at the Rio Bar and nursed a brandy and soda along, waiting for that all-important telephone call. I wondered what it must be like for a woman to go with them all, short and tall, fat and skinny, old and young, rude and polite, eager and bashful, dark-haired and blond, high-pitched and sonorous, happy and morose, stingy and generous. I wondered what it must be like to have all of their hands probing under her skirt, fumbling at her brassiere, pulling at her panties. I wondered if she enjoyed them all, or if some of them were so repulsive that she'd have to close her eyes, hold her breath, and make believe they were someone else. I tried to imagine the counterpart. Women coming into my room every night, short and fat, old and young, pretty and ugly, all peeling off my clothes, tugging at my sex, and pulling my tenderest parts in between their yawning thighs, salivating all over me like affectionate bitches, and putting my lips up against their sagging mammaries. I must say, the thought didn't appeal to me at all. I felt sorry for Anne.

No matter how sorry I felt for her, however, I couldn't quite see marrying her. And that's what she asked me to do. Out of a clear blue sky one day, when I came up after she returned from one of the wealthier patrons' house at two o'clock in the morning. She was expecting a third child, she said, and she had had enough of this way of life. I had told her myself what the last consequences of it would be. She wasn't getting any younger, and she had to think of the future some time. This was as good a time as any. She hoped I was happy about her decision.

"You should've thought about the future before," I said. "When you decided to take on all these men as a way to pay your bills. Sooner or later, you not only were bound to get pregnant again, but you're going to be found out at the store, where they'll certainly give you the boot right away. It was all bound to happen, and it's starting now."

"I thought I could count on you in an emergency," she said reproachfully.

"You should be able to, but unfortunately I can't help you either. I'm a poor man, and I can't afford to marry a family of four at this point."

"But you can afford very well to crawl up here at two every morning and get what somebody else has paid for, can't you? And you can talk pretty and play with the kids as if you wanted some of your own, and snuggle up to me nice and close, can't you? And you can tell me about love and sentiment, and all that sort of crap, can't you? You're real good at that, aren't you?"

"Please, let's not have words," I begged her. "Everything you say is true. Now quit laying it on. I agree with you. I'm a cad."

"Cad isn't the beginning. You're . . . you're . . . you're . . ." she burst out crying. Whenever she was at a loss for words, she cried. Her beautiful black hair was tousled around her head, her face was lined with the dastardly work which the tears had wrought on her makeup, and her mouth twitched with pain.

Billy came running out of his room. Instinctively, he ran to his mother. "Why's she crying, Phil?" he asked me, full of confidence.

She reached out for him and pressed him to herself in a gesture of protectiveness, but also a gesture of searching for protection.

"Because we're never going to see each other any more, Billy," I replied. "I must go away now, for a long time. Maybe I'll never come back. I've got work to do that won't wait for me."

"Don't cry, Mom, he'll come back," Billy consoled her, "and I'll stay with you, always. Don't cry, please don't cry."

"Goodby, Billy. Shake hands. That's it! And when you grow up to be big and strong, ask your mom where I am. She'll tell you where to find me."

"I love you, Phil," Billy cried. Tears flowed out of him, too, and the two of them made a pitiful sight. "Mom and I both love you."

"Shush, Billy, don't tell Phil any lies," she tried to make Billy be quiet.

"It's not a lie. You said so yourself," he cried even more. "You said that we both loved Phil, and he was going to stay with us always."

"Well, it didn't work out that way, partner," I said to Billy. "Sometimes, grownups have their own reasons for doing things, and sometimes they aren't even very good reasons, but I've got to go. Take care of Mom for me."

"I will. Goodby, Phil."

I heard them both crying when I walked out of their front door. I had to fight to stop myself from crying, too. I was sorely tempted to go back and tell them I'd marry them all, mother, son, and daughter, with the unborn child and whatever unpaid debts they had. If I'd had the money to support them decently, I might've done it, but as it was, I left their house a lonely man. It was cold outside.

VIII Suzie: Korean Caper

South Korea in the days of Syngman Rhee was one of the few
remnants of ancient tyranny, administered capriciously, a
haven of corruption and deception, a den of thieves and
thugs, populated by a downtrodden people whose sole concern seemed to be an escape from the misery of grinding
poverty through any means, fair or foul. The major industries
of the country were graft, rice growing, and prostitution.
Sanitation, public communications, transportation, law en-
forcement, education and welfare, trade and commerce, the
liberty and safety of the individual—the most vital business
of any government—were all neglected. The prices of or-

dinary goods of consumption were enormously high, often four or five times their American equivalents, if one figured by the official rate of exchange. Even at those prices, the merchandise was often shoddy and unappealing. Rhee had clamped down an iron lid on imports from the most logical source of cheap goods in the Far East—Japan—on the general principle that the Koreans ought to have no truck with the Japanese who had tried to annex them and make Japanese out of them. As a result, imports had to be brought in from hard-currency countries a great distance away, so that the transportation alone would have made them very expensive, and few goods were allowed to be brought in at all, because Korea didn't produce enough for export to earn enough foreign money or gold. And so, the Korean people had to pay vast sums for home-made Korean merchandise, which usually wasn't very good. Most Koreans did without most of the material things that we take for granted. Many of them longed for the finer things of life, however, and they turned to the only available source: the American servicemen who were stationed in Korea and who had access to the PX system. Consequently, Korea ran largely on illegal currency, the Military Payment Certificate, which only persons serving in, or affiliated with, the armed forces of the United States were allowed to have. With these MPC's, Koreans might persuade Americans or other United Nations troops to purchase goods in the PX for them, which amounted to a personal importation from the United States.

The chief way to obtain MPC's and with them the possibility of buying on the American economy, was prostitution. Women were the only salable item in which Americans were interested and which was available in great plenty in Korea. An internal export of sex supported the Korean standard of living. Rhee's dissatisfied millions depended in the long run upon the glandular secretions of their whores for their most wanted commodities. It was the one item which Rhee made few attempts to regulate, ration, or control, although he certainly taxed it. Rhee's economic system, whether he acknowledged it or not, was largely an economy of scarcity tempered and supported by the world's most ancient, though not most honored, profession. It was immorality stark naked, so much the more so because it pretended to be the result of a staunch national pride.

The United States government on several occasions tried to put a stop to this misuse of its MPC's. There were several unannounced changeovers to new paper bills, which any one person could buy only for himself, and which one was allowed to buy only once. In this fashion, the unauthorized holders of MPC were supposed to be caught flatfooted and left holding the bag. The entire system based on the sale of love was exposed, or at least punished. Koreans of all ages, who were directly or indirectly involved in the flesh market, or who made their living preying upon those who were, were left holding the bag full of worthless paper. They stood at the gates and fences and on the streets leading to the military installations and waved their MPC's at anyone in uniform or obviously a foreigner. They were now willing to give a better rate of exchange than before. Although they always had been shrewd bargainers and unyielding hagglers, it didn't do them any good now, for no one could use their paper any longer. Previously, they refused to accept *hwan* (Korean money) from Americans and insisted on MPC, always charging twice the normal price if the American absolutely wouldn't part with his military currency. They were a bit sorry now. Yet soon they were accumulating the new kind of paper money. The

Oriental is patient and persevering, and it takes much more than one experience of failure to discourage him. The girls went back to work and hugged the foreign soldiers on the horse-hair mattresses or the *tatami* (rice-straw mats), and through their instrumentality new savings of PX money filtered through to the rest of the population, from cabinet minister to honey-bucket carrier. As was proved by Prohibition in America, it's difficult to enforce the law if everybody is involved in breaking it. After all, you can't put everybody in jail. Rhee found it easier to silence his critics than to correct the conditions which they criticized. The U. S. government co-operated with him as much as feasible for he was an ally; after all, a demand for American merchandise was a good thing rather than a bad one, and one couldn't restrict all military personnel to the bases for the duration of their stay in Korea, which usually was one year, because the men would all go stir-crazy. What they did on the outside was hard to control. There were strict regulations on the matter. But the police force doesn't look over everybody's shoulder in the United States. When the law is such that everybody must be watched all the time, the American people either disregard or change the law. That's basically what was needed in Korea. Rhee's senile obstinacy stood in the way of a sensible approach to the question of Korean international trade. That, no doubt, was one of the major reasons for his deposition when it came. We couldn't very well institute a police state among our own troops in order to help him.

Out in the provinces, life was pretty close to the soil. The Koreans lived in shacks built of flimsy wooden frames and matting, and covered with mud and a concoction that smelled like dung. Near American bases, they often "modernized" by using leftovers for building materials: pressed tin cans, orange crates, ammunition boxes, corrugated metal sheets from discarded metal quonset huts, and paperboard of all sizes. Roofs were often covered with tar stolen by the barrel from American stores. All the neighborhoods near the American installations reminded the casual observer of the Great Depression, with its shantytowns on the outskirts of the major cities. The difference was that the Koreans had never known anything else; in fact, this represented the peak of prosperity to them. They came from far and wide to live near American bases, so this must've represented luxury. Life really became tough only when there were no foreigners around to throw away old orange crates and beer cans, and when there was no tar to steal. That's when the Koreans reminded the onlooker of Siberian nomads who are their cousins in language and appearance.

Many Korean women were "in business," and those who weren't could easily be persuaded to join. Their brothers, cousins, and children came out and solicited for them. Anything to bring some rice into the family pot! By the time the little ones were adults, they were expert panderers, ready to take on the bigger responsibilities of life. They also learned a few handy skills by that time. For instance, Korean thieves deserved to be named among the world's foremost. Their tiny tots could outsteal most grownup Westerners. By the time they grew up, they were ready to contribute to their country's economy, which depended on the noble art of doing unto one's neighbor what he'd like to do unto one, only doing it first. Starting in the pimping business, they had a good course of training for their ladder of success. For just being a pimp was an art, demonstrating a keen instinct for survival and for sensing the stupidity of others. No one in Korea really needed a pimp. Anyone who wanted a woman could simply patrol the streets and look for a Korean girl wearing lipstick and Western-style clothes, walk up to her, and ask her if she'd like him to go home with her. Chances were ninety-nine in a hundred that she'd come up with the prize.

In the towns near the American bases, they relieved one of the necessity of asking them for they themselves accosted their prospective customers. In the late afternoons, the girls turned out in force and approached everything male and foreign. Their enthusiasm often led them to lash out with belts and handbags, shawls and clotheslines, or even to take a swing with their solid fists at anyone who spurned their offers of dubious bliss. In Seoul, the capital, they walked the streets by the thousands. The most attractively dressed and cultured ones used to hang out at the Chosen Hotel, which was a very swanky place, indeed, and was then inhabited almost entirely by members of the various economic missions to Korea. The ground floor and restaurant of the Chosen Hotel served as the main American officers' club in Seoul, and that's where the slender Korean beauties slinked and meandered along in the corridors in high-heeled shoes and tight Chinese dresses with long slits at the side. It was like visiting a burlesque house, for those dresses could be fairly revealing, and when a girl with a slit dress crossed her kness, you could see all the way up to her panties. Outside the entrance to the hotel, the girls who couldn't afford to dress quite so nicely or who somehow hadn't managed to gain admission stood queued up, waiting in line for a chance at the men coming out. The Chosen Hotel acquired a well-earned erotic reputation, which made people put on a knowing smile at the mere mention of the name. It became a favorite vacation spot for all our personnel in Korea who could gain access to it. Mentioning the Chosen Hotel was somewhat like mentioning Valhalla, except that you didn't have to die to go there; all you needed was enough for a couple of drinks at the bar and a five-dollar bill for the girl. At those rates, Oriental Valkyries became a popular item. One could hardly afford to do without them. Unfortunately, the revolutionary régimes have since closed this haven of refuge, thus eliminating one of the few amenities that made life bearable to foreigners in their country.

It was in front of the Chosen Hotel that I met Suzie. Naturally, that wasn't her real name, but all Korean names seemed to be the same, and with my pronunciation of Korean it was far safer to call her by her adopted Western name. All the girls working in and around the Chosen Hotel had adopted Western names for the convenience of their customers. Some of them were known only by these names even to their Korean friends and colleagues, and hardly known that well by their landlords, so that they lived in a limbo of near-anonymity which completely enshrouded their former personalities. Once having lost track of one of these girls, one couldn't possibly find her again. They came and went like bees to flower gardens, staying only long enough to collect what honey they could and vanishing into thin air when their business was done. One girl might come to the same place daily for several months and suddenly disappear, so that never again would anyone know of her whereabouts. The dirty, bumpy alleys connecting the shacks and shanties of Seoul's poor districts swallowed her up, never to release her again. Symbolically, these alleys crisscrossed and zigzagged in all directions, forming an impenetrable labyrinth in which it was quite easy to get lost. Crowded with sales booths and stands, rice wagons, dogs, cats, and scores of thousands of scrawny children, all of these passageways looked the same. Since most of us didn't know the Korean alphabet, it was hard for us even to recognize what few markets there were, and since we spoke almost as little Korean as we could read, we couldn't ask for directions except at the very large places of business where someone might speak a few words of English. That meant we were strictly on our own in those little alleys. And for a foreigner to find someone vanished into that strange, noisy, amorphous, and dirty world without the co-operation of the local merchants and beggars was practically impossible. A foreigner was lucky to get out of those parts of town without having his pockets picked. To him, all Koreans looked the same, all Korean houses looked the same, and Korea was a confusing place. He did well to find a girl named Suzie and stick to her.

Suzie took me by the hand and guided me along the large thoroughfares in what seemed three-quarters of a walk around a huge block. Then we ducked behind an awning at a butcher shop and stumbled down a dark alley, where I kept stepping into puddles and on small piles of collected garbage, though I noticed she didn't seem to have such troubles. She yanked me around an equally dark corner, down another alley by some wooden fences, and past a mangy cur, through someone's backyard, into another walk, where a small lantern revealed an unusually rutted and rocky passage. All this time, I was halting, stumbling, and almost falling, holding to Suzie's hand for dear life and supporting myself against various odd shapes that loomed in the dark and which usually turned out to be pieces of walls or buildings. My ankles hurt from being turned so often, I felt wet and dirty, and I began to get the feeling that I should've been much better off staying at home and getting a good night's sleep all by myself. But now it was too late. I didn't know where I was, couldn't possibly find my way out of the block again, and found myself fairly much at Suzie's mercy. Fortunately, we had just reached home. Suzie undid a little trick lock that permitted her to open a tiny square door, like the entrance to a pigeon coop. Having opened that one, she found the handle to the door and pulled it toward herself. The door wasn't very large either, and we had to stoop in order to crawl inside. But anyway, we were inside a building.

We stood in a tiny hall with a dirt floor, a square about four feet each way, from which wooden steps led upwards into the inhabited parts, as in every Oriental house. She groped in the dark for a naked lightbulb, which she turned on, so that she could insert the key into a wee lock on her door. She slid the door open—most Oriental doors open and close sideways by sliding on rails—and we climbed into her room, leaving our shoes on the steps. Her room was also very small, perhaps six feet by seven. Nearly half of it was taken up by the double bed with a horse-hair mattress and a blanket, without linens, and a hard horse-hair pillow. In the middle of the room, almost preventing access to the bed, stood a tiny Korean stove. The room also contained a miniature table and a chair barely large enough to place half of a European posterior upon. All this furniture completely filled the little cell, so that one could barely move, and with both of us moving we had to watch ourselves so that we shouldn't hurt each other and had to climb over each other and the furniture.

She invited me to sit on the bed and she sat on her chair. From a small drawer in the rickety little table, she took a photograph, smiled at it, and handed it to me. It was a picture of a Korean couple in the act of copulating. It was a fairly sharp photograph, which must've been taken with a flashlight at close range, almost close enough for the flash to burn the couple in some sensitive spots. The view started with their buttocks and was cleverly angled to cover the man's silhouette and the woman's ecstatic face. One could see a small part of the man's organ uniting with the enraptured woman. The effect was magnified by the fact that the camera had been close to the people's rear ends, so that their private parts were enlarged by the perspective. Suzi chuckled.

"Sleepy?" she asked me.

I shook my head, indicating that I was just waking up, but she was evidently distressed at such alertness on my part. Apparently. I should've indicated my desire to go to bed by pretending that I was sleepy. Since I hadn't professed such a desire as yet, she decided to do one better and pulled out another photograph. This one was even racier, taken from an angle above, showing the boy kneeling before the naked girl, in the act of making the voluptuous approach to her body. It was so sharply focused that one could've counted the hair on their abdomens. (Contrary to what the Japanese say about them, the Koreans do have hair in all the usual places.) All the folds in the girl's delicate skin were clearly caught by the camera. That photographer must've been a true artist.

"Sleepy?" Suzie asked me again.

"Yes, yes," I eagerly nodded.

There followed the negotiations about the money. Naturally, she wanted MPC's, but I was scared stiff that somehow it would be found out and that I'd get into trouble. We had regulations against giving MPC's to Koreans, and it would be just my luck for the girl to be interrogated and to give a blow-by-blow description of me to the authorities. I therefore insisted on giving her *hwan,* which she didn't want to accept. Seeing that I wouldn't part with any of my MCP's, however, she finally consented to take about twelve dollars worth of *hwan* instead of a five dollar bill in MPC's. Rather than give her anything with which I might be nailed by the Korean police, I would've given her twice the amount she extorted from me. The transaction was unnecessarily complicated because I also exchanged my money through the U.S. finance office rather than through the black market, which paid twice the U.S. rate. But at least I was safe. Nobody was going to put the finger on me for illegal disbursement of MPC's. I wanted neither an American court-martial nor to rot in a Korean jail. Suzie disappeared with the money into the other part of the building where her landlords lived. Presumably, she was paying her outstanding bills. Meanwhile, I was to disrobe and make myself at home on the bare mattress and the square rock that they used for a pillow. I approached both objects with a profound distrust. As I suspected, they scratched and were very uncomfortable.

When she returned, she removed the loose skirt and tight sweater which she used to cover her person on the street as well as the simple panties which were her only other item of clothing. Seeing that I was still fighting the problem of making myself comfortable on her bedstead, she decided to divert me with a little sideshow. She pulled up one leg, inserted one finger into that certain spot, and moved it around a bit to create the necessary glandular activity. Once properly stimulated, she placed a pencil, a cigarette lighter, and a ring on the table and proceeded to pick them up without the aid of her hands. She had a little trouble with the cigarette lighter which kept slipping from her hold, but she did beautifully with the pencil and ring. In fact, she waved the ring around in a circle and dropped it with a precision worthy of a nobler art upon a nail sticking out from the bed. Still without using her hands, she picked up the end of the pencil, shoved it inside of her by pushing it against the bedstead, and laughingly threatened to write upon my naked body with it. It was quite a game, and she chased me all over the bare mattress with it. I hadn't had so much fun since I caught a stallion making love to a female jackass in front of an old farmer's barn, so that the old gaffer couldn't get out and had to wait for the stallion to finish his business.

Suzie was full of little tricks. One of her best ones was with a lengthy balloon into which she poured some water. She twisted it in such a fashion as to leave a little water in one end and stretched it out, placing all the rest in the other end. The end with the small amount of water she approached as if it were a phallus. After she amused herself by wriggling and shaking it around for a while, she gradually pressed the ballon like a tube of toothpaste, feeding more and more of the water into the business end. The thing finally swelled to an impressive size, with some of it visibly tickling her where she was most sensitive. By swishing the liquid back and forth, she could produce all the local effects she craved, and she seemed to enjoy herself no end. But perhaps the ceremony was too much even for her, for she suddenly became very awkward with her toy and jerked it. The poor, elongated balloon, twisted all out of shape, naturally burst in the middle, and the water streamed out all over the cement floor. Suzie sat there, the broken balloon still partly in her hand, laughing loudly. Worse things than water, no doubt, had been spilled on her cement floor. She gathered up the pieces of the balloon and carelessly flung them aside. There was another in the drawer, which she filled with water to repeat her fertility rites. Apparently, the balloon act was an old habit of hers, and she kept a good supply of them in stock.

While we were so pleasantly occupied, there was a knock on the paper door, and without waiting for a reply, whoever had knocked slid the door aside. A woman came in with a bucket full of coal. She paid no attention whatsoever to us, lying there in our birthday costumes, and amusing ourselves with adult games. Calmly, she filled the little stove with coal. When she was finished, she addressed some words to Suzie, and Suzie apparently sent her away.

"She Ajima," Suzie explained. "She okay. Mamasan house."

As far as Ajima was concerned, it seemed, nothing unusual was going on and everything was precisely as it should be.

After Suzie was tired of displaying her carnival talents, she stroked me to put me in the right mood for the business of the evening. Her big, bony body without any breasts wasn't exactly my idea of beauty, but I finally got to the point where I thought I'd be able to give the girl some satisfaction. It was hard for me to mount her, because she decided to play a dirty trick on me and to use all of her muscular co-ordination to keep me from reaching my objective. With her legs open and all the rest of her in position, she kept herself closed more tightly than a locked safe. I thought at first that I miscalculated my anatomy and tried to find the proper locale, but she kept guiding me to that locked door. Knock as I might, that door wouldn't open. All the while, she wore a malicious smile upon her moon-shaped face. She was having a little jest at my expense. I kept shouting, "Come on, let me in, let me enter," but she only intensified that Buddha-like smile of the mysterious Orient. Finally, out of sheer exhaustion and just from the friction involved, I finished in an unwonted fashion and sank back with a sigh of frustration. She was still grinning when she noticed what had happened. The little bitch thought it was very amusing.

I would've liked to go home, but in the meantime it had got to be past midnight, and we had a curfew in Seoul. No foreigners were supposed to be out on the streets after the magic hour. The little wench knew, of course, that I was stuck with her for the night, and she probably enjoyed my predicament royally. She had a bowl of water there from which she had drunk before and got the water for the game with the balloon. Now she used it to wash herself before retiring to bed. The dirty water she dumped into the doorway.

"Excuse me, I'm hungry," she said, in almost perfect English. "You want to come along? I go Ajima room."

She slipped into her panties, skirt, and sweater, and I dressed in my trousers and white Oxford shirt. We climbed through the hallway, up the stairs to Ajima's apartment. The little lady was sitting crosslegged next to a boy of some five years of age, who was sound asleep upon the *tatami* with which her wooden floors were covered. She had a better-class Oriental place, with some low, Japanese-style furniture and plenty of room to move around. Her *tatami* were reasonably clean. The two women exchanged some words, and Ajima went into the kitchen to make some hissing sounds. After a short while, she came back with the rice pot, which she placed upon the stove, a rice bowl, and another bowl with some diced and spiced Korean meat. She ladled out the rice for Suzie and gave her a pair of lacquered chopsticks. Suzie ate with all the appetite of a starved bitch. Instead of carefully balancing the food on her chopsticks, she used the chopsticks like little shovels to pour the food into her avaricious mouth. She slopped the sauce from the meat all over herself and spilled globs of rice upon the *tatami*. I was thinking to myself that I knew how to use chopsticks better than she after my first few days in the Far East.

After she finished her second rice bowl and consumed most of her second bowl of diced meat, she put the bowls down and took out time to burp.

"You want some?" she asked, pushing the bowls over to me.

After watching her eat, I didn't feel too hungry, and I declined the honor. Besides, it smelled to me as if the meat had some *kimchi* in it. *Kimchi* consists of cabbage soaked for ages in brine and garlic and all sorts of other spices, and if you think garlic-eating Poles smell bad, you haven't begun to find out how bad smells really can be. *Kimchi* smells for blocks. It has an absolutely deadly odor, guaranteed to paralyze the olfactory nerves upon first contact. On my first day in Korea, I made the mistake of walking between two Korean women who were chatting on the sidewalk. I never made that mistake again, for I almost fainted from sickness since they'd both evidently been eating *kimchi*. Our employees handling food or waiting on us in mess halls and clubs weren't allowed to eat the stuff. Suzie had described herself as a *"kimchi* worker." Now she must've been partaking of some of the fruits of her labor. I had visions of getting sick when I climbed back in the sack with her. I surely wasn't going to eat any of that food. Even if she had the best table-manners in the world, I wouldn't have touched the stuff. And her cleanliness left something to be desired.

On the wall, there were some photographs of Ajima with a man in Japanese uniform. He had some decorations on him, and I thought he might be an officer.

"Lieutenant?" I guessed.

The two women laughed. Apparently, he wasn't that high up in the ranks. Suzie got up and gave me a great, big kiss. The odor of *kimchi* almost killed me.

"That husband in big war," Ajima explained. "Japanese soldier then."

I thought that was fairly obvious. It was the man's rank that was left to be established. He wasn't a bad-looking chap.

"Where's he now?" I asked.

"He go out, drink saki."

The conversation drifted around to other topics, and like women everywhere, the two were curious. They wanted to know whether I had a family, where I lived in the States, and what I did for a living back home. They wondered about life in the Midwest and in California. Naturally, they wondered whether there were any Koreans in those places. As far as I knew, the only Koreans I had ever seen were in Hawaii, though there were a few hanging around the Chinatowns of San Francisco, Los Angeles, New York, and Chicago, of whom I knew by hearsay. I tried to describe something of American ways for them, but the language barrier proved to be too high to hurdle. After a while, Ajima decided to put the child to bed. He had been soundly asleep on the *tatami* floor all this time, and I didn't understand why she should go to the trouble of putting him anywhere else, but I didn't want to risk exposing my ignorance by asking. She was going to retire, too, and we bade her good night. The two of us went back to Suzie's little room. Suzie was considerate enough to pour some water into the ubiquitous bowl and wash her mouth out, and Ajima appeared once more to fill the stove with coal, so that we shouldn't have to freeze. It was bitterly cold outside, and those mat-and-mud walls didn't keep out as much of it as a tent. I didn't see how the Koreans stayed out of the hospital under those conditions. If we had to live like that in America, we'd all have attacks of double pneumonia a least once a year. No doubt, a person can be habituated to the cold, as is proved by the Eskimo.

Since she'd recouped her strength and had all that new energy to dispose, I thought we might as well try again to have a little fun. When Ajima left us alone with a blazing fire in the stove, I lay down on the horse-hair mattress with her and made her take her clothes off.

"Not the other way," I tried to explain to her. "Open up! This ought to go through the night, and you should be helping me, not fighting me. I can't batter you down all night, I've got to have you with me, not against me, if we're going to have fun all night."

"Okay, all night," she grinned.

She understood. She laid her bulky frame on its back and gave her typical Oriental thighs the general outline of a nutcracker. When I came near her, she looked down and strained to welcome me. One could see that she was straining to be hospitable. The portals were swinging wide open this time, and when she knew that I had arrived, she started swinging sideways. It was a curious manner of handling a man, and this is the only way in which it can be described: She swung it sideways, somewhat like a cradle, with as little forward motion as was possible. This felt pretty good, for it excused me from lunging out at her all the time and straining my muscles. All I had to do was wiggle around a little while she assumed all the responsibility for the work. Her mouth opened in an animal gesture of delight, and her eyes turned over to their whites frequently. It was just as if she were given a kind of narcotic to upset her emotional equilibrium. She didn't make the untoward noises that Western women often make. She was probably trained not to do so for fear of waking the landlords and all their neighbors who would certainly hear any unusual noises within a block or so in those flimsy huts. She just kept rocking and swinging away, and I kept fiddling and diddling, and it was a case of who could keep up the swinging motion longest. After a while, the body accustomed itself to the motion, and it became rhythmical like a hypnotic African dance to the accompaniment of the tom-tom.

We were disturbed first by some loud shouting, clinking, and cracking that seemed to be nearby. I got worried that there might be violence and that it might involve me. Suzie carefully disentangled herself from me, pulled on her clothes, and went out to see what had happened. Since she didn't come back for a while, I put my shirt and trousers on and went out to join her. We stood in the vestibule behind the chicken-coop door and watched some Negro troops rolling empty beer bottles into the pot-holes on the dark alley and throwing whiskey flasks at a mangy cur that barked at them. The windows of the two-story house across the street were open, with the heads of more Negro troops and Korean girls popping out and disappearing again. There was little doubt in my mind about what sort of establishment the building across the alley might be. Two of the dusky soldiers stood near the door and sang hoarsely, clinking their bottles now and then to accentuate the rhythm. Most of the girls stayed inside, but two of them were out in the alley, collecting the beer bottles which two drunken men had rolled into the darkness. In Korea, everything is valuable; there might be as much as two cents paid for each empty bottle if one knew the right junk dealer. A profit like that couldn't be overlooked! It was downright irresponsible of the happy drunks to take chances on breaking these bottles! The girls and the men inside tried to persuade the drunkards outside that they had better come in, reminding them of the curfew and of the trouble they might have if they were caught by the MP's. To make matters worse, one of the black troops came out into the alley fighting with a Korean wench. They were hitting each other with their fists, slapping each other, and tearing each other's clothing. The other girls and troops joined in the fray, shouting, screaming, pulling hair, throwing punches, kicking, and biting for good measure. In the darkness illuminated only by the faint light emanating from the windows across the alley, it was a ghastly scene. Someone must've called the cops, for suddenly Korean policemen came running down the alley in their black uniforms when the riot had been going on for about ten minutes. One of the soldiers was badly cut up. A general shouting and denouncing scene ensued, with everybody pointing an accusing finger at everyone else. American Military Police came rushing in a jeep that barely squeezed through in the alley, with two more MP's closing the exits on the other side so that no one should get away. The Korean and American policemen jointly invaded the brothel and returned with more colored men, who were protesting loudly that they hadn't been involved in the fighting and wanted to be permitted to stay. Mercilessly, the American sergeant issued a command, and he and the Koreans departed in a jeep while the remaining American MP's walked the reluctant celebrants away toward the Army compound. Theirs would be the job of explaining in the morning what they had been doing out on the town after curfew, what had happened to start the fight, and why they had to arouse the hostility of our Korean friends and allies. The

girls stood out in the alley, shouting after them, and after
the men were gone they argued among themselves for a while
until finally they became tired and went inside. Everything
went back to normal, dark, inscrutable, smelly conditions,
with nothing but the cur left on the street to sniff for booty.

Hardly had I recovered my satyromaniacal enthusiasm for
the person of my girl Suzie on that horse-hair mattress when
we heard loud Korean shouts, ending in "Ajima!" and a
tremor shook the entire flimsy building. Someone was club-
bing the house with a heavy object in a drunken effort to
arouse Ajima's attention. From the lengthy scene that followed, I gathered that it was the "lieutenant." By this time,
it was about four in the morning, and I was angry at all the
disturbances in my lovemaking as well as tired to the point
of irritability. I could've gone out and lynched the bastard
all by myself, had it not been for Suzie who calmed me down
by continuing that swaying, rocking movement with her
muscular, *kimchi*-working hips. While I loudly cursed the
man and told him to shut his trap, she kept closing in on me
and shushing me to keep me occupied. Obviously, I wasn't
going out there to beat the drunken "lieutenant" to a pulp
as I wanted, as long as she rocked me into a state of erotic
bliss. And she did exactly that, gave it a good workout, and
played the scale of her muscles like an expertly performed
physical sonata. In the meantime, the drunken and desperate
man, afraid that Ajima would leave him out there to freeze,
had picked up something very heavy like a rock and began to
pound the walls with it. Those matting-and-mud walls
weren't constructed to withstand much of this battering
assault, and so the building shook in its foundations and loud
cracks and rents could be heard. The bastard hit on our wall

twice, and in the process he knocked off so much of the dried mud that there was a bare spot showing and the cold wind whistled through unimpeded. Along a wide crack, an entire wall threatened to collapse. "Ajima!" the "lieutenant" shouted, and there followed some words which I couldn't understand, but which I'd hesitate very much to repeat to a well-bred Korean lady.

From Suzie's garbled explanations, I gathered that the "lieutenant" did very little but drink most of his days, and Ajima had to provide for the family, which she did in part by renting out rooms to Suzie and another girl. Instead of working, the man took what money he could from his wife and drank it up with his boon companions. Naturally, Ajima didn't take to this treatment very well, and when he came home too late, she locked him out. But she always relented and let him in again. I hoped to God, Wotan, Baal, and Manitou that Ajima would weaken this night too, so that the "lieutenant" might not knock down the house around our ears and force me to walk home during the hours of curfew. That would've entailed using the streets, and thus having an argument with the MP's regarding violation of military orders, or perhaps having dealings with one of the rapacious Korean taxi drivers who attempt to extort the most outrageous sums from helpless Caucasians, especially after midnight when they know they're at their mercy. I was hoping against the odds that the shaky mud walls would take the beating without crumbling. In fact, I gave serious consideration to the idea of going to the house of ill fame if the man kept up the noise, just in case the police should reappear. I couldn't afford a scandal involving the Korean police, either. Because of the curfew, I was absolutely trapped. Probably, there wasn't another spot in all of Seoul where I ran so much of a risk of involvement in unpleasant incidents. Somehow, I picked it. Just my luck!

For safety's sake, I submitted to the ultimate sacrifice and told Suzie to go out there and sow peace between the warring couple. Once more, we had to separate at a stage where it was most frustrating, and she climbed bravely out of bed and put on her panties to talk to Ajima. It seems she didn't talk to her without her panties on, even though Ajima saw her give the works to her admirers in bed. The pigeon coop door was opened for negotiations, and a crestfallen "lieutenant" sniveled some abject words in a hoarse voice, before Ajima's kind heart consented to his admission. Suzie came back to bed, but by this time we were both so tired that there could be no thought of a resumption of activities. She unscrewed the uncovered lightbulb with the words, "I love you for breakfast tomorrow," and we wished each other a good night. So far, I had seen a lot of Korean life but hadn't yet achieved the sexual satisfaction for which I had come.

Suzie was just as good as her word. Naturally, I didn't sleep a wink on that uncomfortable bed. All I was capable of doing was to listen to her suggestion of a snore and cuddle up to her under the blanket so that the cold wind which came sweeping through the punctured wall shouldn't reach me. The first hour seemed like an eternity, but after that, I sank into a kind of torpor which made the long wait bearable, and I felt a little disturbed when Ajima knocked on the door at seven-thirty and produced a steaming pot of tea and two rice bowls. This time, I wasn't reluctant to accept her hospitality and thanked her profusely. When Suzie had eaten a few nips from her rice-laden chopsticks, she bent down and took an active interest in the part of me which I let no one but my girl friends see. Since I made no protest, she kept up this game between mouthfuls of rice. It was fairly stimulating. Finally, after she finished her rice and devoted herself to her task more attentively, she succeeded in extracting what she wanted. It had taken me a long night to be satisfied, but I finally made it. It was my first night on the town and the last time I went looking for a girl in Korea.

IX Hisako-San: The Glutton

Tokyo hostesses vary in price and quality from the big name clubs, where you pay a hostess-charge of a thousand yen per hour or four thousand yen for the evening, merely for the girl's presence and above and beyond the drinks, down to the small honkytonks, where they wish the girl on you without charge and you can buy her a drink for as little as three hundred yen. (One dollar, in my day, was equal to three hundred and sixty yen.)

Ordinarily, though not always, the looks, social graces, and linguistic ability of the girls vary with the price. In Tokyo, like everywhere else, you get what you pay for. The thousand-yen-an-hour hostess would be a social asset at a cocktail party in New York's swankier hotels or at a ball given by Parisian industrial magnates. The three-hundred-yen-a-drink hostess isn't the type you'd take home to meet mother or that you'd take dancing at the Ritz. This doesn't necessarily mean that the expensive one is always preferable to the cheap one. Many a hostess from a large club turns out to be a conceited bitch who thinks she owns the city and who specializes in the noble art of separating the sucker from his hard-earned cash, whereas many a small club girl is a good-natured kid who'd give her right arm to help out a chap in need. When I speak of quality in connection with hostesses, I'm referring more to good breeding and biological desirability. And there were some real beauties among the high-class hostesses. In fact, there were very few who weren't exciting.

The institution of the hostess is typically Japanese and probably goes back to the geisha. But the geisha still exists today and is something else again. Geishas in the old days were the experts at conversation, games, and dances, whose company was among the most expensive luxuries that the Japanese could buy, even though these pleasures weren't followed by the slightest sexual liberties. As for physical pleasures, Tokyo had the largest red-light district on earth until its abolition by the Japanese Parliament on April 1, 1958. There still are some geisha houses where one may easily drop a few hundred dollars a night, enjoying the society of the high skilled and trained Geisha who rank among the most respected and worshiped people of Japan. But the nightclubs worthy of that Western name all have bar-girls called "hostesses" by the ingenuous Japanese who find a euphemism for everything and somehow manage to put the Occidental at a disadvantage before every negotiation. "Hostess," to me, had always implied that I was a non-paying guest in the Western world; but in Japan, I was taught better. There, the presence of a "hostess" made me so much the more of a paying guest, and a guest who entertained his hostess at a great deal of expense. On the other hand, a good hostess is an excellent dancer, admires and fawns over her guest, laughs at his jokes, tells him how wonderful he is, and manages to keep a lively conversation going all the time. Furthermore, if she happens to like him and he propositions her with any skill, she'll declare herself available for his private amusement after closing time—for a slight consideration of five or ten thousand yen, of course. And if he doesn't want to wait until the club closes at four o'clock and all the girls are paid for the day's drinking, there is the possibility of buying her way out of the place—for another little consideration of three to five thousand yen, of course. Managers and overseers always appear stern and uncompromising on this problem. They make it seem a personal favor to allow the customer to buy the girl's freedom for the night by paying for the drinks she doesn't consume, because they don't want to let their places become depopulated. The truth is, however, that it's pretty good business for them, since they're selling the drinks that they don't have to pour and therefore can sell over again. Sometimes, if one consistently buys the time of a girl in a club, the Papa-San may even forget himself and look happy, thinking of the nice profits he's getting for nothing, by just playing Cupid. But it doesn't happen often. Oriental shrewdness demands that they're doing you a big favor when they're actually doing something to promote their own interests. In that way, they think, you'll appreciate them more.

The thousands of Tokyo hostesses keep not only the nightclubs busy but also provide the mainstay for hundreds of downtown stores and restaurants which cater mostly to them and to their customers. There are the beauty parlors and ladies' fashions stores which locate themselves close to the entertainment districts in the Ginza, Asakasa, Shinjuku, and Shibuya for the express purpose of preparing the damsels for their missions of attracting men with expense accounts or holiday savings. There are the tiny little eating places near the clubs where the girls will go when they're paying for their own meals, and there are the plush, expensive joints where they will steer their customers if they're asked out for dinner. There are the jewelry shops that provide them with little trinkets to attract attention and sell expensive rings, bracelets, and clips to the boys who want to make a big impression. There are the drug stores specializing in medicines to stimulate desire and capacity for sexual intercourse, to prevent pregnancy, to keep the skin young, to gain or lose weight, to aid digestion, to counteract the effects of alcohol, etc. Finally, there are the hotels, large and small, of all kinds and gradations of comfort, hidden and advertised, downtown and farther out, new and old, but all of them discreet, where one may disappear for hours, days, or even weeks, sending out for all things necessary to sustain existence and refusing to communicate with the outside world on the other side of the garden and the great wall. Without the hostesses of Tokyo, they'd all be down to their last rice bowl. For the Japanese are one of the most diligent and constructive peoples on earth, but they're still poor. Luxuries are the privilege of a very select few, of foreign tourists and American military people, and of girls who can charge five or ten thousand yen per evening, which is about as much as a poor little teenager may receive for working as a salesclerk for a week or even a month. Hostesses easily make twenty times as much money as their less sophisticated age-mates and represent one of the most important "industries" of the world's largest city. Not only that, but, statistically speaking, one could probably make a case for the opinion that the hostesses are responsible for the gigantic success of the tourist business in Tokyo and constitute a major attraction of the great city for both Japanese and foreigner. Without them, Tokyo would not now be the largest city in the world.

The club was one of Tokyo's finest. Uniformed personnel and people who weren't well dressed hardly ever managed to gain entrance to it. You walked upstairs above the shops on the street-level, left your overcoat at the wardrobe, were looked over by a number of Japanese of uncertain functions and welcomed by a head-waiter whose business probably was to steer you away from the bar and to one of the little tables, where chances were that you'd leave more money and order a hostess with your drinks. The hostesses sat on the other side from the bar in several rows of seats, one lovelier than the other, dressed as if they were going to a wedding, well-groomed, young, sleek, elegant, and radiant. They had to look appealing in order to get invitations, and they knew their business. Their looks were their most time-consuming concern both when they were and when they weren't at work, and they were experts. Some of them had been in their profession for years.

Most Japanese dance bands sound like a mob of teen-agers practicing for a high school jam session, but at this club they were pretty good. Microphones were located all over the club to carry the sound from the bandstand in one corner of the gigantic room to every niche and cranny. It made them sound as if they were two-hundred strong, though there were only about ten of them. In Japan, all night clubs catering to Americans have enormously loud music, almost loud enough to blast a person out of his chair. The Japanese will tell you that they're doing this because Americans are used to it from home, though I've been all-over the United States and I've never found a nightclub with music as loud as it is in Japan. The likely explanation is that these loud noises make it impossible to talk and thus help the foreigners bridge the language gap. When you can't speak, all you can do with a girl is dance and smooch, and there's always plenty of both going on. In this club, too, there was some fast and furious dancing, and some good, old-fashioned necking. The slender hostesses in their slit-up Chinese dresses turned and twisted their posteriors and swung their legs to the time of the music, so that the tight skirts slipped up and one could catch a good glimpse of the naked thigh above the stocking. Others wore wide, ballerina-type dresses and twirled so fast that one could tell what color of panties they were wearing. Some of their panties were skimpy and scanty things, and in the red illumination of the club it was easy to believe that in a moment of terpsichorean frenzy one could make out something dark above their thighs, surrounded by flesh made luminous by the lighting. One never went wrong by bribing the band to play good, fast dance music, for that's when the fun started. The younger men, Japanese and foreign alike, exhibited some of their best contortions and rhythmic snake-dances, while the Japanese girls were a smiling mass of legs whirling in various states of nudity, of slim posteriors wiggling insinuatingly in time with the fellows' movements, and tiny breasts shaking below the low-cut gowns. One didn't need to be told that all of that was flesh on the hoof, eager, ready, hot, and willing to be sold at prime beef rates.

Hisako-San was one of the hostesses sitting and waiting for an invitation when I passed by to go to the little boys' room. There was something outstanding about her. Most Japanese girls are flat-chested, but she had a pair of tremendous breasts, even though she was a short girl and otherwise had a slender figure. This circumstance sufficed to endear her to me. On the way back to my table I picked her up and took her along.

Like all Japanese girls, Hisako-San was very conscious of the mammary situation, and since she was so well endowed along those lines she discussed it with me at great length. Naturally, she wore nothing but low-cut cocktail dresses in order to enhance her sales appeal. Several of the other girls, she informed me, had an operation performed, in which some of the fat was removed from their hips and grafted to their breasts in order to make them protrude more. It was a poor substitute, however, for the artificial breasts never had the shape or elasticity of natural ones, since the body doesn't so easily absorb artificial parts in that region. In many cases, the cells of the fat tissue just weren't provided with nutriment by the usual processes at all, and the poor, ambitious females had to return to their surgeons every couple of years to have the old rinds of bacon taken out and new ones put in. It was a painful operation, but the Western clientele demanded solid and substantial breasts, and a good hostess will do anything to please a customer. Many of them also had their eyes operated upon to remove the Mongoloid fold from the upper lids. This was a comparatively easy and inexpensive operation of permanent effect. The woman in question then had a pair of round, helpless, little eyes between her high, Asiatic cheekbones and her little nose, which gave her a curious hybrid effect and a lifelong expression of surprise. "Japanese girl-san try very hard, be just like American girl-san, make American boy-san feel like home. Good josan make lots of money, maybe marry and go to Stateside." But Hisako-San didn't think it was necessary in her case. "I got plenty of bosom now, no?" she asked, stretching amiably and blowing some cigarette smoke in between her bulbous pride. "Maybe I have eyes fixed, but I do okay without operation."

"Don't have yourself changed at all," I advised. "You're pretty just as you are now. If you try to look like a Western girl, you'll be neither one nor the other. As a Japanese girl, you're a beauty. If you're a Japanese girl, be a Japanese girl. Always be yourself and make the best of what you have."

"You talk like my mother," she replied.

"I've got four days of vacation left. Would you like to spend them with me?"

"I'd love to," she answered. "But before we go, I got to tell you something maybe make you mad. I got to ask money."

"How much?"

"All josan this club have agreement, always ask ten thousand first night."

I pretended to be taken by surprise. It was about twenty-seven dollars, and that was about tops for prime beef on the hoof around Tokyo. In the midst of the whirling, swirling gayety on the dancefloor, with the girls carrying on sophisticated conversation, and obsequious waiters smiling and bowing to them like little princesses, one sometimes forgot the harsh realities of the moment. Actually, the elegant clubs with all their luxurious furnishings were places where assignations were contracted for at stipulated prices. I was never given to any illusions about the matter; I was more taken aback by the unabashed manner in which the little slut asked for such sums of money than by the fact of her asking.

"For this, you'll stay two days," I said firmly.

"Okay," she grinned, "if you keep me satisfied two days."

"Let's go," I said.

"I have to stay till four o'clock, unless you want to give money."

With my three thousand yen safely in the hands of the manager for permission to leave early, and another five thousand in the pocket of the waiter for the few drinks we had, we finally managed to get out of the club without paying any more, albeit we had to pay off the woman who cleans the ladies' restroom and the boy who runs errands for busy josans. Hisako-San owed money to them all, she said. Having run the gauntlet of the avaricious servants, we finally escaped from the building and caught a taxi. Here, I was in my own element and directed the driver along the shortest route to the hotel, much to her chagrin and to the welfare of my pocketbook. The very elegant manager of the hotel bowed and smiled noncommittally when he saw the reason for my late return home, which would net him another five-hundred yen guest-charge. A soft-spoken bellboy brought us some ice to use in my whiskey and asked if he could do anything else for us. After that, we were left alone at last.

She was completely at home in the situation and felt happy as a child at a Christmas party. The drinks tasted pretty good, and then she was all for taking a bath. No real Japanese girl of good family will ever go to bed with a man unless she's properly bathed and, if possible, has scrubbed the man thoroughly from head to toe, in order to make sure that he's clean, too. Since she was evidently well-reared and bred, I left her

strictly alone in the bath at first, but she was astonished at
such an antisocial attitude on my part and asked if I wouldn't
like to scrub her back and have her reciprocate the compliment. Whether I liked it or not, there was no getting around
the fact that she wanted to go bathing together before she
indulged in any more intimate activities. Not being especially
bashful around women, I hung up my clothes and climbed
in the tub with her, where she splashed my head full of soapy
water and played around like in a swimming pool. At last, I
got my scrubbing. It was a thorough job and felt more like a
massage. When she finished it, I was absolutely sure that I was
clean. Nothing could be hidden in any of my pores. Casually,
she touched a couple of forbidden spots and watched for the
results with the expectancy of a baker watching for his yeast
dough to rise.

Hisako-San was a mixture of all the racial influences which
helped to shape the Japanese people into one of the most
heterogenous groups that pass for a single nation. She knew
that her mother was partly of Aino descent and traced to these
strange, nearly white people the amazing blessing of her large
mammaries, which are so often encountered among the Ainos
but practically never among the purely Mongoloid Japanese.
In addition, she had a very light complexion, even considering the fact that many Japanese aren't at all dark-yellow like
the Chinese but tend rather to look lighter than most Euro-
peans. There's also a strong Polynesian influence noticeable
among the southern Japanese, which gives them an especially
happy combination of grace and elegance. From that lineage,
she inherited a very heavy growth of heavy-structured black
hair and a suppleness of movement which made one dream of
the temple-dancers of Bali, as well as that peculiarly strong
passion which made her yearn for the pleasures of the body

with an intensity altogether atypical of a Japanese girl. Her facial structure was round and rather characteristic of Japan, but the proportions of her body—because of the Polynesian or the Aino influence—were more like those of a white girl than the long-waisted, short-thighed women one finds in the Japanese countryside. Hisako-San, properly dressed and with a little make-up, wouldn't have looked out of place at a European party or an American town-meeting.

Japan has short-time girls, girls for the evening, and girls for long stays. The short-time girl, like her colleagues of the Place Pigalle in Paris, the Soho district of London, or of the Bahnhof area in Frankfort, goes up to the room with her man, turns a quick trick—the quicker the better—and hurries back to the street to peddle her favor to the next comer. The girl for the evening charges a bit more money, but she stays with her customer for an hour or two, until his passions are abated and he's satisfied for the night. She may go out to look for seconds or not, depending upon what time it is and how good he was. The long-time girl will remain to have breakfast with her customer in the morning, maybe enjoy a quickie after the breakfast eggs, and, if he so desires, stay for the week end or even longer, leaving only for short visits with her numerous girlfriends, members of the family, her barber, her manicurist, her cosmetics adviser, her tailor, her seamstress, and any other members of that ubiquitous staff that derives its livelihood from her need for salable beauty. She's the closest thing a bachelor can have to a wife, and she has the added attraction that she'll go home when the first thrill has worn off, so that he need have no domestic quarrels.

Hisako-San was, by nature and inclination, a long-time girl. She didn't hurry through her drinks, her food, her dressing operations, or her sex. She was a girl who not only liked to take her time but who couldn't get enough of the rites of Eros, no matter how protracted. And what she was really looking for was a boyfriend whose desires ran along the same lines and who would share his bed with her for all those wonderful, long hours of delight which she was capable of providing. In other words, Hisako-San and I had been looking for each other a long time when we found each other. It was like Plato's unreconciled half-personalities suddenly meeting for one lengthy, orgiastic, quivering, flesh-and-saps union. We were twin souls of the boudoir, playmates of the reproductive process, siblings of coital yearnings, fellow-addicts of the same narcotic, colleagues in blissful oblivion, co-workers engaged in producing a common climax of nervous exhilaration, joy-filled lips joined in forming the identical happy sound.

"I'm a nightclub-girl, I can't love with my heart," she used to say, "but I love you as much as I can. I love you with all my sex. That's the best thing I've got to give, it's the part of me that loves best, because I can't afford to give my heart. I love you with all my sex." And she gave that delicious part of her a little wiggle that made me wish for even greater potency.

She had a wonderfully shaped posterior. I used to study it assiduously. Not too large and not too small, but just right for the soft pad to sit on and to rest on when she curved the torso upwards toward me, just sufficient to absorb the shock of bearing down on her, when she curled herself in such a way as to complete our union perfectly and when she performed a kind of pillow-mambo that increased her thrills. She had nice, round, upholstered cheeks, not wobbly like those of girls who've been copulating in every crib they could find, but firm and fleshy, with a layer of fat beneath the skin to stop them from acquiring a masculine appearance. This delicious rounding of the flesh went gently around her person and didn't stop abruptly at the pelvis, as do the posteriors of so many girls who've been plying the trade. It gently wound itself, like the petal of a tulip, to the front, gently as an egg, and even when she spread her legs and lay flat upon her back, there was but the faintest suggestion of bones sticking out of her soft, feminine mass. Nor did it suddenly end like the broad top of a table to rest upon her thighs, but it gradually tapered off into the thighs on both sides with swinging, undulating lines, giving way to legs so exquisitely chiseled out of light jade that one feared somewhat to touch them, lest one put a blue mark on that delicate shade of yellowish-pink. In the back, the cheeks could be seen in geometrical curvature, revealing a bare minimum of anus, and sloping off in the middle toward the sensitive, darker folds surrounded by sparse hair. It was black hair, tinged slightly with the brownish sheen of the Ainos, and began at the exact halfway point between those thighs. It grew with some abundance all around her private parts and halfway up the Mons Veneris, only to lose identity as it straggled upward and to disappear at the line of the belly. She was as well-proportioned as a Hakata doll.

Above the posterior, she sloped into an exceedingly narrow waist. It was almost a skinny waist, because it clearly formed an arc toward the spine along the entire back half of her person, revealing the top of her pelvic bone ever so slightly to balance the side of the pelvis which barely became visible on the side when she lay down. Because of her round, rather bulky posterior, the effect of the narrow waist was surprising and strangely enticing. Her skin—like that of all Japanese women—appeared to turn a deeper shade of yellow on the waist. Along the front portion of her torso, the waist accentuated the absolute straightness of the line from her navel to the Mons Venus. The navel, like that of girls all over the earth who don't get much exercise, already sat in the midst of a flabby region that rippled to the touch of an eager hand and receded at the slightest pressure like the surface of a pudding. On her belly, the yellow effect of the waist left off, and she was almost white, so that one might've thought it a white woman's belly, had it not been for the solid, kinky substance of her pubic hair, which characterizes the Oriental and Malayan races. When she spread her thighs apart, her stomach was as flat as a board, while still providing the soft cushioning of a wad of cotton.

Above the waist, she proudly carried her pride and joy, the swollen tokens of mature femininity which the male mammal likes to touch, fondle, and kiss. For a Japanese girl, she really did have large breasts, akin somewhat to those of a well-fed Italian or Spanish woman in shape, round, standing forth like halves of grapefruit when she stood up, though tipped by spigots the size of blueberries, embedded in round, red lamellas larger than half-dollars. So large were those bulbs of hers that I couldn't close my hands around them. They spread into pointed cushions on her chest when she leaned back and prepared herself to receive me. Her nipples were in the habit of standing up erect for long periods at a time, waiting to receive the eager lips of the male. She didn't often let me touch my mouth to those dark-red nipples, because someone had convinced her that the male kiss of desire would distend and extend them and flatten the breasts, and she wanted to retain those lovely roundings as advertisements for the pleasures of her body. She took a childish delight in stroking them, massaging them, pressing them from the side, and giving them rubdowns with soap and water, always conscious of the fact that they probably had made it possible for her to collect many a ten-thousand-yen fee that otherwise would've gone to josans with the operational fat rinds in their bosoms. She regarded them in much the same light as a pianist views his hands, an actress her face, and a hunter his eyes: they were her bread and butter. More than that, they were the object of an almost Narcissistic worship on her part. She loved to look at her breasts almost as much as I did. The two of us sometimes were in competition for them when we sat in the bathtub or stood in front of the mirror together. They were toys which made her popular with the other children, but she was most reluctant to let anyone else play with them, because she wanted them for herself.

Her face reflected her personality better than I've ever seen an Oriental face indicate what was behind it. Perhaps this fact may be explained by her partly Aino extraction, or perhaps it was due to an extreme self-willedness that was so strong that she spurned the Oriental habit of speaking only with a view toward a calculated effect and adopting a smiling exterior to hide one's true emotions. It was an unusual face in a sea of similar Japanese faces which, to the foreigner, tended to look alike. A face which was at one and the same time shrewd and childish, lewd and deliberate, cruel and sensitive, proud and inviting, aesthetic and materialistic, barbarous and cultivated, radiant and yet controlled. It was unmistakably Japanese, but it still showed enough of the alien influence to attract the attention of the male passer-by. It was not what one would call an uncommon face, and still it hit the beholder like a stroke of lightning. And it was variable: She could make herself look enticing or forbidding, distant or attentive, cheerful or bored, at will. When she didn't control herself and let herself gesture naturally, she often looked like a little girl asking for favors, and yet she caught herself every time and sparkled sophistication and a kind of superiority to compensate for the loss of composure that had given her a weak spot. During the love act she could relax her facial muscles and let herself be a simple young woman who could never get enough sex to satisfy her longing. When the climax occurred, she could open her lips to utter shouts of joy and roll her eyes, as if she couldn't stand another moment of it while her arms and legs pressed me to her and ensured that I'd continue through the night. Her eyebrows could adopt an angle to her half-closed eyes that made her look doubly Oriental and schemingly inviting, as if she had to go on the offensive to obtain what she wanted, although I was constantly having another go at her and hardly gave myself the time to recover from the exertion. Her narrow nostrils quivered and opened sideways like those of a nervous horse, her cheeks lengthened as she drew her jaws apart, and her mouth sought out mine with a ravenous appetite that could be accounted for only by her relatively young years. There wasn't a wrinkle in her face, yet she could look old beyond her calendar age when she was disappointed or angry. Above all, however, she had the faculty of looking ecstatic, rapturous, thrilled beyond the point of communication. She used her face like a language, and the words which she communicated with it composed paragraphs of sexual intoxication, whether it was in the anticipation, during the act, or in the remembrance of past events. She didn't just talk and act sex, she looked it, in a transitive meaning of the word which is suggestive of telepathy in the sensations.

Being alone with Hisako-San was synonymous with stripping and jumping into the sack as quickly as one could. There was no such thing as being dressed in her presence except when it was time to eat and the waiters had to bring us our food. Even then, we sometimes hid in the bed while the table was being set for us. The waiters, who were all very young, grinned and stuttered, handing me the bill and a pencil with which to sign it where I lay in bed, and withdrew smilingly after they had my John Henry on the paper. We'd dash out of bed like two happy children, sit at the low table naked as nature had equipped us, and gulp our food.

"This is very good dessert," she'd say, when we got around to the honey-fried apples, the pineapple syrup, the Lychee nuts, or some other Chinese delicacy, "but I want a second dessert. What about you?"

"Me, too. And I know just what I'd like."

And I'd kneel before her and warm her up for the next act by kissing her thighs and fingering her breasts, suckling on her breasts and stroking her spinal cord, or kissing her on the mouth and trying to ascertain whether the food had restored her energies. Hisako-San was a girl of practically unlimited sexual potency and could always be depended upon to recover from the exertions of a busy afternoon between the courses of a good Chinese dinner. Without more encouragement than another drink, she'd be ready for more of the previous treatment. She'd repeat that suggestive line about "I love you with all my sex," and snuggle up to me like a cat in heat, letting the sparkle play in her brown topaz eyes and parting her lips ever so slightly to simulate the ecstasy of another orgasm. Her body meant to her the alpha and omega of pleasure, the source of her success in life, an inexhaustible fountain of joy, a perpetuum mobile of carnal thrills, an indestructible toy which renewed itself with the mere supply of fuel to be available again for limitless rites celebrating the beauties of erotic contact. She viewed with pleasure in her

face every attempt to intensify the magnitude of her sensations, and her only wish was to remember what it was that
had enabled her to feel even more than she had known before. She was aware of her attractions for the opposite gender
in a lively manner and used everything with masterly skill in
order to evoke even more of an effective love-play from her
partner.

"American boy-san always like me," she confided in me.
"Usually I'm not very lucky, because the old men who have
the money don't appeal to me. Young boy-san who appeal to
me don't have money. So, I have a good customer, I go out
after the club, maybe to another cabaret, maybe to a late-hour
restaurant, maybe to a party, but I always go home alone, and
he give me money to come back. I never go back. If young
boy-san come, I want to go right away, but he no have the
money, so I can't go. We sit and I have just a few drinks and
dance, and pretty soon he have to go home, because no money.
If young boy-san come and have the money, I'm lucky. Then
I see if he really want me, and if he really make my heart
beat, I always go."

"But without the money, you might have a better time if
you're with someone that you'd really like?" I objected.

"No money, I no go," she protested violently. "If nightclub
hostess go with customer, he must have money. Otherwise she
stay poor all her life."

"In other words, I must always give you money if I want
you?" I asked.

"Always. That's how I know you love me. If you give me
much money, I know you really care for me. Nightclub girl
must always have much money."

"Suppose I don't have any money?"

"Oh, I'm very lucky with you, you nice boy-san and always

have money," she smiled. "That's why I love you with all my sex," she wiggled her shapely posterior.

Obviously, there wasn't much to do under the circumstances except to grab her in her full bosom, kiss her tongue, snuggle up to her abdomen, and let nature take its course. She was absolutely and irrevocably convinced that money was the exponent of true love, and I'd never be able to convert her to a more civilized concept in the short time that I was likely to spend in the Tokyo area. All she knew was what the other girls had told her. Her mother had tried to rear her as a conventional girl, but she thought her mother was "old hat," as so many young people do all over the earth. Japanese social problems were roughly the same as those of the West. The older generation still clung to the ideals of hard work, honest effort, unswerving loyalty, dedicated relationships, and faithful partnership capped by the marriage vows, whereas the younger people often were attracted by the lure of the bright light, the enjoyment of promiscuous affairs, the excitement of permanent courtships and the accompaniment of jazzed-up music, the intoxication of a gay nightlife, the whirl of the most daring modern dances, and the tingling sound of free and easy money. The youth of Japan rejected wholeheartedly the austere and diligent life of their dignified forebears. Hisako-san's father had been high up in the circles of the war party in pre-war Japan. Her mother still cherished his memory with all the ardor of a lonely widow and surrounded herself with the trappings of her former days of glory. But Hisako-san's own life was the life of New York, Boston, and Philadelphia much more than the life of the shinto temple, the cherrytree branch, or the lacquer cabinet. She looked good in a kimono and was proud of it, but she didn't own very many of those old-fashioned and cumbersome garments and had two closets filled to the point of congestion with Western clothes. She knew how to perform the ceremony of pouring the tea and knelt beautifully behind the sliding doors, but she did such things only in derision and felt truly at ease only when she was wearing a skirt and sweater and turning on the dance floor, or when she was dressed in her cocktail outfit, sat in a modern American chair, and guzzled her gin fizz. Her face was Japanese, but her smile was Occidental. She was a symbol of the Japan that grew out of the defeat of 1945.

Even her lovemaking was Westernized. The average small-town Japanese female has a holy horror of copulating in any fashion except the straightforward approach, which in the South Sea Islands is well-known as the "missionary position." It's the obvious and easiest way to most people—except the Polynesians—and it joins face to face, breast to breast, waist to waist, lock and key, so that it involves the least amount of imagination. One could tell a Japanese girl who had never slept with foreigners by the fact that she'd refuse absolutely and with abhorrence in her voice any suggestion of using the more animalistic and less dangerous technique that has become known as the French method. "No Frenchy-Frenchy!" they always shouted, repelled by the very idea of such an imposition upon their chaste habits. But Hisako-San liked the French method best of all. "Delicious!" she always grinned. In her indulgence in this technique, she was as insatiable as in the other positions we tried, only more so. Fully engaged in providing a maximum of voluptuous delight to the man, she only demanded to be given the same treatment, and there wasn't the slightest chance of one's disengaging oneself from this situation for several hours. She writhed and convulsed with an almost painful pleasure for hour after hour, and she strained herself to the fullest of her ability to stimulate the container which, according to what she said, is the fountain of a woman's sole source of true joy.

Rodin must've had a girlfriend like Hisako-San, because there are several watercolors in which he treats the entire female head and torso as a kind of barely sketched ante-chambers to the abdomen and thighs. He portrays the thighs as gigantic, forceful columns, glaring in fleshy nakedness at the eyes of the observer, as if they meant to surround him with the soft prison of feminine love. His statuary shows him to have been a ladies' man, but his watercolors truly show him for the voluptuary that he undoubtedly was. It was in that image that I always thought of Hisako-San: Her cruelly beautiful face, her pomegranate breasts, her tight waist, her white belly were the parlor, while her thighs contained the living room of her person, and the shrine on her house's altar was forever burning with desire for the rites of love. The eye accustomed itself to the proportions of her legs as to familiar surroundings, considering the slanting line of her Mons Veneris as the proper background, and accepted the pinkish yellow of her skin as the typical color for night and day. The intimate bulge of her hips was the frame of the picture, the horizon which bounded the perspective of daily awareness with geometrical perfection. She was shaped so well that I understood for the first time why beautiful properties are the properties of functionality. She had me admire her functional qualities and put them to good use from the time I looked at her smiling eyes at breakfast till the time she began to look a little tired in the afternoon, and from the time I saw her smile at me encouragingly with the dessert until we got up for eating supper in style. As soon as she returned from her club in the wee hours of the morning, she wanted more of our reciprocal caresses, and I stayed with her until I heard her gasping for air and I knew she couldn't take it any more.

"Let me got to sleep now, please," she'd say. "Tomorrow we make love again. Now I dream of your wonderful body." And she'd pull the sheet over her face, turn her body partly sideways, and fall into a deep slumber, with her legs spread wide apart and lots of room for her to move, so that occasionally she could stretch joyfully and make motions as though we were still at our game. She always went through erotic contortions when she dreamed of me, she said.

Unfortunately, there was one thing she liked still better than "Frenchy-Frenchy" love, and that was money. With a truly Oriental persistency, she hounded me regarding this commodity whenever we met. No matter how much her sex may have loved me, or in whatever way she was involved with me, the cash register in her head certainly never stopped turning. At first, she was content to ask for five thousand yen a day, but then she thought of the idea of adding presents to this sum, and when I thought of using these gifts as a substitute for cash, we had our first disagreement. A particularly disagreeable habit of hers was that she never would stick to a bargain. If she received her share of the division in an agreement, she immediately held her hand out for more. If she had been paid according to previously stipulated terms, she wasn't slow to think of a good reason why the price should be increased *ex post facto*. If she convinced herself that there was no point in asking for more, she'd coddle, embarrass, nag, or cajole me into giving her something else. No gift was ever good enough, no item expensive enough, no amount of cash large enough, and no favor quick or perfect enough for her to be satisfied. One always found himself indebted to her. She hadn't invented the word "enough" as yet, and she never would. She revealed herself to be one hundred and fifteen pounds of solid greed, nicely proportioned, wrapped and packaged, but repulsive in its contents nonetheless.

At first, I reasoned somewhat along the following lines. I was in Tokyo to have a good time. She spent my first four days with me and was very good about the things that she was bad about later. I returned on week ends and vacations to make love to her again, and each time she turned greedier. If that's the way she feels, I figured, I'll be the same way. I'll get everything out of her that I can, pay no attention to her well-being, and drop her like a hot potato when I'm through with her. Meanwhile, I thought, it makes no difference what the stupid little girl says or does. I'll use her for my bodily comfort and close my ears and my mind to her attempts at extracting the contents of my bank account from my pockets. I'll keep her for an exerciser until I'm sick and tired of her, and then I need have no remorse or scruple about bidding her adieu.

Later, it became difficult to put up with her constant barrage of requests. I argued and reasoned with her, but in typical Oriental fashion she let me talk myself tired and then started all over again in her begging procedure. She had her native persistence on her side, and she could confidently count on the fact that she could wear me down every time, for she was a creature without nerves when it came to annoyances. It became much more of a torture to me than the pleasure was worth. And so, when business took me out of town again, I told her that I'd send for her and had resolved in my mind not to see her again. On our last date, she flirted with a man across the room. As far as I was concerned, she could have him. She probably had him more than once—him and a tribe of others. By now, she may be taking over the directorship of a bank.

X Rita: Tragic Nymph

"Germany has become the playground of nations," the Germans themselves often told me, when shortly after my conclusion of duty in Japan I went to the old Fatherland. There was much bitterness in that expression: Comparisons with the days when Germany was among the proud members of the exclusive club known as the Great Powers, regrets over the many mistakes that had led to the occupation of their country by its enemies and the dismemberment of many of its provinces, ethical condemnation of the immorality of those particular Germans who'd do anything for money, and the insinuation of an accusation against the foreigners whose massive

power and monetary means succeeded time and again in cor-
rupting the Germans to do everyone's bidding. For it was a
known fact that anything could be bought in Germany at
highly competitive prices, from books to blondes, from jets
to jewels, from nuts to notoriety, and that the average American or Algerian, Turk or Hindu, Sicilian or Swazilander
seeking joys and thrills on vacation had more freedom with
license in Germany than anywhere else. Perhaps the Germans
envied the foreigners their entertainments which they themselves could seldom afford. As always under such circumstances, the righteous indignation of many self-appointed
judges of public morality had a close affinity to the losers in
the competition for the possession of the female who was the
primary object sought by the vacationing foreigners of all
colors and the best-selling article on Germany's rapidly expanding internal markets. And say what you would about the
strength and solidity of the German "economic miracle,"
there's no disputing that the German female was much in
evidence everywhere and that men, young and old, came from
far and wide to patronize her in her native habitat. Hers was
a prosperous business with reasonable prices, rapid turnover,
maximum competition, high sales appeal, modern promotion
technique, wide profit margins, and virtual tax exemption.
If Germany was the playground of the nations, she was the
toy that attracted children.

Like most other countries—except the Moslem states which
frown on all contact between their women and the hated
foreigners—Germany had its share of streetwalkers, who
abounded in droves in the cities where a great deal of money
changed hands, and of girls of easy virtues of all gradations
who picked up their customers in certain bars and cafés,
where they made their headquarters and which, in some cases,

were the only homes that they knew. In addition to these, there were the bar-girls, who got paid for the drinks they managed to hustle, and who also were sometimes to be had after hours. Bar-girls, therefore, often had to carry green license cards just like those of the streetwalkers and the recognized, registered, and medically inspected prostitutes who operated indoors. There was also what was called a learner's license, designed for girls who were allowed to go to bed with strangers as much as they liked but weren't allowed to take money for their favors—an especially fine nuance of legalistic meaning in the bureaucratic administration of the world's oldest and not least honored profession, worthy of commendation by all lovers of red tape. Then there were the waitresses and bartendresses in the nightclub trade, who might or might not lean in the direction of promiscuity, depending on their inclinations. Finally, there were the plain goodtime girls who had regular daytime jobs but found life a little too dull and boring in that type of routine and sought additional thrills and adventures in the dance halls, cabarets, beer joints, cafés, ice cream parlors, and wherever else they might meet young men of similar inclinations who'd give them a good tumble.

A special institution was the American bar, of which there were several wherever an American military unit happened to be stationed and wherever American service personnel went on leave for the amusement of vacationing soldiers, sailors, and airmen, and the convenience of the local maidens who arranged their assignations there. An American bar attracted a certain type of clientele. The usual girl who went there was very young, optimistic, cheerful, somewhat stupid, overly impressed by anything and everything as long as it came from the United States, and more American than a third-generation Iowa farmboy. She used far too much makeup, because that's what she had seen in the Hollywood movies that she attended religiously, danced only to American jazz music, and that only in the latest style, spoke pretty good English of the common, colloquial variety, dressed like something out of the advertisements of the cheaper American magazines, smoked nothing but American cigarettes, and liked men only with crewcuts. She dreamed of the day when some red-blooded American boy would fall madly in love with her, gesture like Van Johnson, sing like Pat Boone, talk like Rock Hudson, and dance like Fred Astaire, sweep her off her feet, and whisk her away to his penthouse, there to enjoy the millions in which all Americans are rolling, and to produce a tribe of children. Time and again she fell in love with one of these young men, gave herself unstintingly, quarreled over trifles, or was deserted in the end when her dreamboat had to sail home. Over and over, she partook of this experience, and because a few of them succeeded in trapping their quarry, the rest had their confidence in Lady Luck bolstered. In the end, the girl usually turned out to be a drink hustler or a whore, or both, like all the others, because she was necessarily disappointed over and over again, and each disappointment made her so much the more resentful, not only against the particular men who acted like cads toward her, but against men in general. Besides, a girl has got to earn a living somehow, and there's a limit to the amount of time she can spend in bars and look for boyfriends and still work. Men ordinarily were more than willing to sleep with her, and often they'd just as soon give her some money and know that all their obligations to her ended with it, rather than tremble every month before the crucial days arrived for fear that they might become founders of a family. At first, she'd take money only from friends, with no definite connection between the sex act and the gift, but soon it would become evident to all concerned, including her, that there wouldn't be any gifts without the pleasures of the bed, and so, she'd turn the argument around and simply arrange her life in such order that there would be no sex without money. Having gone that far, it always is a short step to accept anyone who doesn't seem too repulsive, provided that he gives her the stipulated sum, and that's the approximate stage where most prostitutes operate. Only toward the very end, when the lines in their faces make them objects of pity, and when their nerves are so shattered that they can't wake up without a pint of whiskey before breakfast, do they usually take all comers. And from there, it's but a short step to the point where they must accept one of the two horrible choices: either straighten out and go to work on a regular job, or end up as a permanent patient in a hospital for the demented or the disabled and indigent. Depending on their constitution, they may last two years or twenty. And often they can cut their career short by marriage, for amazingly enough the top quality prostitute averages at least one proposal of marriage per week. A man of the world often can't help wondering how many of the respectable middle-class women he sees walking with their husbands and children really are reformed whores. The statistics would probably shock the ladies of high society were they to be published.

American bars, then, were the perfect observation laboratories for a person interested in sociological patterns and patterns of human behavior. They were the resorts of the last-attempt, out-and-out old prostitutes; the disillusioned little girls who were on their way to becoming members of the same tribe; the working girls who were constantly surrounded by a network of intrigue on the part of their customers and their employers to drag them into the circles of whoredom, too; the genuine sweethearts who met their boyfriends there; and the occasional young woman who came to look for adventure, in addition to the hopefuls who were in between these various stages and most likely were sliding the scale of human values.

Rita was in her mid-thirties when I discovered her in an American bar in Munich. She bore the traces of time and suffering, yet one could see that she must've been a great beauty in her younger days, and she was still good-looking and exuded a charm which comes only with intense activity of the soul. She was a short girl with a mature figure, blue eyes, and platinum-blond hair, which she wore in a very severe, simple arrangement that brought out the delicacy of her facial characteristics. It struck me immediately that she wasn't the type that usually could be encountered in the large, smelly halls with loud shouting, noisy jukeboxes, dirty tablecloths, rickety barstools, invective exchanged by the females, and drunken curses from the mouths of lonely soldiers. Rita was more nearly the kind of woman whom one expects to meet in an elegant cocktail lounge. She was out of her class.

I sat down beside her. She made no response at all to my attempts to involve her in conversation. Rather than be rude, she brushed me off with a word or two. And only after I had stopped saying banalities and meaningless phrases, such as one uses in picking up girls, did she talk to me. Then she spoke to me as one intelligent human being to another. It was like meeting someone who sat in the same seminar at the university or who was engaged in similar research in the library. Forgotten were the nasal hillbilly songs on the jukebox, the quarrels about a few *pfennigs* which occupied the energy, and

above all the vocal cords, of the other girls, the bantering of
the GI's in their open-necked sportshirts, and the malodorous
fumes of stale beer and tobacco that hovered in the room.
Forgotten was the fact that we were both slumming among
people younger and more limited than we were. Forgotten
was the fact that we were strangers who had just met. We
knew the same expressions, sensations, cities, and thoughts,
had read the same books, and had drawn identical conclusions from our many experiences. Only after a couple of
hours was there a lull in our conversation, and then we agreed
to leave together and continue our conversation elsewhere.
She led me away from the newly reconstructed business streets
of downtown Munich into an area where there still were ruins
from the extensive wartime bombings, and we walked into a
small restaurant half hidden among the debris. It was a fit-
ting background for us to withdraw to from the world of the
young people who were only babes in their mothers' arms
when these charred ruins first smoldered and sank to the
ground. The two of us belonged to the generation which had
lived through the years when Europe and Asia stood in flames
and millions of people perished in the battles, the bombings,
the deportations, and the disorganization which is always
the aftermath of war.

"We'd like a quiet place where we can carry on an intensive conversation," the girl said to the proprietress. "We've
got a lot to talk about."

"Take the booth in the corner there," the hulking woman
replied, not the least bit surprised. "No one will disturb you
there. What may I bring you?"

"Red wine, the best you have," I ordered, without looking
at the menu. I was sure that Rita would agree that red wine
was the thing to drink when you were "talking intensely." Be-

sides that, I was in a mood to drink a lot and yet to talk, and this combination always goes best on a good, dry wine that wets the throat without dimming the ability to reason. As I had foreseen, Rita was delighted with my choice. I was to find throughout my relationship with her that, although we disagreed on many basic issues, her taste was as impeccably good as I deemed my own. We sat there until four o'clock that morning and guzzled red wine.

"Would you like to come home with me and have a cup of coffee?" she asked, when the hired help began to put the chairs on the tables with gusto and to sweep the floors of the little restaurant.

"Sounds like a good idea."

Without further ado, I paid the bill and we walked to her house. Naturally, I wondered about her. She certainly didn't look or act like a pickup, didn't have the typical habits of a lady of easy virtue, and had none of the characteristics of the good-time girls. She didn't giggle, didn't pry into my personal affairs, didn't bother to find out how much money I might have along, didn't act coy, didn't tell me stories about the many men whose advances she had refused, and didn't try to impress me with her dire need of money. She spoke to me as one friend to another. And yet, since she was an attractive woman and obviously a woman of the world, she must know that my presence in the American bar could be explained only in one way. As far as that was concerned, her own presence in the American bar held a similar meaning. What was her game? Was her intellectual conversation her come-on with which to lure me to her body? Or was she using the promise, however veiled, of her body as a come-on to win a partner for a night of conversation about things intellectual? She could talk philosophy, religion, politics, literature, sociology, history, or economics, and she had an astounding command of her language with which to express her views lucidly and coherently. I couldn't help wondering if these admirable attributes had been cultivated at the expense of her physical abilities, or if they went hand in hand with professional competence in erotics. I'd probably soon learn the answer if I went home with her.

She lived in a shabby room on the top floor of a multi-story building in a half-rebuilt neighborhood. The rooms had cold running water. Even the bathroom, which she shared with a dozen other tenants, had no hot water tank. I couldn't help wondering whether these people ever bathed, and how the "economic miracle" had passed by them. But then, I remembered that the German housing authorities were just propagandizing and working for the project of installing a complete bathroom with hot water in every apartment. Rita's room was small and appointed with rather ancient furniture that was old without being antique. It also was so cold that it made me shiver. Rita moved an electric heater into the center of the room next to my chair and focused its rays on me. I'm afraid she read on my face the disappointment I felt over her happy home. Somehow I had expected more.

Her story was an interesting one. Like most German females whom one meets in bars, she came from the Soviet zone. Her father had been a highly placed official during the Nazi régime. I could tell from the places she knew and the people she mentioned that it was true. She knew her way around pre-war Berlin pretty well. She grew up in the capital of the Third Reich, and she was at just the correct age to participate not only in all the youth movements but also in the social occasions and gala events which her family's status made available to her. She showed me pictures of herself from those days:

young, blond, beautiful, statuesque, proud, radiant, conscious of her position—everything that a good young woman of the top echelons was supposed to be. True to her obligations to the Fatherland, she married during the war and had a child. Her husband was killed on the Russian front. And so, when the debacle came in 1945, she was in all the wrong categories for a woman who wanted to survive and succeed in life. She was captured by the Russians and maltreated by them. She still had the scars to show on her arms where her bones had been broken in the beatings. She didn't say what else they had done to her. The image of her body with both arms broken and twisted out of shape sufficed. But she survived; and somehow she recovered from her wounds and resumed her studies at the university, which she had interrupted in order to get married. She completed her course of study in psychology, passed the governmental examinations which in Germany qualify the applicant for various positions, as the bachelor's degree does in the United States and, asked the Soviet Zone authorities to employ her. They used her professionally in the creation of orphanages and for the counseling of delinquent children. She cared little about their politics, having had her fill of political activity, and as long as she managed to stay away from the inner guidelines of the party, she was all right. She found herself a new husband, gave up her position, and produced three more children. Unfortunately, however, the husband was an irresponsible bum who wouldn't or couldn't take care of his family. She stood it for about five years and then decided to separate from him and go back to work.

By now, she had advanced far enough and acquired sufficient experience to cause the authorities to draw her into the political cesspool of the Communist Unity Party. That was something she couldn't tolerate, and so, despite all the blandishments which they could offer and the love she bore her children, she took them to her mother-in-law's house and fled to West Germany. Freedom, however, meant cross-examinations and internment at first, and even later never led her back into her profession. In order to earn some money, she became a saleswoman for a company that made artificial parts of the body and orthopedic equipment. And so, the psychologist, who could be helping thousands of young people, spent her weekdays on the road, seeking out the oldsters and trying to persuade them to take a new lease on life through her products. The high official's daughter stayed in cheap inns and was the daily companion of ignorant farmers' wives and boisterous salesmen as well as the victim of the advances of every lonely drunk who discovered that she was traveling alone. She came back to Munich on week ends, to keep house in her shabby room, dream of her distant children, and occasionally seek a grand thrill by frequenting American bars. It made me feel a bit ashamed to realize what she was missing and how much she must miss it.

Over the telling of this story, my verification of the people, places, and facts to corroborate it, and the showing of pictures and souvenirs, another hour or so had passed, and I was getting very tired in spite of the two cups of coffee that she served me.

"I'd better go home," I said. "It's been very pleasant, but I need some sleep."

"You may sleep here, if you like," she responded.

It came out so simply and matter-of-course, and there had been so little preparation or advance notice of such a turn of events, that I was surprised. Naturally, I didn't want to miss the opportunity, though I didn't know what to say in my acceptance speech, and so I said as little as possible. I thanked her and said I was glad. Then I began to strip my clothes off and go to bed, while she went through innumerable ablutions and lavations at her cold water sink and made herself attractive for bed, in the manner of most women who always waste tremendous amounts of perfectly good time with ceremonies that appear to have no results whatsoever and usually leave them only less desirable than they were before. In the meantime, I slipped under the heavy covers, because it was still cold in the room and I was very tired. I remember watching her unctuous rites of cleanliness and aphrodisiasm for a while but growing tired of it, and I must've been asleep when she finally finished and joined me in the pre-warmed bed. I don't know how long I had been asleep, but it restored me perceptibly. I was awakened by her rubbing her breasts against my side and lowering her freshly scrubbed face over my neck. It was a pleasant way to be disturbed, and with my eyes half closed, I reached out for whatever part of her my sleepy hands might grope at. She guided them to suit her fancy: the left one to her breasts and the right one where she craved my attentions even more. It was very co-operative of her, I thought.

What followed can only be described as my rape. It was incredible, and if someone else were to tell me about it, I'd probably not believe him. Yet it happened nonetheless. The woman raped me, my genital organs, my mouth, my eyes, my nose, my chest, my stomach, every part of my anatomy. She almost choked the breath right out of me, but I had fun.

As soon as my fingers touched her nipples and found their

way to her most sensitive spot, she exploded with a torrent of emotion as if someone had electrified her. Her entire body wound itself and writhed against my hands and against my sides to gain some contact with me. Not content with merely touching, she stuck out her tongue, turned her head sideways, and licked the left side of my face and the left ear. Her tongue slipped deep inside the ear, so that I thought she was going to carry the eardrum out with her if she ever withdrew it. Inside my ear, her tongue skipped around and bandied about like a crazed snake, which produced, a quaint feeling all over the nervous system. Shoving my hand aside from her breast, she then bent herself over gradually and lowered the upper portion of her body upon my chest. She used her full, fleshy breasts almost like weapons, whipping me with them, bringing them together so as to stretch my skin, or squeezing them up against me and alternately raising and lowering them, so as to produce the maximum friction for her nipples which stood erect like well-drilled soldiers. Finally, she also withdrew herself from my right hand and raised herself over me to bring herself directly in line with my torso. She rubbed herself giddily all over my belly, clutched every part of me as if to convince herself of our intimate contact, and finally bounced herself on my thighs. Meanwhile, her arms had worked themselves under my neck, and she raised my head toward herself. Her tongue by now was giving an altogether complete bath to my neck, exerting an unbelievable strength and an insatiable appetite for the touch of my flesh. Her hands alternately raised and lowered my torso a bit to accommodate the continuous contortions of her body with frictional contact on my own. Her body probed for its proper connections, tried time and again to find them, almost caught hold a few times, but failed at least a dozen times. I wanted to use my hands to complete the junction, but she wouldn't let me touch her that way.

"No, let me find you myself!" she cried hoarsely between moans and groans. "Just a little more patience!"

When finally she located what she wanted and her eyes closed, it felt as if a well-lubricated vacuum pump were dragging me into a bed of wagging tongues. She felt hot beyond words. From her mouth and throat issued a succession of jungle sounds reminiscent of a tigress stalking her prey. She roared and hissed in addition to moaning, groaning, gasping, rasping, squeaking, howling, and squealing.

"Please, complete it inside of me!" she begged me. "Please, please, let me be a mother! I want a child from you! Please, give me a little one! Don't hold yourself back! Let me have all your strength, all of it, please, holding nothing back! Now, now, ah, yes, that's it! That's it, now darling!"

At last her prayer was fulfilled, and the climax arrived and passed. She collapsed on top of me with something between a growl and a purring hiss. Before she returned to the cold water sink, she gave a long, grateful kiss. While she stood and washed herself, I couldn't help remembering Benjamin Franklin's advice to consider the older and more mature women, because they had more to offer and were more grateful. Right after that, I again thought of Axel Munthe's theory that women always tried to compensate for missing children by creating more. Rita had made the sacrifice of her children in order to escape to the West. The little ones were in the care of an eighty-year-old grandmother somewhere in Brandenburg. Rita's fervent hope was that somehow the old lady could be persuaded to take the children and run the risk of escaping to the West with them. It wasn't much of a hope,

even before the erection of the Berlin wall, for it was un-
likely that the old woman would have the good sense to understand how important such an action would be for the little
ones, or the energy to carry out anything like a concerted plan.
Unfortunately, it's usually been my experience that the older
people are and the less time they still have to live, the more
careful they are about saving their own skins at the expense
of others. Besides, to an old lady like that, the difference between Communism and capitalism may not have been too
clear. Chances of Grandmother's risking such an escape, which
would gain her very little and mean a terrible gamble to her,
were very slim. I tried to tell Rita to take a logical outlook on
this matter and make peace with the fact that she wasn't likely
to see her children again, but she wouldn't surrender those
illusory hopes. Deep inside her mind, however, she must've
known that I was right, and she was already compensating for
this realization by a desperate desire for a child: my child. It
was unfortunate that it was left to me to arouse this desire,
for she'd recently had an operation to rid herself of an unwanted embryo. This operation meant that chances were
practically nil of her conceiving again during the next several years, according to what her doctor had told her. By
the end of those years, however, she'd probably be undergo-
ing the change of life, and so, she'd probably never have a
child again by me or anyone else, no matter how ardently she
might wish for one. Perhaps it was this feeling of never being
able to bear children again which was most responsible for
her mad desire to have another one, much as a medical prohibition of sugar creates an insane longing for sweets. Poor
Rita! She wanted the impossible, and she wanted me to provide it for her. She didn't ask for a thing, not for marriage,
nor for money, nor for presents, nor even for all my week

ends. She was willing to take as little of me as I was willing
to offer, or as much, but above all, she wanted my child. She
strained herself with longing for it. And it was the only thing
that I couldn't give her.

This matter of the children we were going to conceive became the major topic of conversation and the strongest tie
between us. She cultivated the idea with such care that it
became an obsession with her. It dominated her mind and
made her humble herself before me as no other woman has
ever done.

The second time I went to see her was two weeks after the
original assignation. I had been away on business and barely
managed to squeeze in a week end in Munich before I left
again. We had arranged to eat supper together and met on
schedule. All through the meal, she was fidgety and on edge.
I could tell that she was anxious. When we were finished, I
didn't bother asking her where she wanted to go. It was only
a five-minute walk to her house, and we walked there mechanically, as if Providence had steered us. She trotted along-
side of me obediently, unlocked the door, climbed up the
stairs ahead of me to turn on the light, opened the door to
her room, and threw off her overcoat. I took my coat and shirt
off while she was in the bathroom. When she returned, she
crowded me into the easy chair in the corner and felt my
muscles while she undid my shoe laces and took off my belt.
She couldn't get me into bed fast enough. Though we didn't
have a thing planned for the next two days, we were in a mad
rush. She even hurried through the ablutions and ointments
with great speed while I warmed up the bed in the cold room.

This time, she let me go on top and provided the proper
spring action and stimulation with her body from below. She
moved more slowly and with greater care not to cause a pre-

mature climax. The moaning and the groaning, heaving and panting was a bit more subdued.

"I just hope this is as wonderful for you as it is for me!" she told me several times. "I can't describe how beautiful it is. I just hope you're feeling it too."

Unfortunately, I had forgotten about the matter of the children during the two-week interval. The truth of the matter was that I had spent the previous week end with a much younger girl whose greatest worry in the world was that she might become pregnant. My mind, therefore, was still set upon being extra careful, and when the occasion arose again, I reacted instinctively. Without thinking about who my bed partner was this time, I readied myself for instantaneous caution with the first joyous signs of danger. And so, when the moment arrived, I hurried to comply with my promise—to another girl.

Never have I seen such a look of consternation upon the face of any woman, before or afterwards. Rita was absolutely crushed when she noticed what I had done. Her forehead wrinkled, her eyes expanded as if she were in terror, her mouth opened as if she were going to scream, and wrinkles appeared upon her cheeks. She was the face of horror.

"How could you do this to me?" she asked. "After what I told you . . ."

But it was too late now to do anything about my mistake. I couldn't do a thing except face the ordeal with the cold water, which after the sex act is something like a dive upon a fakir's needle-board. The entire rite of Eros had turned into something of a fiasco, because I considered it even more tactless to explain to her what had been on my mind when it happened, and so I simply claimed that I had forgotten about her request. That was altogether incredible to her, and she insisted that I had tried to insult her and that I should come back to bed and do my duty. I assured her that I would if I could, and she broke out crying that it would never be the same now, and that she'd have to give up her most cherished desire, which was my child. She cried into the pillow, lying there naked, with her legs apart, not caring how she looked to me any longer. The two of us were a perfect illustration for the fact that no two people ever really come close to each other in a casual affair, and very few do in a lifelong relationship. We were caught in an unheated room with one another, each for reasons of his own, and we weren't likely to give each other true satisfaction. No matter how much we might share in the same ideas and interests, and no matter how much our bodies might enjoy each other, we didn't really know each other, and we were still too different in our purposes and ways of life to fulfill one another's needs. I was a naked fool, standing in the cold next to a woman who cried in her bed for my child, which she'd probably never be able to conceive. I had no idea what it was like to want my child, for I never longed for children. And she had no idea what it was that I wanted from a woman, which was mostly glamor, beauty, and partnership. Both of our urges were biological, yet mine were centered on my own person and the enjoyment which lay open to me, and hers were rooted more deeply in nature and involved the reproduction of the race. And while I lay down next to her and put her head upon my shoulder to give her security, it occurred to me that men and women could rarely satisfy one another, because they lived in different worlds separated by invisible walls, and no matter how eagerly one reached out for the world of the other, one never penetrated those divisions. Even while our bodies were joined and we enjoyed each other's nerves and muscles, we were separated

unmercifuly by the different aims that we pursued. Nature
dealt cruelly with us, it seemed to me, to condemn us to loneliness in the midst of the most intimate acts.

When I knock off for the week end and take the trouble to
go to another city, I'm looking for fun and not for a heap of
tragedy into which to stick my face. It may be irreverent of
the dignity of my fellow humans, it may be inconsiderate of
their sensibilities, it may be insensitive toward their troubles,
or callous toward their problems, and it may even be an indication of gross egocentricity, but that's the way I operate.
During the week end, I like to go on a joy ride. I don't want
to have my nerves put through a meat grinder.

Rita had suffered from the men to whom she had been
married, and she suffered also from the absence of men in her
life. She suffered when she had lovers, and she suffered when
she had none. She suffered from the necessity of having to provide for her children, and she was then suffering even more
from the fact of separation from them. She suffered from the
political turmoil which she had seen and partly experienced,
and in her deepest recesses she suffered from the fact that she
couldn't approve of the politics of postwar Germany. She suffered from disrupted family conditions from her earliest
childhood on, and now she was suffering from the fact that
she virtually had no more family. Rita was a single composite
of suffering. For a nervous, sensitive, emotional woman, these
ordeals had been extremely difficult to endure while retain-
ing her sanity. In fact, she had developed some of the oddities
of an overly nervous and insecure woman of her years: a nervous, hoarse laugh, a constant need of reassurance regarding
her importance and good looks, and a craving for esteem
that led her sometimes to imagine implications and insinua-

tions which no one had intended. She longed desperately to be at the center of someone's universe, and the truth of the matter was that she moved at the outer periphery of the solar system of all the people with whom she still had contact. Her children were growing up into strangers who knew nothing about her. All the people who really cared deeply for her had been removed by the sweep of Fate's sickle. For this reason, she was a difficult woman with whom to have an affair.

She might've been a difficult wife to the best of husbands because of certain characteristics of hers. Perhaps some of these were attributable to the fact that she had learned the secrets of life from her father. Whether it had damaging effects upon her, only a psychologist could judge; at least, it was highly unusual and may have given her that appetite for sex which was her most pronounced trait. In every man who made love to her, she saw and sensed the father whom she had idolized when she was a little girl. She learned all the tricks of the bed at a very early age, so that she was able to perfect them while she was still young. Now that she was a middle-aged woman, she had such a repertoire of amatory talents that sex was better for her than for most women. And so, she longed for it more, too, in addition to the fact that she was a passionate creature by reason of her constitution. She confided in me that she spent many a night crying in her pillow, because she was lonely and her tender spots ached with longing for the solid substance of a man caressing them. Yet her upbringing had prevented her from associating with men too freely, and so she chose to suffer again, as, indeed, she was suffering all the time. She had the misfortune of having been born fiery and at the wrong time, in the wrong place, and of the wrong family. Moreover, she was unlucky in her associations. All of her being cried out for a good man to share her life, yet she had found none.

She told me how it had happened the first time. Her father and mother were divorced, and her father had remarried, but he didn't get along well with his second wife either, and so Rita and her father had formed a tacit alliance in the household against her stepmother. It was an unnatural arrangement, but social pressures made it impossible for her father to be divorced a second time, since he occupied an important position in the hierarchy of the German state. Whenever he could, he came to her to speak privately without the noxious company of his second wife. One time, when he returned from a vacation and hadn't seen her for several weeks, she dashed out of the shower to tell him to wait until she dried herself. He looked at her in that peculiar way which men have just before the sex act. She hadn't understood, dried herself, and came out in her bathrobe. He kissed her, stripped her with one jerk of the hand, and laid her on the carpet. She trusted him, loosened up, co-operated freely, and enjoyed every moment of it. He was fifty-one, she was seventeen. After that, whenever they could maneuver the stepmother out of town overnight, or better still over the week end, they slept together. It had been a pleasant arrangement while it lasted. And she drifted straight from the arms of her father into those of her first husband. She said that it hadn't taken much effort or persuasion.

Yet one could tell from her attitude toward men that it had affected her profoundly. Each time, she looked for her father in her bed-partner, and since of necessity she had to be disappointed, she didn't have a husband any more. Disappointment makes women obstreperous, shrewish, capricious, stubborn, and cruel. Joined to her other sources of behavior, it made her impossible as a permanent companion for me. And so, sooner or later, we had to part company.

Whereas in the beginning we agreed on everything, we now disagreed on everything with equal predictability. She took the opposite stand from mine on practically all questions from soup to nuts. We had long and bitter arguments about her future and mine. I just wasn't doing anything right, it seemed, and I wasn't going to get anywhere in the world. Considering the fact that I was making four times as much money as she, I thought that was a particularly ludicrous argument. My ideas on religion were no damned good either, for we must have trust in something, she thought. I reminded her of all the injustice and inhumanity which she had witnessed and partially experienced on her own body; mundane arguments of this type never impressed but only annoyed her. She then simply put that silly "wise" expression on which always used to drive me berserk in my parents, and assured me that "some day" I'd understand. This old standby, using a hypothetical time and a conjectural change of mind in the person addressed, is a true idiot's delight, used by all ignorant fathers and mothers when their children become a bit too inquisitive for them to be able to stall and stump them with fairy tales. When Rita used it on me, I always blew a fuse, imagining that she was using the same techniques on me which she had applied so successfully on her children in the East Zone. I was also wrong, it seems, about my theories on man and his relation to society, for I believed that no one should ever get from his fellowmen any more than he had contributed. Rita was smitten by socialist ideas which she had probably picked up in the Soviet orbit or even in the West German Republic, where they have them too, and kept telling me about the obligations of the state toward the individual. This also infuriated me after a while, for I've seen myself for some years as the unwilling contributor to the welfare of a great many people whose welfare doesn't concern me one iota and without whom I'd be a lot better off. According to her, I was wrong about practically all subjects on earth. Toward the end, she even quit telling me how wonderful I was in bed and reproached me with a lack of tenderness.

That did it. I was on the verge of breaking relations by a simple "Goodby" when I had to go to Paris for some months, and during all that time I didn't make one gesture to arrange a meeting with her. She suggested one in letters a few times, and she tried to write interesting epistles to captivate my imagination and make me reply. But seeing the whole relationship from the wider perspective of distance, not to mention the more wordly perspectives of the Queen of the Seine, I discovered the hackneyed phrases in her letters and found all the faults of her reasoning with disgusting clarity. And so, I decided to be another one of the cads who have disappointed Rita. They probably all had their reasons. I could think of dozens of them without even trying. I stopped writing. She must've understood, for she stopped at the same time. And so, we wound up with an ideal situation: a dissolution by mutual agreement.

XI Epilogue: On Women

I'm a bachelor. As such I'm a favorite target for the paternal comments and unsolicited advice of all my married friends. Since most people who've passed their middle-twenties seem to be married, that means I'm subject to more counsel than an accused culprit with a staff of lawyers. Everybody believes that even if he isn't an expert on anything else he's at least an expert on the science of living; and to prove it, everybody is more than eager to dispense his wisdom to all comers. The odd fact about this is that most of the people who hand out this "sagacious" advice aren't particularly happy. Usually, their excuse for counseling me at all is that they want to save me from the troubles which they had to endure. And by this admission and justification, they disqualify themselves in my eyes, for I don't need anyone to speak to me about his agonized suffering; I can easily find a good way to suffer on my own. What I need is someone to speak to me from the full plenitude of happiness. But those individuals are difficult to find; and where they exist they're not at all eager to communicate their secret.

As long as these married friends are in mixed company and comparatively sober, they always praise themselves as the luckiest people on earth.

"Ah, there's nothing like marriage," they always tell me, with a meaningful glance and a pat on the back. "Honestly, I didn't know what living was until I got married. You ought to get married too, Phil. Honestly, you won't be sorry. A man of your talents and looks ought to be able to get himself a wife. What about that little blonde I saw you with the other night? Why don't you marry her? Now there, I thought, was a perfect couple."

And so on and so forth. Whenever they see me with an attractive female, they want to hook me, attach me with ball and chain, drag me to the altar, make me swear the eternal vows, and endow me with a litter of "tiny tots" to give that "true meaning" to my life. They can't find words enough to describe their ethereal bliss to me. As long as they're sober, that is; and as long as the little woman is listening with a suspicious glint in her eyes.

But as soon as I've poured a few drinks into them and they're beginning to get stars in their eyes, when the boys and I manage to get away from their wives and children and have ourselves a stag evening out on the town, it's an entirely different story. That's when their inhibitions are gone, the alcohol has shunted aside the veils of conventionality from their brains, and their true inner selves are communicating with me.

"You don't know how lucky you are," they cry in their beers. "Don't ever get married, Phil. It's the absolute end. You can still pick up and go anywhere, whenever you please; you can go with whomever you please; you can spend your money the way you like; you have no cares or responsibilities to tie you down. Why, if you had a good mind to, you could pack your bags today and bid this stinking town farewell. Nobody can tell you when and what to eat and to wear, nobody can take your money away from you, and nobody is going to bring a nagging mother-in-law into your house and make your days miserable for you. Jesus, how I envy you! Believe me, if I had it to do all over again, I'd live just like you!"

This significant difference of opinion between my friends when sober and the same friends when drunk has puzzled and discouraged me from ever taking the fatal plunge. "Suppose," I've often asked myself, "suppose you were to parade one of your chicks up the sacred altar and, by the common ceremony, make her your sweet and ever-loving wife. Wouldn't you wind up like those pitiful bastards, too? Wouldn't you be trying to hypnotize yourself into a phoney happiness, while deep down inside of you, you were full of envy for the lucky and provident bachelors who still had their freedom?"

And then I think of all the fun that I'd be missing, if I were married. I could no longer afford, financially or socially, to search for new material for my amatory exploits. If I had been married at an early and respectable age, I'd never have met most of the girls in the foregoing ten chapters. I should've been forced to rise early in the morning—that in itself is a repugnant thought—earn a living for myself and my family from eight to five, come home, help change the diapers, listen to my wife's domestic concerns, and figure out how to deceive my creditors until next payday. I should've been forced to spank the children if they were "bad," or take them to the circus if they were "good"—and I don't know which would've been worse on my nerves. Maybe I'd even have been forced to buy a dog and let the beast salivate all over me just to please the little darlings upon my return from the office. There would've been no more of the hot, erotic nights, none of the clasping of a zealous girl to extract every ounce of joy from her beautiful body, none of the thrills of a new lover in my hungry arms.

No, I could never quite see this promise of "forsaking all others" for the sake of one. Sooner or later, something has always happened to make my women less dear to me, to destroy the illusion of perfection, to detract from their attentiveness to my desires, to make them too secure in my affections and therefore to elicit their everyday banalities and silly idiosyncracies, when I had just become fond of their holiday exterior. Even the best of them has diminished in attractiveness with daily contact, and soon the old longing for the gamble with the unknown, the search for the beautiful stranger, the satisfaction of the eternal male longing for the female of one's dreams has broken through. The only possible exception to this rule was Florence, and she is dead, long turned into dust. Perhaps, if the circumstances of intrigue had been stripped from my relationship with her, and if we could've lived together for a while, the same rule would've applied to her. For man has his *Wanderlust,* as does—for that matter—woman; and in man's case, there's no consideration of pregnancy or fear of middle age to restrain him, which hold woman back from becoming too adventuresome in most cases.

Homo sapiens isn't a monogamous animal, and no matter to what institutions or conventions he may pay lip-service, he'll never become anything but polygamous except through extreme domestication. Only if he's deprived of all the attributes of his primordial beginnings and becomes as tame as a lap dog under the combined conspiratorial influence of priesthood and the matriarchal institutions of our society will he shed his polygamous tendencies; and even then, there's no certainty. The tamest cats and dogs become rebellious during the rutting season. And man has the advantage over most animals that his rutting season never ends, and the female is always capable, though not always willing, to accommodate him. No other mammal can make that statement.

Because my very mode of existence is an offense against conventional morality, I've always been attracted to the women who also defied old-fashioned Pauline ethics. Looking back to the ten women I've described in this book, I can't help noticing that not a single one of them would've passed the scrutiny of the Puritan divines in the days of America's infancy: Odette, Suzie, and Hisako-San were common prostitutes; Marsha and Anne were simply better remunerated and more successful members of the same profession; Florence and Rita were adulteresses; Claudine was a loose woman; and only Lynn and Laura, each in her own way, came close to being "good" in the Pauline sense of the word, though even they would've had to do a lot of praying to enter Heaven. And yet, with the single exception of Lynn, who didn't have the good sense to submit, I certainly enjoyed them all, and what happiness they brought me!

Despite the moral censures that might be invoked against them, they brought me a blissful release from the doldrums of an existence hemmed in by the restraints of narrow minds and masochistic superstitions. Without them and their sisters, my life would've been as empty as a shell without its nut. Expertly, they bestowed upon me the spice which makes the food of tellurian existence at all palatable. They gave meaning to the struggles of my days through the joys of my nights. They crowned me in triumph and consoled me in defeat. In the midst of the confused meanderings of the human species, they contrived to inspire me with a purpose. Beautiful were the days and night I spent with them, and vapid were the ones I spent alone.

Our ethics unfortunately are prescribed by the matriarchy that rules mankind in this century; or more specifically, by the housewives who've made up a code of ethics which allows them to be respectable without the possibility of admission to that status of their competitors. And yet, it's an entirely artificial classification, based upon the theory of the monogamous human who doesn't exist, and upon a gradation of invidious value judgments that place a premium on dullness and a penalty upon those human sentiments which alone can release man from the prison of his materialistic routine and make him pulsate with the heart-throb of emotion. Our ethics are lamentably based upon something which the housewives describe as "common sense," but which, far from being rational, is nothing but poison to a sensitive human being. The matriarchal division of all females into "good" and "bad" women doesn't deal with the male perspective at all but merely indicates whether the conduct of a woman is *good or bad for the matriarchy*. For the matriarchy is a self-perpetuating system, and any system perpetuates itself through the manifestations of force and reward: in this case, the penalty of ostracism as opposed to acceptance into the company of ruling matrons.

But I've steadfastly refused to capitulate before the value judgments of the matriarchy. I judge my women not by whether they're good for the matriarchal system but by whether they're *good or bad to me*. For I'm a conscious person, and as such I'm the center of my own moral universe, and therefore, the ethics of the housewife have no relevancy to my existence. What's considered unfair competition by the housewife is perhaps exactly what I need, and what the matriarchy condemns as designed to lessen the social security of the aging female may be precisely the right type of behavior in my book. For I'm not interested in providing financial security and social supports for women who don't contribute to my happiness. I'm interested exclusively in my own happiness, and it has to do a great deal with women who qualify by their appearance, intelligence, and mode of conduct to occupy a place of importance in my life. The women whose welfare I'd consider least worthy of endeavor are those who're the most adamant ones in maintaining the matriarchy, i.e., the ugly, the ancient, and the heavily committed females. The women whose welfare I'd consider most desirable and worthy of my own efforts are precisely the ones against whom the others are always busy guarding themselves, i.e., the young, the beautiful, and the uncommitted ones. For the moralistic housewife will never give me anything more attractive than a pot roast, but the gorgeous young female can give me happiness.

The difference between the ethical levels of the diverse groups of women is subject to great exaggeration. The women who've achieved respectability see to it that the narrow divisions are artificially broadened into chasms which surround

their pitiful positions like moats encircling a crumbling me-
dieval fortress. When one subjects these positions to the ar-
tillery fire of closer scrutiny, however, it often turns out that
they turn to dust at the merest touch of the battering ram.
It's largely a matter of morality for the sake of morale.

What's the most immoral action of which a member of the
human community can make himself guilty? Clearly, it's the
usurpation of something that he hasn't earned, the acquisition of services or property through lies and deception, the
appropriation of other people's affections under false pretenses. Next to criminal acts of violence, it's easily the most
hideous offense against the standards of decency which are
universally recognized. And yet, the traditional moats of respectability protect many a matriarch who reigns over a love-
less household and tyrannizes over an unloved family in the
name of an emotion which either was never present or has
been dead for many years. Married women who deny the
pleasures of their beds to their doting husbands, husbands
who thought that the inequities of marriage would at least
procure a steady bed partner for them, are infinitely less
ethical than prostitutes who deliver with punctilious prompt-
ness the merchandise which one obtains from them. Matrons
who deceive their husbands into thinking that they love them
and secretly betray them behind their backs—whether in
thought only, or in the bed of a lover, makes no difference—
are infinitely guiltier of immorality than the girls who sell
themselves at a stipulated price. Xantippes who use their
dominance in the household and their discretion to dispense
or withhold the sources of enjoyment so as to hold the whip-
hand over their spouses are infinitely less worthy of esteem
than the streetwalker who earns her living on a quid pro quo
basis. For let's face it: Marriage is based on the understanding

of physical union and mutual enjoyment, and a woman who doesn't live up to her part in this agreement is worse, from a moral point of view, than a whore, because she refuses to deliver the merchandise which has already been sold, and which is being bought over and over again. And she gets away with it in more cases than not, because she and her protagonists and identical twins rear male and female children alike, and instill in all of them the basic concepts of life to which they'll be subject for the rest of their natural days. The matriarchal system forms the basis of these concepts. Its walls and moats are described as if they were drawn up along the only sensible, serviceable, and possible pattern. Its ways are, by definition, the only ethical ones. And so, it's constantly being reinforced and it continuously receives new champions from among its victims. No matter how inequitable the role assigned to the male, he's persuaded not only to accept it but also to consider it the natural and only moral pattern of conduct for him to follow. He's the dupe in the grand deception which turns serfdom into the illusion of bliss. He's the sacrificial victim, firmly convinced that he must defend to the utmost the principles under which his jugular vein is severed upon the altar.

Next to tyrannical and unloving wives, the worst women are the goodtime girls who thrive, more or less, on the business of the implied promise which they never fulfill. They allow themselves to be waltzed, wined, and dined at all the fancy places, they almost require the men to court them—several men at once, if it can be arranged—they throw their hips around like burlesque queens and rub their bodies against their escorts, they may even be generous with their kisses and fervent embraces, but when it comes down to brass tacks, they'll fight to the utmost against the supreme enjoyment of all. The teasers—whether through actual physical contact or through the mere suggestion of words, which can sometimes be even more potent in enthralling the imagination—are easily a close second to the Xantippes. If there were an Inferno of the type that Dante so eloquently described, special little compartments ought to be reserved for their incessant torture for all eternity. And when one considers the tremendous mental anguish they cause to countless men, and compares it with the scant hazard to public health caused by the whore, then the prostitute appears as a veritable angel next to the parasitical goodtime girl who never makes delivery on the implied promise. Probably no country is as heavily afflicted with this particular species as the United States, and there may be a close affinity between this fact and the statistic that American men outnumber women in insane asylums by far. The "virtuous" goodtime girl would be enough to drive anyone out of his mind.

There's only one category of honest women who make believe that sex is truly an evil rather than life's greatest blessing, and those are the women who really have nothing to do with men, the old spinsters and the nuns. Even if they're as wrong as human beings can be, at least they're not hypocrites, and that's the most important consideration. If they want to ruin their own lives and voluntarily dispense with the crowning jewel of life's presents, that's nobody's business but their own. At least, in depriving themselves, they don't raise false hopes in a number of frustrated male admirers, don't displace willing females who might deliver where they won't, and don't drive men out of their minds by teasing and stalling. Any honest answer is preferable to the "waiting game," even if that answer be no. In fact, a straightforward no is almost as good as a straightforward yes. It settles the issue. It decides one's course of action. It relieves the courter of all further efforts to try to win his courtesan. It unravels some of the complications which are always snarling up people's lives. Nuns—both inside and outside their proper abodes, the nunneries—are real people. I'm willing to accept them long before I'll accept a woman who's married and still lets her husband dangle on a string of false hopes.

Just as there are several types of unco-operative women, so there are also several types of co-operative ones, whom the matriarchy always tries haughtily to lump into one and the same highly uncomplimentary rating, in order to enhance its own prestige. For detracting from the merits of others has always seemed an easy manner of building up one's own standing. In lieu of actual merits and deserts, the petty little people who'd like to make themselves seem bigger always attempt to advance themselves by stepping on the ruined reputations of others. It's a psychological necessity with those who have no other claim to fame.

First of all, there are the numerous girls in show business, in offices, and behind counters who actually don't have the qualifications for their jobs and wouldn't hold these positions except for the fact that they permit certain privileges to important gentlemen who determine their status and careers. The number of these females, no doubt, is much larger than at first would meet the eye. It's the major objection to permitting women to escape from home and garden and letting them take jobs formerly monopolized by men. For the world is full of lonely men—married and single—who'd like a little something on the side, and the world is no less crowded with little girls who wouldn't mind putting out now and then to get ahead. Since these relationships usually don't rest upon true love alone, one ought properly to classify them with any other type of commercial relationship and call them instances of prostitution. Yet our whole social system might be upset if we, through some sort of wicked coincidences, could unravel all these complicated stories before the public eye, and so we spread a generous veil of ignorance over the entire subject and make believe it doesn't exist, and all promotions are based on the merit system. Of course, it's hypocritical, but the prevalence of the matriarchy forces us all into the mold of hypocrisy, whether we like it or not. It's one of the characteristics of an unnatural system that it forces everybody to lie or to deprive himself of his sanity through drink or dope.

Secondly, there's the more difficult category of the good-time girl who does co-operate in order to get what she wants out of her man. The man has no reason to complain of her. She stretches out dutifully in the back seat of his car or on his living room couch, leans back lazily, and obediently awaits his approach. Maybe, when she's had a few drinks, or if she feels particularly passionate that day, she'll even convey the impression of enjoying the sex act. Yet, does she really? By definition, she's in that back seat or on that living room couch, ready to go, not because she feels a particularly strong desire for the caresses of *this* man, but because she likes the expensive presents which he gives her, the exclusive nightclubs to which he takes her, and the excellent food with which he stuffs her, perhaps even the champagne with which he plies her into submission. He's deceiving himself into a false state of affection and the expectation of reciprocated emotion by cultivating this girl, and she's taking advantage of that fact. She's actually prostituting herself just as much as the whore who pounds her beat on the downtown pavements and collects the money in cash which the goodtime girl makes her man spend on goods and services. And often, this type of girl gets more in the long run in terms of presents and high living than her despised sisters earn with all their professionalism, and with less choice of partners. Yet at least, the goodtime girls who deliver are morally immensely superior to the goodtime girls who don't do anything to justify their existence. A man can accept them and create a place for them in his world, and he doesn't feel they're exploiting him. A reluctant laborer isn't immoral, but a parasite is. One simply has to know how to use the services of such girls and how high to gauge one's expectations.

The girl who fits into the co-operative goodtime category often drifts into the next group in order, which is that of the mistress. Mistresses don't always derive financial benefits from their relationships, but there probably are more who do than who don't, and if the circumstances are right, no one could possibly blame a girl for enjoying a free ride at the expense of her lover, provided he can afford her. The mistress who derives all or part of her support from her lover is, speaking from a point of view of returns on dollars and cents, probably the best investment for the male seeking sound and satisfactory companionship. As long as she's faithful, he enjoys all the privileges of the married man and all the comforts of the soul that go with marriage, without incurring any of the unpleasant obligations and liabilities of marriage: legal permanence, the wife's claims upon his property, the obstacles placed in the way of severance of the relationship, and the mental burden of facing the necessity of spending several decades of one's life with an old hag, just because the good priest said so. A mistress, if she's a good one, is a pleasant partner during many a good day, week, month or even year, without becoming a millstone around one's neck. For unlike the wife, whose legal status ordinarily leads her into making unreasonable demands, letting out her moods upon one, and rationing the use of her body which underlies the structure of her security, the mistress has to earn over and over whatever status she may have and must be conscious at all times of the threat of desertion, without even the satisfaction of the severance pay granted to the lowliest employees. A mistress is probably the only type of woman who more than earns her keep. Whenever a man has the chance of making a faithful mistress out of a chance acquaintance, he's a fool if he doesn't follow up the lead. For that sort of relationship is designed more than any other to favor him.

Unfortunately, mistresses are often badly paid, neglected or abused, and so they frequently go another step down the ladder and try to maintain several relationships with men of their acquaintance. This situation also often grows out of the weakness of the first and the potency of the second lover. At any rate, it sometimes begins to balance the scales in the wrong direction, for the competition of the males—who naturally always find out about each other—tends to raise the girl's market value, and she winds up getting ever higher bids, like a blue chip stock during a Wall Street boom. Furthermore, the feel of money is likely to prove a pleasant experience and lead to an appetite for more, and so she's apt to make exorbitant demands upon her lovers and ultimately to increase their number. While she may still be good company and an even more enjoyable bed partner, her attitude can't possibly be the same toward six men as it was toward her one and only sweetheart. She's bound to compare her admirers, use them to make each other jealous, and drive up the price of generosity. A definite change always comes over a girl in that approximate stage. She becomes hardened to appeals to her emotions, insensitive to pleas of love, unreceptive to requests that cause even the smallest amount of trouble to her —in other words, she becomes callous. At that point, the man is wise not to overdo the act with her, to watch his step lest she take advantage of him, and not to extend the relationship beyond the time when the mutual ardor has cooled. Generally speaking, a personal mistress may be good for two years, but a mistress shared with other men outlasts her usefulness after a period of three to six months.

Finally, there's the whore, the object of so much unmitigated hatred on the part of the housewife, the butt of innumerable jokes and wry comments on the part of the man. She's the creature who makes an outright business of selling the use of her private parts without the pretext of affection or emotion. And because she is an unadmitted support to one of the holy sacraments, a necessary evil which the clergy of most nations have been trying to ration and control for the better efficiency of their rule over men's minds, she's usually rated at the bottom of the social pyramid, right after the beggars and the lepers. Moreover, because our society is dominated by the matriarchy and it imposes its value judgments upon everybody, the whore herself usually classifies herself—or, if not herself, at least her colleagues—at the bottom of the pile, too. But if one considers the problem objectively, there isn't actually anything wrong with the whores except the hazard to one's health involved in such promiscuous association of the lower parts of the body, and this peril can be practically eliminated through frequent and regular visits to a physician. The whore is a businesswoman like all other women engaged in the pursuit of making money. She provides a service, like a masseuse, a hair-dresser, a manicurist, a seamstress, or a dentist. Her job is the care and treatment of a certain member, the appeasement of the craving for sexual intercourse for a reasonable period of time, the provision of physical contact with the female of the species which men are conditioned to require and which the matriarchy uses as the ultimate source of its power. This service is what she provides, and it is this service for which she gets paid. If men are dissatisfied with whores, it is usually because they're stupid and expect more from the woman than they've contracted to buy. A whore doesn't give her customers more than the merchandise for which they've paid, just as a shoemaker doesn't make two pairs of shoes for the price of one. Expecting a whore to fall in love with one is about as reasonable as expecting love from the masseuse, hair-dresser, manicurist, seamstress, or dentist. If the whore is good in her profession, she'll make enough of a show of affection to stimulate the man, who frequently requires tenderness even more than he craves the performance of the actual act of love. But it must be understood that these manifestations of tenderness are part of the service and can't spring from the heart. It may be that sometimes whores fall in love with their clients, just as surgeons sometimes find a case which captures their interest and as tailors sometimes put their heart and soul into a suit that they've always wanted to make. Yet obviously the prostitute cannot fall in love with every man whom she takes to bed with her. If, therefore, a man is dissatisfied with the services of a whore whom he's engaged for the night, it is usually because he's incapable of understanding the merchandise which he's buying, or because he's unreasonably vain and thinks himself obviously superior to other men. If he could think about his situation without his ego standing in the way, he'd realize that a whore is less likely to fall in love with him than the girl who sells him his toothpaste, the girl who takes him up the elevator, the girl who takes dictation in his office, or the girl who serves coffee in the local cafeteria. For none of the other girls are in a position where he might do them some physical injury or cause them pain whereas the prostitute not only takes a chance on that but also smells his perspiration.

Naturally, there are very few human beings, indeed, who could pass for archetypes. Though perhaps a majority of all women could be classified into the categories mentioned above, there also are a great many who don't quite belong in one or the other, because they're in transition. One could find women at all intermediary levels between the categories listed here, women who may think of themselves as belonging to one but actually belong to another, women who've recently been subjected to disappointments, and therefore deliberately change themselves into something they're not, women whom economic distress or physical concupiscence lead into adventures among another class, women who've managed to rise from one class to another through sheer force of willpower or through the generosity of a lover, and women whose minds are befuddled and whose willpower is so low that they really don't belong to any definable class but belong to all of them at the same time. The human race offers all varieties and an infinite possibility of combinations, and because of the delicacy of the brain and the precariousness of mental balance, there are no hard-and-fast rules by which human behavior can be accurately predicted. And since women are possessed of very little logic as compared to men, and love the game of secrecy and deception so well that they often mystify themselves by their own intrigues, they often adopt poses which place them in different categories of mankind, depending upon the people with whom they happen to associate. With one man, a woman may be a sexless angel; with another man, she may be as lecherous as a mink in heat; and

with a third one, she may be *la femme fatale,* driving her admirer out of his mind before she'll finally condescend to give
his passionate body the benefit of her experience. For women,
for the most part, hate making up their minds about exactly
what kind of woman they are; and so, they'd rather take turns
at being several different people at one and the same time.
Candida the day before yesterday, Ophelia yesterday, Penel-
ope today, Lady Macbeth tomorrow, and Circe the day after.

Many women have told me that they make themselves over
into different types merely to keep themselves interesting to
men. This statement is an indication of how absolutely dependent women are upon men, how their entire lives are
organized with a view toward their relations with men, ap-
proaches by men, support by men, attractions for men, appearance to men, impression on men, and benefits from men.
Whereas men have their business, their politics, their sports,
their card games, their discussions, and their friendships,
women essentially exist by and for love only. Love is a woman's life as well as her living, her instinct as well as her intelligence, her avocation as well as her profession, her purpose
as well as her pleasure, her interest as well as her weapon. To
women, all things are determined in the long run through
love; and that means, all phases and facets of life relate to
latent or fulfilled dreams of sex. Women discover sex earlier
than men and make it their lifelong preoccupation. Even the
women who for moral or religious reasons never indulge in
the act of coitus make sex the focal point of their lives, for
whereas fulfillment is the ambition of the others these women
center their lives on abstinence. It's certainly no accident that
Freudian psychology didn't appear until the matriarchy took
over. For the one-sided interpretation of life as standing
solely in the sign of the sex act is typically female thinking

transplanted, in this case, into the male. The matriarchy through such "science" implants its concepts upon the man and makes him more pliable and helpless than ever. All that's lacking then is to convince the man thoroughly of the permeation of any and all things with sex, and then to dispense it with caprice, irregularity, and cunning. The variable and unpredictable woman is the reverse side of sexy psychology. She plays the game in such a manner as to reap the greatest benefits from a complete dependence upon her which her own intrigues have created. And in this fashion, she creates a mutuality of dependence which more than compensates for the consequence of her natural inferiority in brute strength. If she alone can offer the fulfillment of all man's desires, she turns her dependence upon man into full power over his happiness, and since she convinces him that this is his entire happiness, it also becomes power over his sanity. All monopolies confer absolute rule. In a sex-dominated world, a monopoly on sex means uncontrolled domination.

It's apparent that the Battle of the Sexes is nothing new, though the female has been winning it only recently. All we have to do in order to discover its persistence through history is to read the ancient Greeks. In works like *Lysistrata,* we find that the struggle for predominance was waged as long ago as the Golden Age of Hellenic culture. Characteristically, the women are on the losing side in that play, whereas in modern days women have more closely resembled Krimhilde who won her battle and thus defeated herself in her own revenge.

Nonetheless, we can learn an important lesson from *Lysistrata:* that women depend upon men not only in the struggle for survival but that they also need them for the satisfaction of their own sexual instinct, which, for strategic reasons, they're in the habit of denying. The facts of biology are easily ascertainable and presumably well known, yet so thoroughly has the matriarchy entrapped us in its webs that we often tend to forget or ignore the facts of life when it comes to the Battle of the Sexes. A feminine sense of courtesy forbids dragging such realities into the realm of human relations. Yet deny it as they might, women simply aren't the hapless victims of pursuit by bestial males. Rather, they fortunately have sexual cravings as strong as those of men. Though men may think they're suffering alone when they're itching with a yen for possession of a passionate female, the women they're chasing may have a craving for possession of a man which they're obscuring by their shrewish attitude. The Battle of the Sexes is more a war of nerves to determine who can hold out longest and exact the price of surrender than a one-sided pursuit. The only reason that it is usually portrayed in an erroneous light is that this war of attrition is customarily decided in favor of the female; and so, she has the moral triumph of yielding with pleasure to an embrace which she herself would have to plead for, were it not for the pursuing male.

This important message of *Lysistrata* was hidden under a cloak of "decent" secrecy for many hundreds of years, while the women managed to depict themselves as the helpless victims of male cupidity, and the men were taken in by the fiction. Only in this, our own age, has it become possible once more to speak the truth, and even now it isn't quite respectable. For the dominance of the matriarchy is as strong as ever, and male self-determination is at an all-time ebb. The only reason that the truth isn't being suppressed is that people have come to desert all ancient standards and beliefs, and protests against the traditional order are so common that their novelty is practically nil. They are taken seriously only by those who are already converted, and they gain few new adherents. The truth is a luxury which a well-established order can afford without essential damage to itself. And so, *Lysistrata* has been produced in recent years as a play, a television program, and a motion picture, and the protests it evoked were so feeble as to seem negligible. The informative value of the piece is hidden from the public eye because of the public's callousness. There have been so many well-calculated shocks administered to mankind in recent years—be it for reasons of commercial profit or for purposes of political persuasion—that even the truth can no longer ruffle people's equipoise. It disappears among the trash-piles of half-truths and lies and is forgotten as soon as they are.

But to the discerning eye of the connoisseur, the truth always carries a special appeal, and to him the lessons of *Lysistrata* can't be lost. The play means nothing more or less than that the Battle of the Sexes is won, not through the indifference or natural frigidity of woman, but through the superior control that woman exercises over her nerves. In other words, if the message of *Lysistrata* is true—and there are few honest scientists who dispute it—man loses in the Battle of the Sexes only through insufficient mastery of his emotions, through a lack of calculation, and through an absence of patience. He yields on all important issues and overpays woman's price only because he insists upon plunging into a trap of his own making. In claiming superiority and trying to determine the time and place of the action, he actually places himself at a great disadvantage to the more patient and calculating female. Nor can he win this game until he puts his superior energies to work on the task of playing it according to her rules.

Until that day arrives, woman will always hold all the

trump cards. For hers is the kingdom of erotic heaven, the
power of bestowing sexual salvation, and the glory of the incarnation of everything beautiful. Hers are the charms of
softness and the suggestiveness of an ever-present promise.
Only she can clasp man to her bosom and make him quiver
with desire and shiver with delight. Only she can release him
from the tortures of tension and relax his tautest urges. She
can raise him to the skies and send him crashing down into
the deep pit of despair. She can stimulate him to exert himself or send him into the torpor of nihilistic despondency. She
can tame him into meek devotion or infuriate him to the
blackest rage. The only requirement is that she have the jewel
for which man hunts throughout his life without ever being
able quite to appease his longing: beauty.